To my parents Rosemary and Victor, with my love and immense gratitude

The Natural History of
SKOKHOLM ISLAND

by

Graham Victor Frederick Thompson

 www.trafford.com

North America & international
toll-free: 1 888 232 4444 (USA & Canada)
phone: 250 383 6864 ♦ fax: 250 383 6804 ♦ email: info@trafford.com

The United Kingdom & Europe
phone: +44 (0)1865 722 113 ♦ local rate: 0845 230 9601
facsimile: +44 (0)1865 722 868 ♦ email: info.uk@trafford.com

10 9 8 7 6 5 4 3 2

Facing page: Figure 1: Skokholm Island viewed from the south, with (from left to right) Skomer Island, the tiny
island of Middleholm, and the tip of the Marloes Peninsular. Behind them is St. Brides Bay.
Photo by kind permission of Sid Howells.

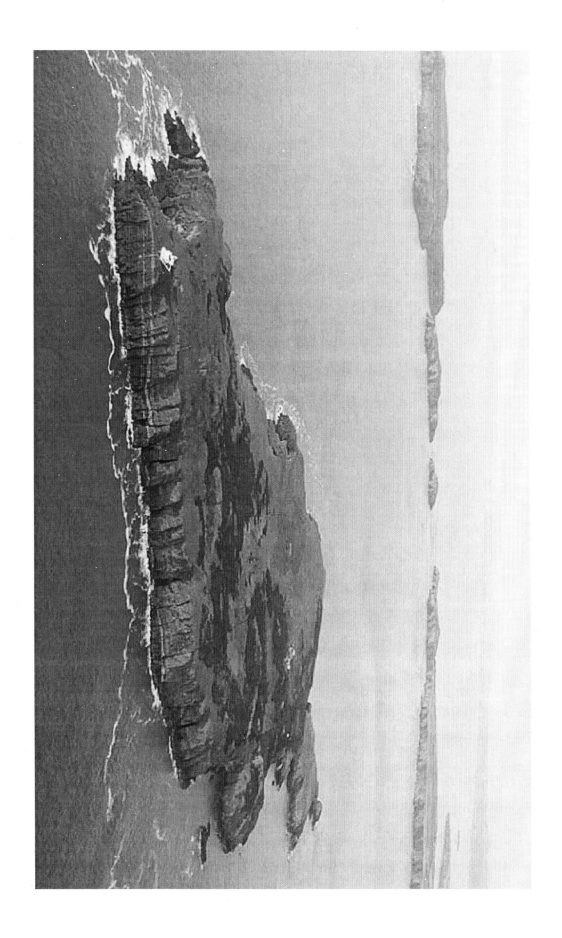

THE NATURAL HISTORY OF SKOKHOLM ISLAND

Contents

CHAPTER 4: FACTORS THAT MAY AFFECT THE FEATURES – A PRECIS

Page no.

CHAPTER 5: EVALUATION FOR NATURE CONSERVATION   223

FIGURES

APPENDICES

Preface

"Far away and long ago an island stood, forlorn and deserted by man, alone in the racing tides off the most westerly coast of Wales. Viewed from the mainland through the haze of Atlantic gales which battered its low cliffs the island had the appearance of a huge dismasted ship, a long black hulk with sea-stained superstructure, abandoned to the moods of the winds of heaven which control the storm-waves of the ocean.

"When the blue calms and long still sunlight of summer lapped the western sea, the island shone with glowing colours, its sandstone cliffs a deep rose-red above the glittering diamonds of the restless currents. Its surface became an enchanting mosaic of flower hues: purple-blue acres of bluebells, delicate flush-pink of the cliff-top thrift, soft yellows of celandine and primrose, snow-white of campion and scurvygrass, vivid greens of grass and fern. The island irresistibly stirred the imagination."

An extract from *The Island*, by Ronald M. Lockley (1969)

After my small, close-knit and wonderful family of mother, father, sister, and darling wife Theresa, Skokholm has been <u>the</u> thing that has meant the most to me in my life of 42 years so far. I first discovered the island during the spring of 1976, when I was 11 years old. I caught sight of its distant, intriguing silhouette through the bright but hazy atmosphere from a cliff-top vantage point on the neighbouring island of Skomer, where I was spending the day bird-watching with my parents and sister during a family holiday. I had not at that time encountered the many books of Ronald Lockley (a man I was to emanate in at least one respect), but the two paragraphs of Lockley's that I've duplicated above would come to express the very essence of what the island was to become to me. Skokholm, completely isolated in the sparkling sea to the south, instantly gave me the impression that it was a wild and perhaps forbidding place, a place for adventure, and thus somewhere that I, a mischievous youngster from the heart of London, would feel quite at home. But getting there was another matter for I had heard that, unlike with Skomer, there was no opportunity to visit for the day. One had to stay there for a week at the very minimum, with a maximum of only 17 other people. Thus it sounded even more appealing than it looked! But Wales is a long way from London, and as a family we didn't return there for some years, so it would have to wait.

I first managed to visit Skokholm six years later, as a teenager in a 'young persons' week' on what can only be described as the most amazing adventure holiday that I could have dreamed of at that time. A friend came with me in search of an escape, and birds, and we were not at all disappointed. It was late April 1982, bird migration was underway, and I saw species that I'd admired in my field guide but only dreamed of actually ever seeing. And it was then that I saw the delightful Puffins for the first time. I could not have imagined that one day I would be living amongst them. We'd also explored some of the many caves (without the Warden knowing, of course, but we carefully avoided disturbing any of the nesting birds), sampled what was effectively a journey back in time (Tilley lamps for lighting, a bucket for a toilet, and a driftwood-fuelled fire), and actually felt that we'd become a part of history. I was smitten, and returned again in late summer, with two different friends. None of the three found the island adventure to their liking and never revisited.

Opposite: Figure 2. The author on Skomer Island on a cold March day, with Skokholm beyond. This was a re-creation of one of the first times he ever saw Skokholm, and is probably the only one that most visitors to Pembrokeshire – undertaking a day visit to Skomer as one of the hoards of holidaymakers – ever have. Very few of them would enjoy a stay on Skokholm.

After numerous visits, including occasional week-long stints as a "Volunteer Warden", and at a time when I was totally disillusioned with life and work on the "mainland" (where I was frustrated that wildlife and wild places were obviously not generally appreciated), my wife (then fiancée) Theresa agreed that I should apply for the job as Summer Assistant Warden on the island, a post that would mean virtually no pay, and a spell of three months away from her, but would put me in line for jobs on other Nature Reserves, the only sites where I thought I could work happily. When the time came I was full of enthusiasm for the summer of fun that awaited me, whereas Theresa, quite understandably, felt exactly the opposite. But I couldn't turn back then; I truly believed that it was for our future after all (and undoubtedly because I so dearly wanted to spend the whole of the summer at my favourite place!).

Theresa joined me for the final 7 days of my 13 week contract, after she'd spent a "hellish" 12 weeks alone, making just enough money to pay the mortgage, eating the most basic of foods (and little of them at that – she lost almost 2 stones in weight that she didn't need to shed at all!), trying to sell our house, and thinking of our future as unemployed (short-term we'd hoped!). Our plan was to volunteer for nature conservation organizations in the hope that the experience so gained would lead to employment as a Warden. During that week, we heard that the present Skokholm Wardens were leaving for the Seychelles, after having spent 9 years on the island. We were actually devastated, for I was banking upon returning as the summer assistant the following year, in the hope that after a second or even third summer season I might be in the position to take on the Warden's role – surely their departure was too soon for us?

My stint on the island had gone very well. So well in fact that, a few months later, in September of 1995, we had been appointed as the new Skokholm Wardens, but we still had to wait until March of the following year to go out there. It was the longest winter of our lives, eventually cut short by the grounding of the oil tanker *Sea Empress* just a mile from the island in the middle of February. The spillage meant that we were required out there immediately, two or three weeks sooner than planned, to monitor the situation – but would there be anything alive out there? We were concerned to say the least. We had to wait a further two days as we undertook the many final preparations necessary for living on such a remote place. We arrived to find that, thankfully, the vast majority of the oil was taken by the tides away from the island and the surrounding sea, but it had certainly left its mark on Skokholm. It recovered and our dream of living amongst the seabirds was to be fulfilled (although we are certainly mentally scarred by the dreadful memories of those few weeks).

For the following 9 years we were present on the island for at least 9 months annually, March to November inclusive, but once we went there in January, 6 times in mid-February, and always remained there until early in December. We had of course previously loved the island, but we never could have imagined just how ingrained it was to become in our souls. For the first few years we didn't set foot off of it, until finally we were forced to take annual summer leave – it seems that we were getting too fond of our workplace! Our managers changed frequently, and we had to justify our existence to each one of them (it was that or accept the often ridiculous changes that each of them wanted to put into operation). As far as we were concerned most of our mainland "support" staff members were incompetent and/or interfering and lacked any desire whatsoever to understand and accommodate our unusual situation. It was extremely frustrating to be constantly let down and finally it all became too tedious, especially when coupled with the frustration that nothing was going to be done about the selfish boat operators that had commenced trips around the island, constantly scaring the birds and seals. So we finally took our leave, extremely sad to be going, but pleased to be away from the squabbling between various factions that were all keen to have things their way where Skokholm was concerned.

We are very proud to say that we have undoubtedly spent far more time ashore there than any other person alive today, and throughout this book the reader will see my remark "personal observations" (shortened to "pers. obs.") – this is not just a repeat of other people's observations (although they do form a large part), for I was actually there to witness at first hand many wonderful things.

During our copious time on Skokholm we undertook an interest in as many aspects of the site as possible between the daily demands of maintaining the infrastructure, monitoring birds and plants, and looking after visitors (and keeping an untrusting eye on them); the many written reports of studies carried out over the previous 60 years helped us learn more. We also suffered a great deal, as visitors in the form of paying guests, film crews, some members of the Management Committee, many of the lighthouse maintenance staff and many private boat-owners did their utmost to cause an immense amount of disturbance to the birds and seals by ignoring the all-important guidelines of keeping to the marked footpaths and at a distance from the animals, so it taught us a great deal about Human bad behaviour too! This book is one of the results of 9 years of love and endeavour, telling part of the story of the amazing wildlife that exists there, a story that cannot possibly be unravelled during a week's holiday, and not even in a decade spent there. Our own personal tale of time spent there has yet to be published, as have my extensive natural history diaries.

My one regret is that, at the time of writing, the island has just been purchased by the Wildlife Trust of South & West Wales. Given that this Trust has maintained guardianship over Skokholm since 1948, and employed me there for 10 consecutive summers, this will seem to be an odd statement. However, as the sections on birds and mammals in this book will reveal, there is a huge possibility that, in the Trust's hands, there will be actually be less control over what goes on there than there has been recently, and by this I mean that studies of an intrusive and potentially destructive nature might recommence after a 30-year prohibition. A multitude of animals may once again be subjected to various experiments in order to satisfy the whims of academics or gain a student his or her PhD. Although this book utilises the results of the many studies that have been carried out on the island in the past, having lived there for such a long time has given me the very clear view that unmolested wild animals are definitely more relaxed, more trusting (yes, I had many birds and rabbits trust me!) and hence more photographable and generally more pleasant to be near – for example, gulls that aren't fearful of someone won't defaecate on them when they are walking a harmless distance away from a nest. I always knew where and when the first misdemeanour of any one year had been carried out (by this I mean a visitor – usually an errant photographer – had left the footpath), because the Great Black-backed Gulls nesting nearby would suddenly be very panicky whenever anybody passed by. Thereafter it was impossible to obtain a good photograph!

An increase in available funding will probably mean that there will be an endless list of "improvements" to the infrastructure, whereupon the water supply will probably be stretched to the limit to keep human visitors ridiculously clean, whilst the streams meanwhile run dry; more landing places for boats will be constructed with tons of concrete where presently there are nesting seabirds, further encouraging the growing multitude of private boat owners to undertake unofficial, and extremely harmful, excursions ashore. Skokholm as a wild and (generally) unspoilt place – as I have known it – will undoubtedly cease to exist. I desperately hope that by drawing attention to just how special the island is with regard to all of its wild inhabitants, and the harm that is currently being caused to them, serious efforts will be made to protect Skokholm, and the activities of those people who wish to ruthlessly exploit it for their own short-term gain will be severely curtailed.

Graham Thompson. Central France, November 2006.

Acknowledgements

My immense gratitude is due first to my Mother and Father for encouraging me to expand my interest in nature, and for often helping me financially even in my adult years – working in nature conservation does not lead to much in the way of financial gain! The study of living things has given me an unimaginable amount of pleasure, and I can think of nothing better than to be living in the midst of wildlife, particularly in wild places.

We wouldn't have been in the position to become the Wardens without the help of Michael and Susan Betts, themselves Skokholm Wardens from 1987 to 1995, who very kindly chose me to be one of their assistants in 1995 and thus ultimately put me in the position to become the Warden. I will forever remember that it was they, plus previous Warden couples Graham and Liz Gynn (1981 - 1984), and Rob Wolstenholme and Amanda Holman (1985 - 1986), who inspired me to have the belief that I could one day sit at the head of the table in the famous Wheelhouse. We were appointed by an interview panel that consisted of David Saunders (Director of the Dyfed Wildlife Trust at the time), Stuart Devonald and Jack Donovan (both Island Management Committee members), and we will forever remain grateful to them for giving us the once in a lifetime opportunity.

I would also dearly like to thank the many naturalists, natural history societies, bird clubs, wildlife trusts and so on who have been able and kind enough to make available their knowledge in the form of field trips, habitat management tasks, plus books and journals, magazines and newsletters, the reading of which has furnished me with a huge part of what I know about – and further strengthened my love of – all things wild. Just a basic understanding of what goes on in the complicated lives of these plants and animals cannot fail but to foster a huge amount of respect for them, and ultimately (one hopes) bring about their protection from the ravages of the modern world. May these organisations go from strength to strength, and have greater sway with successive future governments that are, it seems, finally going to begin to appreciate the value of our wild places not just for people to use, but in their own right. If you aren't yet a member of a nature conservation body local to you, please do join!

This book contains information gleaned from the many papers written by naturalists and researchers who spent considerable amounts of time studying the various aspects of Skokholm, and I am extremely grateful to all of them. The first mention must go to Stephen Warman and Carol Hellawell, Skokholm Wardens 1979 - 1980, who wrote the first management plan to be utilized on the island, after a thorough examination of the site's biology through their own observations and by reading the many written reports that were the result of previous studies. Richard Ninnes spent a great deal of time working on the island flora, was in regular communication with me over the vegetation monitoring, and also produced a number of splendid, detailed maps. Much of the work on invertebrates was carried out in the 1950's or before, and subsequent name changes could have created a lot of confusion for me when trying to update them. However, I am indebted to Adrian Fowles, Invertebrate Ecologist for the Countryside Council for Wales (CCW), for taking the time to input a huge list of names I'd sent him into the CCW Invertebrate Database and send me updated nomenclature for all of them. Adrian also took the time to identify, or arrange to have identified, a number of specimens that I'd sent to him. Similarly, I would like to thank Peter Harvey of the Spider Recording Scheme (British Arachnological Society) for taking time out of his busy schedule to identify numerous specimens of spiders and solitary bees and wasps for me, and also Dr Mark Shaw, Keeper of Geology & Zoology for the National Museums of Scotland, for identifying a number of ichneumon wasps and sawflies (these are very difficult groups of insects to work with).

Sincere thanks are also due to Sid Howells, Area Earth Scientist for CCW, for allowing me to accompany him on a number of excursions to study the geology of the island in September of 2003, and for giving me permission to use his excellent aerial photographs. I am delighted also to have been present on the island during numerous biology field courses led by Dr. David Lees of Cardiff University, weeks during which many facets of the island's biology were investigated, including a long-term study of kleptoparasitism on puffins.

An occasional visit to Skokholm by groups of people from various Natural History societies further added to my own knowledge of the island, for while I was busy counting birds in the height of the breeding season, they were able to spend time looking at the many other things I would have loved to have been seeking. In particular, I would like to thank the New Mills Natural History Society, and in particular the amazing Professor emeritus Brian Fox (sadly now deceased), for allowing me to accompany him on his lichen survey during a week in May 1995. Many other things were discovered that week, including the discovery of "worked" flint flakes that were painstakingly analysed by Ron Weston, as were mosses and liverworts by Tony Smith. More recently (2002), Len Johnson searched for mosses and liverworts (not particularly easy to find on an exposed site like Skokholm), and updated the nomenclature on these for me when informed that this book was in preparation. His lichenologist friend Jonathon Guest kindly assessed M. Gillham's (1954) list of lichens and made valuable comments in light of today's greatly-improved knowledge of the many lichen species.

Since leaving Skokholm, we have had a tough time dealing with what we regard as "our huge loss". I must thank Mike Alexander, a former Warden of Skomer Island, and his wife Rosanne for giving us invaluable support in coming to terms with life without the island. They themselves experienced such feelings, and are still coming to terms with them twenty years on. Very few other people would understand.

My wonderful sister, Deborah, has been instrumental in giving me much-needed technical support with the typing of my manuscript, for my knowledge of computers is distinctly lacking and I am most indebted to her. Finally, my darling wife Theresa has given me nothing but encouragement to continue writing when I'd reached sticking points on a number of occasions, and she also reminded me of huge number of wonderful things that I had long since forgotten about in our encounters with wildlife on the island. She has put up with me spending many hours of what could be our time together, in order that I could fulfil my ambition of having my experience of the ultimate in "living and breathing Skokholm" put down on paper for all to see. And of course, without her standing strongly at my side from the very beginning of my career in nature conservation, I would never have been the Warden of the island in the first place. To now have a wonderful son of our own – Geai – really makes our lives complete, and I hope that one day he will visit Skokholm to find the birds and rabbits thriving, and people firmly under control.

I give my heart-felt thanks to everyone who has been instrumental in assisting me with the realisation of this book about a place that will forever remain dear to me, and to the many wonderful people that we met on the island during our time as Wardens. Many of you have become good friends to us, and are too many to name individually, but you have encouraged me to put my thoughts and knowledge about Skokholm down on paper – I hope that you approve, and even discover something about the island that you didn't know before.

Chapter 1: An introduction to Skokholm

Section 1.1: Location and general description

Skokholm Island is located off the extreme south-west tip of Pembrokeshire, South Wales, in the Parish of Dale, at latitude 51° 41′ N, longitude 05° 16′ W. It lies approximately 4 kilometres to the south of the well-known island of Skomer and is separated from it by a stretch of water known as Broad Sound, and is at a similar distance to the south-west of the Marloes Peninsular. The entrance to the Milford Haven waterway – a busy shipping port with oil refineries and marinas – lies some 7 km to the south-east. It is a nature reserve managed by the Wildlife Trust of South & West Wales, and has been designated as a Site of Special Scientific Interest (SSSI) and is part of the Skomer and Skokholm Special Protection Area (SPA), designated under European law. Its foreshore is also part of a Special Area of Conservation (SAC), titled "Pembrokeshire Marine", which includes an area which also encompasses the islands of Skomer, Grassholm, The Smalls, the Bishops and Clerks, and Ramsey. It is of international importance for its breeding seabirds and this is reflected in the SPA and SSSI notifications. Its colony of Manx shearwaters *Puffinus puffinus* is probably the third-largest in the world, of very high density, and containing some 15 percent of the World population. Breeding storm petrels *Hydrobates pelagicus* – a species difficult to census – have been thought to account for up to 20 percent of the EU population, and there also exists about 3 to 4 percent of the World population of lesser black-backed gulls *Larus fuscus* (race *graellsii*).

The island is visited using the boat service operated from Martin's Haven (Ordnance Survey Grid Reference: SM 761092), currently provided by Dale Sailing Company. The vessel *Dale Princess* crosses once or twice weekly to bring residential visitors that have booked through the Wildlife Trust of South & West Wales (WTSWW). It lands at South Haven, Skokholm, which has a trackway running from it up onto the island plateau. More rarely, in the case of strong southerly winds, it will stop at Blacksmith's Landing on the north side of the island, which leads to a series of steps cut into the cliff-slope. Landing from private boats is forbidden, in order to protect the breeding birds.

The sea currents around the island are rather unpredictable. The rise and fall reaches a mean of over 6 metres in extent at springs – coinciding with the period just following the full and new moons – and at full flood and with a tidal stream flowing at 2 knots, maelstroms exist at many locations around the island where shallows and submerged rocky reefs cause the water to boil at the surface. Even during neap tides, the range is relatively large, at a mean of 2.6 metres. The route taken by the *Dale Princess* in order to reach Skokholm is an easy one to navigate if one were simply following the compass. But the combined effects of the tides, the exposure to uncannily unpredictable winds and the tide race of Jack Sound – a shallow, narrow strait situated between the mainland at the Marloes peninsular and the small islet of Middleholm – mean that the crossing can be far from straightforward to the unwary. Once Jack Sound has been negotiated, Broad Sound – a stretch of water over two kilometres wide between Skomer and Skokholm – then has to be crossed. Here the wind can be more of an influence than the tide, frequently requiring a huge degree of counter-steer if a set path is to be followed. With the prevailing winds from the west and southwest, and a huge fetch from these directions, there are many days when this crossing is quite simply impossible to undertake due to a huge groundswell – the combination of wind and tide has caused many a ship to flounder here in days of old. Once the eastern-most end of the island is rounded (at least 40 minutes after leaving Martin's Haven), the relatively-sheltered inlet of South Haven is eventually seen nestling between rugged rock faces either side, but even this sanctuary is only so if the wind is not in the south or southeast, or if a westerly gale has been blowing for days previously.

The island is part of the Pembrokeshire Coast National Park. It is visible from many parts of the coastal footpath on the mainland and is known to evoke feelings of wonder and awe in people observing it from there, particularly to those with some knowledge of the island's history. Many others would undoubtedly simply long to escape here upon seeing it for the first time. At first sight, Skokholm appears as a rather flat-topped and rather featureless island. Viewed from the north and south, it is seen to dip towards the east. It is bound by cliffs of Old Red Sandstone, which are frequently battered by large waves from the south and west. Deep bays and gullies occur all around the coast, with occasional boulder beaches and very few small sandy shores exposed only at very low water. Crags characterise the southern part of the island, the rest being planed-off and generally featureless, typical of a wave-cut platform. Every bay, point and even many of the small rock outcrops have been named, most during the years that the island has been occupied as a bird sanctuary – see the photographs in Figures 3 and 4 (pages 19 and 21). Whitewashed farm buildings are situated towards the middle of the island, in the lee of a rock outcrop called *The Knoll* that affords some protection from the prevailing winds, and numerous part-derelict stone-lined earth banks delineate the fields surrounding them. An unmanned lighthouse is situated at the farthest, south-western tip of the island, with a light that commences flashing every ten seconds as natural light fades at dusk, and continues until the first light of day.

About 8 miles to the west of Skokholm sits the island of Grassholm with its veil of gannets, and further away still the Smalls Rocks and the infamous lighthouse there. Elsewhere, there is the wide expanse of the open ocean. When the sun shines low in the southern sky during the winter months, viewed from the mainland the island is silhouetted against a sparkling sea, mysterious and alone. From the island itself, views are breathtaking – to the southwest lies the open ocean with all of its changing moods; to the north the island of Skomer with its rugged volcanic rock, and more distant the islet of South Bishop; to the east lies the mainland coast comprised of the Marloes and Dale peninsulars with their extensive sandy beaches, the Old Red Sandstone islet of Gateholm and, on a clear day, the view of the Preseli mountains; and above, a night sky full of twinkling stars and even falling gems in the form of the islands' *cause célèbre*, the shearwaters and petrels, with very little man-made light to interfere with the spectacle. The rugged cliffs and outcrops of Old Red Sandstone with a multicoloured shroud of lichens makes Skokholm a paradise for artists and photographers. There are also spectacular displays of wildflowers. It is little wonder that the great naturalist and pioneer R.M. Lockley wrote numerous books about the place.

Once ashore it is clear that the home comforts are never going to approach those experienced elsewhere in Britain in the early days of this, the 21st Century and, in fact, most of the facilities are perhaps – at the time of writing – more reminiscent of the 19th Century! But this is the appeal to many of those who regularly stay on the island and would surely do so to many people who are currently not aware of its existence. Many visitors want to escape the rigours of mainland life (so-called "civilisation") and enjoy being as close to nature as is humanly possible. Lying prostrate whilst surrounded by all things natural is probably the most common activity on the island, which includes having puffins virtually at one's feet throughout the daylight hours. After dark things change just a little, as the "comical" puffins are replaced by awe-inspiring and incredibly vocal Manx shearwaters. Visitors to Skokholm stay up late, some of them until dawn the next day, because the nightlife is unequalled, anywhere!

Facing page: Figure 3. Skokholm from the south-east, by Sid Howells. The names of locations are referred to in various parts of the text.

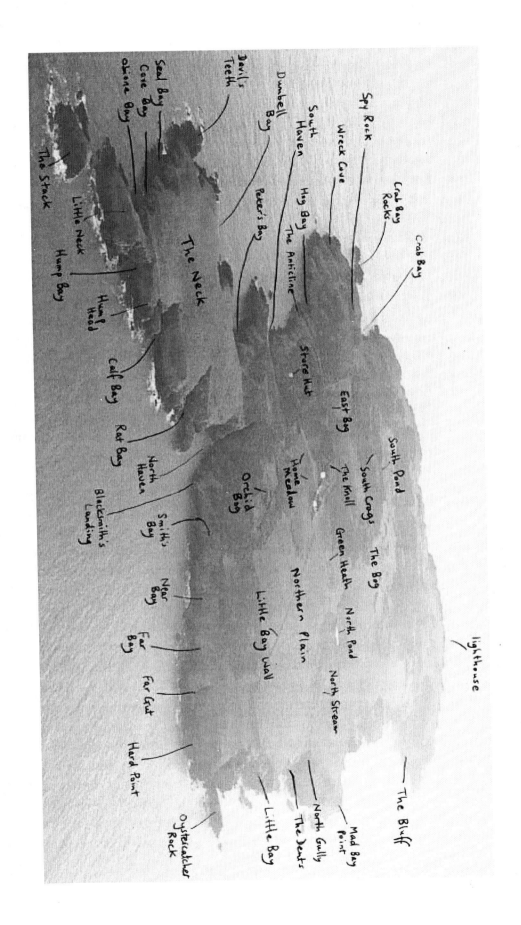

Crab Bay

Spy Rock

Wreck Cave

Crab Bay Rocks

South Haven

Hog Bay

The Anticline

Dumbell Bay

Peter's Bay

Devils Teeth

Seal Bay

Cave Bay

okene Bay

The Stack

Little Neck

Hump Head

Hump Bay

The Neck

Calf Bay

Rat Bay

North Haven

Blacksmith's Landing

Smith's Bay

Near Bay

Far Bay

Far Gut

Hard Point

Oystercatcher Rock

Little Bay

The Devils

North Gully

Mad Bay Point

The Bluff

Lighthouse

North Stream

Northern Plain

Little Bay Wall

Orchid Bay

Home Meadow

Green Heath

North Pond

The Bog

South Crags

South Pond

The Knoll

East Bay

Stone Hut

19

Section 1.2: Land tenure and infrastructure

For two-and-a-half centuries, and until very recently, the island was part of the Dale Castle Estate, but following the death of the owner – Mrs. Osra Lloyd-Phillips – in 2005, it was purchased by the Wildlife Trust of South & West Wales (WTSWW), which had previously leased it from the Estate for many years. This sale did not include a small area at the south-western tip, which is the property of Trinity House Lighthouse Service, Corporation of London, who built a lighthouse there in the early 1900's. The land above the High Water Mean Ordinary Tide (HWMOT) is owned by WTSWW. The foreshore between HWMOT and Low Water Mean Ordinary Tide (LWMOT) is owned by the Crown and leased to the Pembrokeshire Coast National Park by the Crown Estate Commissioners (the SPA and SSSI boundaries extend to LWMOT). The SSSI covers approximately 106 hectares (ha.).

R.M. Lockley and H.W. Shellard took the lease from former farming tenant John "Bulldog" Edwards in 1927, for 21 years. In 1948 the lease was taken on by The West Wales Field Society (of which R.M. Lockley was a founder, now called The Wildlife Trust of South and West Wales), subsequently renewed in 1969 for a period of 7 years at a rental of £500.00. In September 1976, there was a significant change in the conditions of the lease, which then prohibited the trapping of any animal, thereby bringing about the cessation of many long-term studies, and in particular the seabird research. The lease was for a period of 3 years, then 4 from 1979 - 83, for three until 1986, then 5 to 1991, then to 1996, to 2001, and finally for a further 5 years to the autumn of 2006.

The island is managed as a nature reserve, with advice from the Wildlife Trust's "Islands Advisory Committee" which includes members co-opted from the Countryside Council for Wales (CCW), the Pembrokeshire Coast National Park Authority (PCNPA) and the Edward Grey Institute of Field Ornithology, Oxford University (EGI). The day to day management is entirely the responsibility of the reserve Warden, guided by the agreed Management Plan.

The main landing area is in a bay known as South Haven, which has a rough access track for the island vehicle (a 30 cwt dumper truck). On the north coast, steps have been built (in the late 1980's) on the steep slope down to a small concrete landing pad next to Blacksmith's Bay, only safe to reach by boat at half tide, and which is only used when sea conditions dictate that the main landing place is not usable.

The main "observatory" (formerly farm) buildings are situated in the east, in the relative shelter afforded by a rocky knoll found to their immediate north, and were first built in the mid-1700's. They include: an attractive, whitewashed cottage containing a small "common room" and library plus a number of visitor bedrooms; a long single-storey block with numerous bedrooms and a laboratory; a second block with Warden's accommodation, a kitchen, and a dining room which seats up to 19 people, plus a vehicle garage at its western end. There are two recent additions to the buildings, in the form of two small blocks, one which houses the Summer Assistant Warden at one end and has a small workshop at the other; the second has the Warden's Office and a small storeroom that has been used as a gift shop, and sometimes a bedroom for the Assistant Cook. There is also a wooden shed that is currently used as the island gift shop, situated in the shelter of one of the farmyards. Another, more substantial, hut is situated on the cliff-top above South Haven. Formerly a storeroom belonging to Trinity House Lighthouse Service, it is now used by the Wildlife Trust for the same purpose.

Facing page: Figure 4. Aerial photograph of Skokholm from the west. Photograph reproduced with the kind permission of S. Howells.

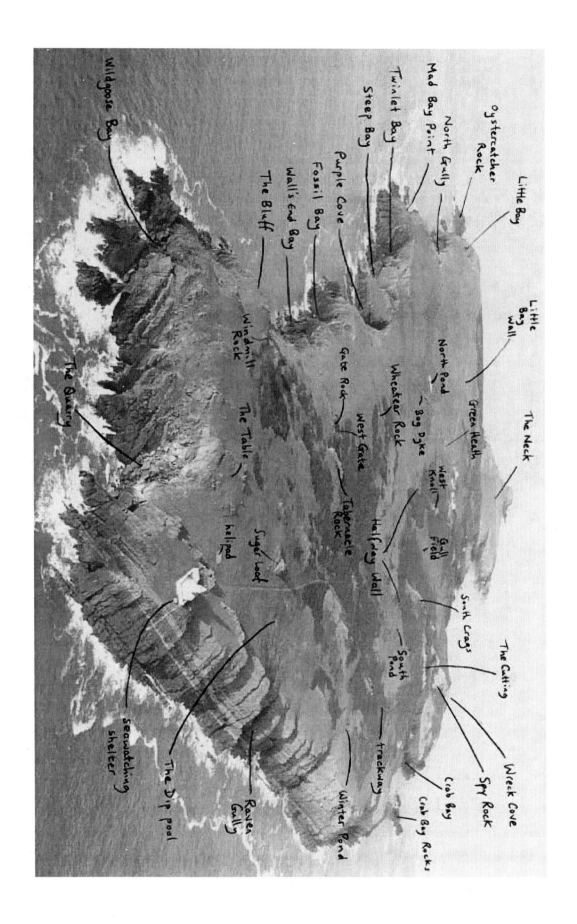

Wildgoose Bay

Oystercatcher Rock

North Gully

Mad Bay Point

Twinlet Bay

Steep Bay

Purple Cove

Fossil Bay

Wall's End Bay

The Bluff

Windmill Rock

The Quarry

The Table

Gate Rock

West Gate

Wheatear Rock

Bog Dyke

North Pond

Little Bay

Little Bay Wall

Green Heath

The Neck

West Knoll

Gull Field

Halfway Wall

Tabernacle Rock

Sugar Loaf

helipad

seawatching shelter

The Dip pool

Raven Gully

Winter Pond

trackway

South Pond

South Crags

The Cutting

Crab Bay

Spy Rock

Wreck Cove

Crab Bay Rocks

21

Figure 5 (above): The "observatory" buildings seen from The Knoll, the site of RM Lockley's first Manx shearwater study-burrows. Skomer Island is just in view on the left, the small islet of Middleholm to its right, and the Marloes peninsular further right still and separated from Middleholm by Jack Sound. The Old Red Sandstone islet of Gateholm is just visible to the far right (through the rain).

The dumper truck has, until recently, been used to transport luggage and food from and to the landing places, and occasionally to transport building materials, and spoil from pond excavations. Its use as a transporter of luggage has now been taken over by wheelbarrows for reasons of safety. Lighting and cooking is powered by propane gas. Other power sources include a wind-powered electricity generator, three small solar panels and a petrol-engined electricity generator, the latter only infrequently used to run power tools.

Water for drinking and cooking is drawn from a covered spring ("The Well") situated above South Haven. It is piped by gravity down to a tank and on to a hydraulic ram pump, which sends it uphill to a large storage tank at the buildings complex. It then flows by gravity to the kitchen tap and boilers. Water for personal- and dish-washing is in the form of rain, collected from the roofs and stored in butts, regularly treated with a weak chlorine solution to kill bacteria and other micro-organisms. Toilets are of the chemical "elsan" type, i.e. a bucket with a "proper" toilet seat on top of it, and waste is emptied into a covered pit situated nearby.

Section 1.3: Archaeology and past land use

Unlike on the nearby islands of Skomer and Gateholm, there is very little evidence that ancient man ever inhabited Skokholm. In the early 1900's, a few flint flakes, probably of Mesolithic age, were discovered, and were, until recently, the only evidence of possible pre-historic settlement (Lockley, 1969). However, recent finds of flint tools – microliths, scrapers, borers and an arrowhead – suggest that the island was possibly occupied in the Bronze Age (Weston, 1995).

Skokholm has a long, if somewhat fragmented, agricultural history. Where evidence exists, it is clear that the island farming followed the mainland pattern of the times, and frequently mainland-based farmers held the island. The first written records show that it was a feudal possession of the Norman barons who had conquered Pembrokeshire. In the 14th and 15th centuries, the island was owned by the Crown and leased to landed gentry, who exploited it for the rich supply of rabbits and seabirds. From 1324 to 1544, interesting records of rabbit catches are listed in Henry Owen's *"Calender of Public Records Relating to Pembrokeshire"*.

Records for 1387 - 88 make mention of repairs to a house, which was probably a ferreters' bothy, and was most likely situated at the site of the cottage that exists today. The island appears to have become uninhabited at some time during the 16th century, and up to the beginning of the 17th century it apparently served for fattening sheep, cows, oxen, horses and the ubiquitous rabbit.

Gulls nested on the island at this time. Owen (1603, in Lockley, 1969) describes the islands of Pembrokeshire as the chief nursery of the seabirds which "are ripe about mydsomer (sic) at which time they become flushe" (they fledge). Seabirds were eaten at the time of Lent, since they were conveniently described as a kind of fish (because of the birds' diet, no doubt). It was apparently not always this way, however – a former owner, J. Lloyd, was quoted in *"A Historical Tour through Pembrokeshire"* (Fenton, 1811, published 1903) and makes no mention of the seabirds (but mentions the rabbits and other farming).

Later, Lockley (1969) mentioned how one of his companions demonstrated how the fishermen of the 1920's caught seabirds – by setting rabbit long-nets along the cliff-top at dusk. In the morning there would be shearwaters, puffins and gulls tangled in the mesh, and the birds were then used to bait lobster pots. Eggs and young birds were eaten. He also mentions finding numerous examples of a "diabolical instrument" called a *barbelé* – a long, flexible stick with a small barb at one end – which was used to hook birds and rabbits out of burrows.

Since about 1750 to just recently, the occupants of Dale Castle on the nearby mainland have owned Skokholm (see Section 1.2). Soon after its incorporation into the estate, a new house was built that probably involved extending around the 4 main walls of the original bothy (see above). Other farm buildings were added (in the 1760's) and approximately half of the island was "walled in" (the walls consisting of earth banks, lined with small slabs of sandstone laid in an attractive herringbone pattern). Agricultural returns of 1870 show Skokholm growing sufficient corn to feed the 15 cattle and 4 horses (i.e. corn not grown in sufficient quantity for export), whilst butter, fattened cattle and rabbits were exported to the mainland. In the late 19th century farming declined and the site was mainly used to breed ponies and later to graze sheep.

Fenton (1811, published 1903), when writing of the early 19th century, records pasture supporting eight cows, and some enclosed arable land which was periodically limed (there is a lime kiln in South Haven). The chief crops were oats and barley (furrow marks are visible to this day in aerial photographs over much of the island, particularly in the east), whilst ryegrass *Lolium* sp. and clover *Trifolium* sp. were mown for hay. Retired sea-captain Henry Edward Harrison was the last person to really farm Skokholm, until his death there in 1881. It was he who cut through solid rock to form the track-way which runs down to the quay in South Haven (Lockley, 1969). He had no son to continue farming the island, and no tenant was found subsequently who was prepared to do so, undoubtedly due to the agricultural depression. The owner of Skomer at that time, Capt. Vaughan Palmer Davies, took over the tenancy of Skokholm for its rabbits and put sheep and ponies on to graze. He relinquished the lease in 1891, at the same time that he left Skomer. Gilbert Warren Davis, who farmed near St. Ishmaels, took it on for a short period until the Boer War, when he enlisted into the army. He did not farm *per se*, but kept sheep on the island and took rabbits. The landlord then held the island himself.

In 1905, the lease was taken over by John "Bulldog" Edwards of Marloes, who farmed the island again, keeping pigs, cows, horses and poultry. At this time agricultural fortunes were improving, and his farming has been described as "perhaps the best the island had ever known" (Howells, 1968). Edwards sent eggs and tubs of butter to the mainland weekly. When the horses and cattle were swum to Marloes Sands in order to sell them, they were said to hold pools of seawater in the rolls of fat on their backs. The rich grazing apparently meant that sheep would have become too fat for breeding purposes, so they were not kept. Edwards also grew corn to feed the livestock. In 1912, he and his wife left the island shortly after the birth of their first child. This decision was made because of the considerable problems they encountered in attempting to get to the mainland for the birth and the customary "confinement" of the expectant mother beforehand, and obviously did not want a repeat of the incident. Bulldog still retained the tenancy of the island, purely for the rabbit-catch.

In 1913, the Corporation of London (Trinity House) purchased about 3 ha of land for the construction of a lighthouse, and built a crane and gantry on the cliff-top in the bay at South Haven. John Edwards then put two horses onto the island for the purpose of hiring them to Trinity House Corporation, which was building the lighthouse at that time and required their strength for hauling materials up from the shore.

In 1927, Ronald Lockley took over the lease. At the beginning of his 13-year occupancy, he fully intended to farm the island, by way of the introduction of livestock and by undertaking limited cultivation. He was determined to completely remove the rabbits in order to provide far more grazing for his sheep, since he described "a bare turf covered with rabbit pellets". He also planned to replace these wild rabbits with the long-haired "chinchilla" breed, that his wife Doris had previously begun breeding on the mainland. Their pelts were worth ten times those of their wild counterparts. For a while Lockley succeeded in reducing the number of wild rabbits, thanks to the extensive use of steel traps, and by 1932 his sheep flock consisted of 100 breeding ewes. Because birds were being killed in the traps in numbers that eventually became unacceptable to him, he ceased using them and turned to using snares and ferrets instead. Ultimately it proved to be a losing battle and in September 1934 Lockley hired two barges and removed the whole sheep flock in one operation (Lockley, 1969).

In 1939 and 1940 "cyanogas" treatment reduced the large number of rabbits (estimated at 10,000 or about 100 per hectare) to just 400. For a short while subsequently, Lockley collected 3 - 4 tons of hay per acre of best land, whereas the grass had previously been nibbled so short as to render hay production impossible (Lockley, 1940c). However, he was ordered by the War Office to evacuate the island in 1940, and although there were inhabitants in the form of lighthouse keepers, the island was not farmed, and consequently rabbit numbers quickly returned to normal. Meanwhile, the global recession in the late-1920's put paid to any chance of him making his fortune from selling rabbit furs (Lockley, 1940a). Just prior to this time, a pig was brought on to the island for the purpose of dispensing of household waste (Skokholm Bird Observatory Report 1940 – 46).

One of Lockley's ponies, named Sugarback by his daughter Ann, was left on the island in order to continue to fulfill his transportation duties for Trinity House Lighthouse Service. Trams laden with supplies were pulled by the pony along a railway track which ran from the landing place in South Haven right up to the lighthouse. In the mid 1950's, mechanized transport was obtained in the form of a three-wheeled motor tractor, deemed to be "more docile" than the pony and tram. Efforts were made to take Sugarback off the island, and reunite him with "his" mares that had been evacuated in 1940, but he would have none of it! So he was allowed to remain on the island, where he remained much an integral part of everyday life, until he finally died there in 1957. He was buried beside South Pond (Lockley, 1969). The railway tracks, meanwhile, were lifted, and eventually R.M. Lockley sold much of the metal as scrap to a Haverfordwest merchant (Skokholm Chatty Log, 1956).

From 1946 a small number of people comprising the staff and visitors to the Bird Observatory (established by Lockley in 1933 – see section 1.4) lived on the island during the spring and summer months. A flock of Soay sheep (six ewes and two rams were given to R. M. Lockley by the Duke of Bedford in 1936 and the flock multiplied, numbering 96 head in 1951), a few goats (see below), a pony and the rabbits comprised the grazing stock. In addition, a Welsh Black cow was brought on to the island in 1946, because the Honorary Warden, John Fursdon could not drink goats' milk and "most stubbornly insisted" upon having a cow (Fursdon, 1983). Caroline was an instant hit with John and other visitors, for not only did she produce "excellent, creamy milk", she was reportedly a "very affectionate creature and observer of *Homo sapiens*", and "she became so tame that she assisted in all outdoor activities, including nocturnal shearwatering expeditions." Caroline was left on the island over the winter period, ended up in poor condition and ceased to produce milk. In 1947 she continued to show her affection for people, advances that were not always appreciated because they were apparently misunderstood. Sadly, and rather bizarrely, she was obviously not held with such affection by the Warden that year (Peter Conder), for she was slaughtered and cut up on the quay in October 1947, just prior to the island being vacated for the winter.

Numbers of Soay sheep fluctuated according to weather conditions and occasional culls (during the war a number of rams were slaughtered). The drought of 1959 left them in such poor condition that some 70 were killed on "humanitarian grounds" in the spring of 1960. A few were allowed to live and there is a record of a "handful" on the islands in 1964 (e.g. Sheard & Ferry, 1964), but they seem to have disappeared shortly afterwards. More pigs were brought onto the island in 1956 (Skokholm Island Chatty Log, 1956), presumably for the consumption of household food-waste, prior to be sent off to market.

Lockley reared half a dozen or so goats in the 1930's and 1940's. A number remained on the island long after he had departed, providing milk and meat to a succession of Wardens and visitors. In 1981, the surviving members of a 12-strong herd, which grazed most of the island and tended to avoid people, were rounded up and taken off the island in the autumn, for the benefit of the vegetation, particularly lichens, and for the burrow-nesting birds which often had to contend with collapsed roofs. Presumably Caroline the cow had previously caused far greater damage to burrows.

In the smaller of the two farmyards, there is a grindstone of approximately 70cm diameter (it can just be seen in Figure 8). Island visitor Brian Taylor described it in July 2001, as follows:

"A runner stone, i.e. the top stone of a pair. It has a very obvious star-shaped rhind for locating the drive. The source of power to turn it could have been human, horse, or perhaps wind. It would have ground meal for baking the household bread; it may have ground corn, most certainly barley, also rye, oats or even beans and peas. The dressing of the stone reveals some interesting information: the angle of the "harps" (grooves cut into the stone to facilitate grinding) indicates a right-hand stone, i.e. it ran clockwise. In old mill terms, this was "with the sun", which made it a lucky mill. Its age? Very difficult to say, probably 19th Century but perhaps an 18th Century stone re-dressed."

Near to the north-western tip of the island, there is a place called "Windmill Rock". Perhaps therein lies the answer to the question of its origin and mode of operation.

Section 1.4: Past conservation status and use

As far as is known, a real interest in Skokholm's wildlife (for means other than food) began under the tenancy of R.M. Lockley who, with time on his hands because of the imminent failure of his farming efforts (see previously) and thus in desperate need of an income, initiated pioneering studies of many of the breeding seabird species, in particular puffin, Manx shearwater and storm petrel. By starting a number of ringing studies and the erection of a "Heligoland-type" trap in 1933 in the Cottage garden, Britain's first Bird Observatory was formed (an article he had written about Monmouthshire's avifauna, published in the journal *British Birds*, led to the editor of the journal supplying Lockley with many rings for the purpose of studying seabirds). In order to generate an income, Lockley invited visitors to come to stay to assist with the work (Lockley, 1936). His work stimulated much interest – members of the 8th International Ornithological Congress made an excursion to the island on 8th July 1934, following a meeting at Oxford, where they were told about the studies on bird migration and breeding seabirds. Lockley encouraged all kinds of naturalists to visit, and much was achieved in describing the natural history. He was forced to evacuate the island by the War Office in 1940, since Skokholm was said to be in a strategic position at the mouth of the Milford Haven estuary and harbour, and there were plans to fortify it. Thankfully these never materialised.

In April 1946, the island was reoccupied by R.M. Lockley, John Fursdon (who then became the first recognized Warden of the island) and a number of other volunteers of the West Wales Field Society (now known as the Wildlife Trust of South & West Wales). As would be expected, much of the infrastructure was in a state of disrepair, although just one of the roofs had ceased to remain watertight. Traps were repaired with wire netting, but metal rings for bird banding were in very short supply, so throughout the year very few birds were actually ringed. However, general observations were made of bird movements and counts made of many of the breeding species.

In August 1947, Skokholm Bird Observatory was officially re-opened by the West Wales Field Society in conjunction with the Council for the Promotion of Field Studies (now the Field Studies Council). The CPFS was attempting to co-ordinate scientific research and wardening of the Pembrokeshire islands through the new Field Centre (its second) at nearby Dale Fort. This had previously been purchased by WWFS on a 100 percent mortgage, and the ever-willing John Fursdon became volunteer warden there early in 1947. Given the immense financial burden faced by the Field Society (having to pay scientific staff and cater for up to 50 people), it was soon passed on to the CPFS for the latter to manage it as a field centre. The CPFS stipulated a condition however, that it would also require to be able to oversee the running of Skokholm, already very prestigious and that would undoubtedly lure people to West Wales – and hence also to the newly-established centre at Dale Fort if so encouraged. The fort was purchased by CPFS from WWFS afterwards, and the money put to good use in the purchase of Skomer Island by WWFS (Lockley, 1973).

In 1948, the West Wales Field Society took over the lease of the island (granted to the society by the previous leaseholder, R.M. Lockley), for a 21-year period, but the practical needs of the observatory were still seen to by Dale Fort Field Centre after the CPFS agreed a license with the WWFS (Dale Castle Estate would not allow a sub-letting). The WWFS continued to produce the annual Skokholm Bird Observatory Report and – through stalwart volunteer John Fursdon, the island's first Warden after Lockley – to publicise the island far and wide by way of film shows and exhibitions. The direct running of the observatory was the responsibility of a succession of resident wardens, employed by the Field Society.

Many ecological studies of the plant and invertebrate communities, as well as the birds, were started in 1947, and naturalists were continually encouraged to visit. By the mid-1950's, probably more information was available on the ecology of the island than any other island site (and many mainland ones) in the British Isles.

The island was mentioned in *Command 7122, conservation of nature in England and Wales: Report of the Wildlife Conservation Special Committee, Appendix 6 - List of proposed National Nature Reserves (NNR)* (1947). Its statement included the neighbouring islands of Skomer and Grassholm, and is reproduced below:

"List of proposed National Nature Reserves: -

NR.19. Skomer, Skokholm and Grassholm, Pembrokeshire (830 acres)

A group of three islands having the most important colonies of seabirds in England and Wales. Grassholm has the only gannetry in the two countries; Skomer has a peculiar vole; much research has already been done on birds and other groups on Skokholm, and a field study centre and bird observatory has recently been set up on Skomer. Lies within the Pembrokeshire Coast National Park."

Skokholm was first notified as a SSSI in 1954 and renotified in 1986 and 2001, and although it was proposed as a National Nature Reserve (NNR) the Nature Conservancy Council did not declare it because of the land tenure. With the ownership of the island now resting with the Wildlife Trust, the island is very likely that it will finally be notified as such in the next few years. The 1986 notification is reproduced below (note that most population figures have since changed):

Date of notification: 1954; renotification, 1986.

National Grid Reference: SM736050

OS 1:50,000 Sheet No. 157

OS 1:25,000 Sheet No. SM 70

Site area: 106 hectares (263 acres)

Description:

A relatively flat island of Old Red Sandstone rocks lying two miles off the mainland, of international importance for its seabird colonies. The maritime grassland of the plateau is a rare example of rabbit-maintained vegetation. The invertebrate fauna contains many nationally rare species, particularly amongst the Coleoptera and Lepidoptera, and the saxicolous lichens of cliffs and outcrops are of great interest.

The rabbits on Skokholm have avoided *Myxomatosis* due to the absence of the flea vector *Spilopsyllus cuniculi* and their abundance exerts on the island's vegetation a pressure which is additional to the effects of wind, salt-spray and nutrient-enrichment from seabird guano. This highly modified maritime vegetation has been the subject of much detailed research. An extensive band of hummocks of thrift *Armeria maritima* occurs on the southern and western coasts, along with much sea campion *Silene maritima*. Further inland and along the eastern coast, red fescue *Festuca rubra* characterises the short sward of the old field systems, with abundant Yorkshire-fog *Holcus lanatus*, common bent *Agrostis tenuis*, buck's-horn plantain *Plantago coronopus* and English stonecrop *Sedum anglicum*. Bracken *Pteridium aquilinum* is encroaching on the plateau grasslands and on the limited areas of maritime heath that occur on the eastern side of the island. Springs and seasonally inundated depressions in the boulder clay that caps the centre of the island have a marsh flora of rushes *Juncus* spp. and sedges, particularly sand sedge *Carex arenaria*, with much marsh pennywort *Hydrocotyle vulgaris*.

About 36,000 pairs of Manx shearwater and 6,000 pairs of storm petrel breed in burrows or crevices, and much research on these nocturnal seabirds has been undertaken since the island was established as Britain's first Bird Observatory by R.M. Lockley in 1933. Most of the studies on the breeding biology of the storm petrel have taken place on Skokholm, where 17,000 - 19,000 individual birds can be present at the height of the breeding season. Four thousand lesser black-backed gull, 2,500 puffin, 500 Razorbill and 200 Guillemot pairs also breed. Other breeding birds in 1985 include herring gull (350 pairs), fulmar (56 pairs), oystercatcher (39 pairs), wheatear (17 pairs), rock and meadow pipit and skylark (about 20 pairs of each), great black-backed gull (11 pairs) and lapwing (3 pairs). The invertebrate fauna has been well studied, and a number of scarce beetles have been recorded, associated with a variety of habitats. About 25 species are regarded as nationally scarce, including *Trox scaber*, which is abundant in bird's nests, the coastal *Gronops lunatus* and the tortoise beetle *Cassida hemisphaeria*, which is found only on sea campion. Several local moths occur, mainly species of cliff vegetation on rocky western coasts, such as the thrift clearwing *Bembecia muscaeformis* and black-banded *Polymixtis xanthomista*, but also species dependant on saxicolous lichens, the marbled green *Cryphia muralis* and hoary footman *Eilema griseola* for example.

The freely-drained soils of the plateau support a few locally scarce plants, notably an enormous population of sea storks-bill *Erodium maritimum* and wild pansy *Viola tricolor* spp *tricolor*, but on the cliffs out of reach of the rabbits, small colonies of tree mallow *Lavatera arborea*, the large, fleshy-leaved variety of buck's-horn plantain *P. coronopus* var. *maritimus* and sea purslane *Halimione portulacoides* persist. The wet depressions also contain interesting plants which are locally distributed in Wales, particularly the three-lobed crowfoot *Ranunculus tripartitus*, chaffweed *Anagallis minima*, nettle-leaved goosefoot *Chenopodium murale*, red goosefoot *Chenopodium rubrum*, lesser water-plantain *Baldellia ranunculoides*, adder's-tongue *Ophioglossum vulgatum* and lesser marsh-wort *Apium inundatum*. A total of about 270 higher plants have been recorded. The 3 - 4 miles of cliffs and the inland outcrops support several interesting lichens, amongst which *Catillaria biformigera*, *Rinodina confragosa* and *Bacidia scopulicola* are nationally scarce, whilst the foreshore and sub-tidal areas are also a marine interest.

The site is within the Pembrokeshire Coast National Park. The island is leased to the West Wales Trust for Nature Conservation and managed as a nature reserve. It is much used for detailed ornithological and botanical research.

The site was re-notified in accordance with Section 28 of the Wildlife and Countryside Act 1981 (as amended) in March 1986.

In 1963, through the efforts of the CPFS's Warden at Dale Fort John Barrett (who oversaw the running of Skokholm from late-1947 until October 1968), the Edward Grey Institute for Field Ornithology (EGI) at Oxford University became responsible for the scientific direction of observatory staff, under the auspices of Dr. David Lack. Until this time the Bird Observatory had obtained a great reputation as a ringing station with respect to migratory birds, but in general there had been little study made of the island's breeding seabirds. With the migration patterns of the other birds relatively well understood, it was the turn of the gulls, the Manx shearwater, the razorbill and storm petrel, and as a result these species became the subjects of several long-term population studies. An EGI PhD student was employed as the Island Warden, and as a Demonstrator of Oxford University, answerable to the Field Studies Council, whilst two assistants were responsible for cooking and the many other duties required on the reserve. Under such a setup there was inevitably some clash of interests as wardening work perhaps became secondary to the research as far as the Warden was concerned (Lawman, 2000).

In 1969, the lease was renewed for the West Wales Naturalist's Trust (WWNT, formerly WWFS), but the long-standing collaboration with the CPFS had previously been discontinued as a result of a dispute with the landlord over the unauthorized erection of a building by the CPFS that led to the owner threatening to severely curtail any research work. This was something the CPFS could not accept, given that its work involved trapping. Relations with the WWFS were not good in any case, with numerous disputes about fees, advertising and production of the annual reports. So the officers of the WWNT became responsible for provisioning and transport. The ban on trapping did not materialise, however, and the EGI continued its seabird studies unabated. But in late 1976, the landlord finally had his way, following yet more reports of cruelty to birds and animals – a change in the conditions of the lease meant that trapping and ringing had to stop, so the Edward Grey Institute for Ornithology withdrew also.

From 1976, the WWNT ran numerous natural history courses on the island in order to attract visitors, and was generally delighted with how things went. So Skokholm's clientele has changed significantly, the island now being primarily a holiday destination, where people seem to like to "get away from it all", with bird-watching and photography the major pastimes.

Skokholm was described as a component (along with Skomer, Grassholm and Ramsey) of a Grade 1* site in the Nature Conservation Review (Ratcliffe, 1977). The citation is reproduced below, but note that all population figures have changed.

"C.45. Ynysoedd Preseli, Pembrokeshire   720 ha   Grade 1*

(a) Skokholm	(b) Skomer	(c) Grassholm	(d) Ramsey, Ynys Dewi
SM7305	SM7209	SM 590	SM7023

The offshore islands of Skokholm, Skomer, Grassholm and Ramsey are mostly bounded by cliffs, and Grassholm is largely a rock cone. They are famous for their breeding colonies of seabirds. On Skokholm there is a large colony of Manx shearwaters (35,000 pairs) and storm petrels (about 6,000 pairs). Rabbits are abundant. Skomer has Manx shearwaters in even greater numbers (50,000 – 60,000 pairs) than Skokholm, another large rabbit population, and there is an interesting geographical race of the bank vole (the Skomer vole) peculiar to the island. Skomer probably has the bulk of the guillemots (3585 birds), razorbills (1540 pairs) and kittiwakes (1630 pairs) nesting on the Ynyoedd Preseli and its bird populations in general are larger than those of Skokholm. Other breeding birds on the island include choughs, ravens, common buzzards and short-eared owls, and breeding colonies of puffins exist both Skomer and Skokholm (c. 8,000 pairs). On Ramsey, the first three species occur at unusually high densities. Also on Ramsey, the Atlantic grey seal has its largest known breeding colony in Wales (200 pups annually). Grassholm is famous for its large population of gannets (16,000 pairs) which forms the only colony on the west side of southern Britain. The cliff and rocky slope bird populations as a whole are the largest in the whole of western Britain south of Scotland, and these islands are currently being much used for studies of seabird ecology and population dynamics.

The vegetation of the interior of Skokholm and Skomer consists of the usual range of submaritime grassland, with moderately halophytic species, and grades into heath in places least influenced by spray. The vegetation of Grassholm over the two thirds not occupied by gannets consists mainly of Festuca rubra sward over a hummocky layer of peat which was extensively burrowed by the once extensive puffin colony. Floristically, these islands are not rich and their interest is largely faunal, though they have been much used for studies of the effects of breeding seabirds and mammals on maritime vegetation, and the character of the biotically modified vegetation is well documented. Areas strongly influenced by manuring and treading have abundance of species such as Festuca rubra, Agrostis stolonifera, Atriplex spp., Cochlearia officinalis, C. danica, Holcus lanatus, Matricaria maritima, Plantago coronopus, Poa annua, Rumex acetosa, Sagina procumbens, Silene maritima, Stellaria media, and Umbilicus rupestris. The rarer plants include Cicendia filiformis, Asplenium billotii and Juniperus communis".

Section 1.5. Past management for nature conservation

In the 1920's the Royal Society for the Protection of Birds (RSPB) embarked upon its Watchers Scheme in Pembrokeshire, where it paid a number of local people to keep watch on rare breeding birds, and this scheme also included the occupants of Skokholm, Skomer and Ramsey. With the further aid of volunteers, in 1938 the whole of the Pembrokeshire coast from Cardigan in the north to Laugharne in the south was covered by such observers.

During R.M. Lockley's 13-year occupation, he pioneered seabird studies and wrote many books describing his life on the island and its wildlife and plants, as well as establishing the Bird Observatory. There was little actual management for nature conservation, though by the process of maintaining records of the wildlife and plants that were present, and investigating their natural history, the foundations were being laid for their conservation. The construction of Heligoland traps necessitated the planting of shrubs, and the limited farming and the control of rabbits did bring about a variety of habitats and their associated animal and plant species that are not present today. The Bird Observatory published an annual report from 1936.

In October 1930, whilst on Skokholm R.M. Lockley witnessed the tanker *Ben Robinson* leaving a trail of oil behind it, which extended some nine miles in the direction of Linney Head to the south-east. On 17th January 1931, a case was brought under the Oil and Navigable Waters Act 1922, resulting in a £25 fine plus "significant costs" being awarded against the National Benzole Company. Lockley himself was unable to attend the court hearing, being stranded on the island.

In 1934, a unique event took place on Skokholm, as about 140 delegates of the 8th International Ornithological Congress undertook a field trip to the island, following meetings in Oxford the previous week. Of special interest to the group of eminent persons – including ex-King Ferdinand of Bulgaria – were the Manx shearwaters, which Lockley showed to the group by removing some from his study burrows on The Knoll behind the cottage. A "well-known oologist" stole the egg of a storm petrel, and it was probably a carelessly discarded cigarette that led to a fire smouldering underground for days after the event, putting the shearwaters all at risk (Lockley, 1947). In the short-term, at least, this meeting could not have been deemed a good conservation measure!

In 1938, Lockley and R.M. Whitehead formed the Pembrokeshire Bird Protection Society (presently called The Wildlife Trust of South & West Wales). This organization was supported financially by the RSPB and effectively brought about the replacement of the RSPB's Watchers Scheme that involved the recruitment of Honorary Watchers (following an obligatory subscription to the Bird Society). Landing tickets were then required by any person wishing to visit the islands of Ramsey, Skomer, Skokholm and Grassholm, rather than have them land without authorisation.

In 1946, the West Wales Field Society took over Skokholm Bird Observatory. From then on, there are good records of management activities in annual reports. In addition, from 1981 to 1987, cards were completed as part of the Event Record Scheme – a Nature Conservancy Council (NCC) project, in collaboration with the Biological Records Centre at Monks Wood Experimental Station – where all events (natural and man-made) that might possibly have a lasting effect on the island, were detailed. These included: any actions by staff or others that were likely to lead to a change in the ecosystem, or which assisted the maintenance of a stable sub-climax vegetation condition and included desirable and undesirable activities; research, surveys and other recording activities; natural occurrences with a lasting effect on the ecosystem; and administrative details that were likely to be of value to Wardens as *aides memoires* in running the reserve efficiently. Notes on other events prior to this period were also entered onto cards, such as information obtained from previous annual reports, island Chatty Logs and various other sources of information (e.g. the many books of R.M. Lockley). A copy of each card was sent to the NCC, and the data entered onto a computer, whereupon a printed summary was sent back to the recorder (copies are held on Skokholm and with the Countryside Council for Wales).

The non-intensive farming carried out from the 18th Century onwards probably led to a diverse flora and fauna being found on the island. For example, Lockley reports of breeding corncrake *Crex crex* in 1930 and the presence of various agricultural weeds that are extremely rare in Britain today. Ploughing would obviously have restricted the distribution of Manx shearwaters (Smith *et al.*, 2001), but lapwing *Vanellus vanellus* undoubtedly fared well. Collection of gulls' eggs would have kept numbers of these predators down, to the perceived benefit of other species.

The site has not required a great deal of conservation management by way of habitat manipulation, with the plant communities mainly under the influence of grazing by rabbits *Oryctolagus cuniculus* and of the wind and salty sea-spray and thus maintaining a breeding habitat suitable for all of the birds deemed "important" (in national and international terms) on the island.

Section 1.6. Present nature conservation status

Skokholm Island is a Site of Special Scientific Interest (SSSI), and part of the Skomer and Skokholm Special Protection Area (SPA). It is part of the Pembrokeshire Coast National Park, which is also the planning authority. The island, together with Skomer and Grassholm, is given year-round "Avoidance" within the Ministry of Defence Low Flying System concerning aircraft training exercises, following numerous occasions when breeding birds were extremely disturbed by passing jet aeroplanes.

SSSI status under the Wildlife and Countryside Act 1981

The second renotification was made by the Countryside Council for Wales on 14th December 2001. The following is taken directly from the schedule, and applies to the present day, apart from the matter of ownership.

CYNGOR CEFN GWLAD CYMRU
COUNTRYSIDE COUNCIL FOR WALES

<u>SITE OF SPECIAL SCIENTIFIC INTEREST: CITATION</u>

PEMBROKESHIRE   **SKOKHOLM**

Local Planning Authority: PEMBROKESHIRE COAST NATIONAL PARK

Date of Notification: 14th December 2001

National Grid Reference: SM 736050

OS Maps: 1:50,000 Sheet number: 157
                                       1:10,000 Sheet number: SM70SW

Site Area: 107.3 ha (approx.)

Description:

The site is of special interest for its maritime grassland, and its breeding seabirds, in particular for Manx shearwater <u>Puffinus puffinus</u>, puffin <u>Fratercula arctica</u>, storm petrel <u>Hydrobates pelagicus</u>, razorbill <u>Alca torda</u>, guillemot <u>Uria aalge</u>, lesser black-backed gull <u>Larus fuscus</u>, which together with fulmar <u>Fulmarus glacialis</u>, herring gull <u>Larus argentatus</u> and great black-backed gull <u>Larus marinus</u> comprise a seabird assemblage, and for breeding chough <u>Pyrrhocorax pyrrhocorax</u>. Grey seals <u>Halichoerus grypus</u> which breed and haul out on the foreshore and the littoral zone are also of special interest. An assemblage of nationally rare and scarce lichens occurs including the scheduled golden hair lichen <u>Teloschistes flavicans</u>. Skokholm is located approximately 3 km south west of the Marloes peninsula. The island is composed of Old Red Sandstone rock, forming the western-most exposure of this rock extending across Wales. The gently sloping plateau surface, 50 metres above sea level at its highest, southern end, is capped with glacial deposits, and the main soil type is a clay-rich acid brown earth. The cliffs on the southern side are vertical, but elsewhere they become much more indented and irregular.

The southwest shores of Skokholm are subject to the greatest degree of exposure. The sub-tidal fringe here is dominated by dense thongweed Himanthalia elongata with an understorey of mussels Mytilus edulis and coralline algae. On the less exposed north-western side, kelp Laminaria digitata occurs with thongweed over coralline and red algae. The more sheltered eastern side of the island supports sub-tidal fringe rock dominated by kelp, including a nationally scarce tide-swept kelp community with sea squirts and bryozoans such as the gooseberry seasquirt Dendrodoa grossularia and the bryozoan Alcyonidium gelatinosum. Lower shores on the exposed south-western side exhibit zones of barnacles Semibalanus balanoides and mussels and abundant coralline algae including Corallina officinalis, above which the exposed form of bladder wrack Fucus vesiculosus var. linearis occurs with S. balanoides and limpets Patella sp. A band of pygmy lichen Lichina pygmaea occurs above this zone, but this band is absent from the less exposed shores. The lower shores on the less exposed side support thongweed with an understorey of encrusting coralline and red algae, above which channelled wrack Pelvetia canaliculata occurs with occasional spiral wrack Fucus spiralis and pygmy lichen over encrustations of barnacles and limpets. Upper shores support bands of black-tar lichen Verrucaria maura, with laver seaweed Porphyra sp. where more exposed, above which a wide band of yellow and grey lichens exists, extending vertically up to 30 metres on the steeper higher cliffs of the south-western side of the island.

The Skokholm rabbits have avoided Myxomatosis due to the absence of the flea vector Spilopsyllus cuniculi. This abundance of rabbits, together with the influence of seabird guano, has resulted in extensive modification to the maritime vegetation that has been much studied. An extensive band of thrift Armeria maritima hummocks occurs on the southern and western coasts, along with much sea campion Silene uniflora. Further inland and along the eastern coast, red fescue Festuca rubra characterises the short sward of the old field systems, with abundant Yorkshire fog Holcus lanatus, common bent Agrostis tenuis, buck's-horn plantain Plantago coronopus and English stonecrop Sedum anglicum. Bracken Pteridium aquilinum dominates sections of the more sheltered eastern coast, but is much more sparse elsewhere and has an understorey with abundant sheep's sorrel Rumex acetosella and wood sage Teucrium scorodonia. Only very limited relict patches of maritime heath remain on the eastern side of the island. Springs and seasonally inundated depressions in the boulder clay that caps the centre of the island have a marsh flora of rushes Juncus sp and sedges, particularly sand sedge Carex arenaria, with much marsh pennywort Hydrocotyle vulgaris. The island also supports a large population of sea storks-bill Erodium maritimum and wild pansy Viola tricolor ssp. tricolor and on the cliffs out of reach of the rabbits, small colonies of tree mallow Lavatera arborea and sea-purslane Atriplex portulacoides persist. The wet depressions also contain interesting plants such as the nationally scarce three-lobed crowfoot Ranunculus tripartitus, lesser water-plantain Baldellia ranunculoides, chaffweed Anagallis minima, lesser marshwort Apium inundatum and divided sedge Carex divisa at one of only two sites in Pembrokeshire. An assemblage of lichen species associated with rock (saxicolous) or the ground (terricolous) has developed on the island, including nationally rare and scarce species such as the scheduled golden hair lichen Teloschistes flavicans, Rocella fusiformis, R. phycopsis and Rinodina confragosa.

The nocturnal burrow- or crevice-nesting Manx shearwaters and storm petrels occur in their thousands, and much research has been undertaken on these species since the island was established as Britain's first Bird Observatory by R M Lockley in 1933. Lesser black-backed gulls, guillemots and razorbills also occur in the low thousands, and fulmars, herring gulls and great black-backed gulls comprise the remainder of the assemblage of seabirds. The chough also breeds on the island, together with oystercatcher Haematopus ostralegus, lapwing Vanellus vanellus, skylark Alauda arvensis and wheatear Oenanthe oenanthe. Grey seals breed in small numbers around the island in the autumn, and haul out on the foreshore throughout the year. Invertebrates recorded on the site include nationally scarce species of butterflies and moths with a distinctly coastal distribution. These include Barrett's marbled coronet Hadena luteago barrettii, whose larvae feed on the roots of sea campion, the black-banded moth <u>Polymixis xanthomista statices</u>, which frequents coastal rocks and whose larvae feed mainly on the abundant thrift on the island and the marbled green <u>Cryphia muralis</u> that is dependent on saxicolous lichens.

Remarks:

The foreshore from Mean High Water seawards is included within the Pembrokeshire Marine/Sir Benfro Fôrol Special Area for Conservation (SAC). Skokholm is part of the Skomer and Skokholm Special Protection Area (SPA).

The SSSI lies within Pembrokeshire Coast National Park. The foreshore is leased to Pembrokeshire Coast National Park from the Crown Estate.

The grey seal is listed in Annex IIa of the EC Habitats Directive (Directive 92/43/EEC on the Conservation of Natural Habitats and of Wild Flora and Fauna).

Golden hair lichen <u>Teloschistes flavicans</u> is listed on Schedule 8 of the Wildlife and Countryside Act 1981 (as amended).

The island was first notified in 1954 and renotified in 1986. It is leased to the Wildlife Trust West Wales and managed as a nature reserve.

SPA status under E.C. Directive 79 / 409 / EEC

Nearby Skomer Island was designated as a Special Protection Area (SPA) by the Secretary of State for the Environment in August 1982, under the provisions of the European Community Directive 79 / 409 / EEC on the Conservation of Wild Birds, which seeks protection of both breeding and feeding areas for internationally important species. In 1988, it was proposed that the SPA be extended to include Skokholm and Middleholm down to the mean low water mark, and this was subsequently confirmed in August 1991.

The following is taken straight from the SPA citation. Note that some population figures may have changed, e.g. Barnacle Geese *Branta leucopsis* no longer overwinter on Skomer.

"EC Directive 79 / 409 / EEC on the Conservation of Wild Birds: Special Protection Areas.

CITATION FOR SKOMER ISLAND AND SKOKHOLM, DYFED

The islands qualify under Article 4.1 by virtue of supporting about 7,000 pairs of storm petrel <u>Hydrobates pelagicus</u> (about 5 percent of the EC breeding population).

The islands qualify also under article 4.2 by virtue of supporting about 137,000 pairs of Manx shearwater <u>Puffinus puffinus</u> (about 49 percent of the EC population), 4,300 individual razorbills <u>Alca torda</u> (1 percent) and 19,600 individual puffins <u>Fratercula arctica</u> (1 percent).

The islands contain a range of habitats including cliff, maritime grassland, heathland, acid grassland, bracken and marsh. The vegetation is considerably modified by the manuring and trampling effect of seabirds and in particular the grazing activities of rabbits *Oryctolagus cuniculus*.

The islands hold the largest concentration of breeding seabirds in England and Wales. In addition to those species mentioned in the above citation, the islands have a range of other breeding seabirds, including herring gull *Larus argentatus*, kittiwake *Rissa tridactyla* and guillemot *Uria aalge*. The islands hold the largest colony of lesser black-backed gulls *Larus fuscus* in Britain.

Several Annex 1 species nest, including peregrine falcon *Falco peregrinus*, short-eared owl *Asio flammeus* and chough *Pyrrhocorax pyrrhocorax*, and barnacle geese *Branta leucopsis* overwinter."

Special Area of Conservation (SAC)

Under the European Habitats Directive (Council Directive 92/43/EEC on the conservation of natural habitats and of wild fauna and flora), the British Government had to draw up a list of sites that require protection because of their special interest, those with species and/or habitats described as "priorities" being considered first. This directive compliments the Wild Birds Directive of 1979 (above). A number of "Possible Special Area of Conservation" sites were identified in March 1995. Following public consultation, the "Pembrokeshire Islands possible SAC" was submitted by the UK Government to the European Commission as a candidate SAC in October 1997. The Pembrokeshire Islands SAC was renamed during the "moderation process" in 2000 as the Pembrokeshire Marine SAC. The following is taken from the CCW description:

Pembrokeshire Marine candidate Special Area of Conservation.

This is a summary description of the habitats and species of the Pembrokeshire Marine candidate Special Area of Conservation. It should be read in conjunction with the official map of the site and the document entitled "Reasons for Recommendation as a possible Special Area of Conservation", which contains a list of the habitats and species for which the area is considered to be of European importance.

The Pembrokeshire Marine candidate Special Area of Conservation (cSAC) extends from just north of Abereiddy on the north Pembrokeshire coast to just east of Manobier in the south and includes the coast of the islands of Ramsey, Skomer, Grassholm, Skokholm, the Bishops and Clerks and The Smalls.

Part of this area was proposed as a candidate Special Area of Conservation in 1996 because of the outstanding quality and diversity of marine wildlife in, on and around its reefs, estuaries, shallow inlets and bays and for its seal population.

The rocky reefs of the cSAC are very varied and extensive. The wide variation in physical factors, such as exposure to water movement, slope, aspect, topography and abrasion from adjacent sediments, is reflected in the diversity of biological communities. Important communities and species found here include tide-swept hydroid (sea fir), bryozoan (sea mat), soft-coral and anemone communities; sponge dominated and sea squirt communities in sheltered areas; tide-swept mussel communities, and rare species of sponges, anemones and sea squirts. Some of the species found on the reefs of the cSAC are warm water Mediterranean-Atlantic species.

The inlets, bays and estuaries range from Milford Haven, one of the best examples of a ria (a drowned river valley) in Britain, to the wide shallow embayment of St Brides Bay. Species richness of plant and animal communities in the sediments of Milford Haven is particularly high; the current swept sponge communities in the upper reaches of the Haven are unusual, whilst shallow sandy/muddy areas support extensive beds of eelgrass *Zostera angustifolia*, a relatively scarce habitat in the UK. The sea bed of St Brides Bay is mainly sandy or muddy, with occasional rocky outcrops near the coast. In tide-swept areas sands are clean and mobile, whilst in more sheltered areas the fine muddy sands support a rich mixture of bivalves and burrowing urchins. Mud runner crabs excavate burrows in the areas of soft mud found within the bay.

The grey seal breeding colonies of the Pembrokeshire coast comprise about 4% of the British population and it is estimated that 900 pups are born within the cSAC annually. The Pembrokeshire Islands population is important because it is the most southerly in Europe of any significant size and is relatively isolated from those elsewhere in the UK.

Following a review of the UK's entire network of candidate SACs in 1999 - 2000, it is now proposed that the boundary of Pembrokeshire Marine cSAC be extended to include the coast and seas off Linney Head, St Govans Head and Stackpole and a small area north of Dale that includes Pickleridge Lagoon. Intertidal sandflats and mudflats, a saline lagoon, sandbanks, sea caves, Atlantic saltmarsh, four fish species (Allis and Twaite shad and sea and river lamprey) and otters have been added to the list of important habitats and species.

The limestone reefs of St. Gowans Shoals and those off Linney Head host many animals that bore into rock such as the rock-boring sponge *Cliona celata* and piddocks. Many of the species that occur here, such as acorn worms, are limestone specialists and therefore restricted to this habitat, which has a limited distribution in Wales. The limestone sea-caves around the Castlemartin coast support a variety of animals and plants, including lichens, encrusting algae, sea squirts, sponges, bryozoans and hydroids. The animals and plants found here are adapted to low light levels and the community is therefore different to that of the surrounding shores.

Coastal saline lagoons are rare habitats throughout the UK and Europe and are listed as a priority habitat in the European Habitats and Species Directive. The cSAC now includes Pickleridge Lagoon on the upper shore of Gann Flats, Milford Haven. Large numbers of the lagoon cockle *Cerastoderma glaucum* (a species found almost exclusively in lagoons) have been found in this lagoon and it is thought that this may be the largest population of this species in Wales.

The intertidal mudflats and sandflats within the cSAC represent a range of different environmental conditions and are very rich in species (including worms, crustaceans and bivalves). Subtidal sandbanks also support a range of species, many of which spend most of their time wholly or partly buried in the sand. These intertidal and subtidal areas of sediment are important in providing a rich food source for birds and fish. Important areas of salt marsh are also found within the cSAC.

As well as grey seals, important species found in this area include the Allis shad, Twaite shad, river lamprey, sea lamprey and otter. Herring-like shad spend most of their adult lives in the sea but spawn in rivers (or, occasionally, in the upper reaches of estuaries) and usually migrate through estuaries on their way to the spawning grounds in April and May. Lampreys are a primitive type of fish that have a distinctive suckered mouth, rather than jaws. Sea and river lampreys spend their adult life in the sea or estuaries but spawn and spend the juvenile part of their life cycle in rivers.

The SAC was officially designated in December 2004. There now exists a SAC "Management Scheme". Its main aim is "to secure and maintain the favourable conservation status of the SAC by ensuring that human activities coexist in harmony with the species and habitats of the site." It should be noted that one aim is "to avoid unnecessary regulation", i.e. it will be based around voluntary local agreement.

As an aside, it aught to be mentioned that the island's most notable building has been given special protection of its own. On 10th December 1997, "The Cottage" or rather the main farmhouse, was included in the statutory lists of buildings of special architectural or historic interest, approved by the Secretary of State for Wales under Section 1 of the Planning (Listed Buildings and Conservation Areas) Act 1990. It is a Grade 2 listed building, described as a "small farmhouse of picturesque and unusual form, probably C18, in superb setting". Listed Building consent must therefore be obtained from the Pembrokeshire Coast National Park Authority before any work involving alteration of the cottage is undertaken.

Section 1.7. Current conservation management

There is a Management Plan that has been in existence since 1980, and which has recently been updated and installed on the new computer programme "Countryside Management System" (CMS) developed for all SSSIs by CCW, which will allow for easy access to all of the required information, and ease of reporting. The plan contains the following: a vision statement; a site description; a list of special features; and conservation objectives for each feature, drawing on a number of areas including favourable status, factors affecting the features, measurable attributes that allow the condition of the feature to be checked, and the rationale, i.e. an outline of the management required to keep factors within "operational limits"; and an action plan and management projects.

The key factors that need to be controlled include: bracken, various forms of disturbance, and mammalian ground-predators, all of which are described in greater detail under various headings elsewhere in this book, and around which management revolves.

Section 1.8. List of important features

The most notable features of Skokholm are listed below.

A. Primary features (those that qualify the site for SSSI status):

<u>Habitats</u>

Special habitats:

1. Maritime cliff and associates. Area 26 ha.
2. Coastal grassland. Area 55 ha.

Mixture components:

- Flush and spring, and standing water. Area 6 ha and 1 ha respectively.
- Bracken. 16 ha.
- Marshy grassland. Area < 1 ha.
- Intertidal. Area 1 ha.

<u>Species</u>

3. Golden Hair Lichen *Teloschistes flavicans*. Listed in Schedule 8 of the Wildlife & Countryside Act 1981 and is on the IUCN's (World Conservation Union) Global Red List of Threatened Species.

4. Manx Shearwater *Puffinus puffinus*. This species also qualifies Skokholm and Skomer for SPA status under Article 4.2 of the EC Birds Directive. The population is estimated to be about 46,000 pairs (Smith *et al*, 2001), probably the third largest colony in the world. It is a Red Data Book (RDB) species and is on the Amber List of the Birds of Conservation Concern (> 20 percent European population in UK, > 50 percent of the UK population in 10 or fewer sites).

5. Storm Petrel *Hydrobates pelagicus*. This species qualifies Skokholm and Skomer for SPA status under Article 4.1 of the EC Birds Directive. There are an estimated 1,009 pairs currently on Skokholm (Thompson, 2005), though past estimates had put the population at 5,000 - 7,000 breeding pairs (Scott, 1970). It is a Red Data Book species and is on the Amber List of Birds of Conservation Concern (> 50 percent of the UK population in 10 or fewer sites). There are only 41 known colonies in the UK (Lloyd *et al*. 1991).

6. Lesser Black-backed Gull *Larus fuscus*. A significant proportion of the UK population of the race *graellsii* has bred on Skokholm. In 2004, it was estimated that 2,000 pairs bred. It is on the Amber List of the Birds of Conservation Concern (> 20 percent of the European population in the UK, 50 percent of the UK population in 10 or fewer sites). The largest number estimated on Skokholm was approximately 4,600 pairs, between 1979 and 1983.

7. Guillemot *Uria aalge.* In 2002, 1,157 individuals were counted on Skokholm, the highest figure ever recorded. It is a Red Data Book species and on the Amber List of the Birds of Conservation Concern (> 20 percent of the European population in the UK, > 50 percent of UK population in 10 or fewer sites).

8. Razorbill *Alca torda.* This species qualifies Skokholm and Skomer for SPA status under Article 4.2 of the EC Birds Directive. In 2002 there were 1,285 individuals on Skokholm. There were about 2,000 pairs in 1937. It is a Red Data Book species and on the Amber List of the Birds of Conservation Concern (> 50 percent of the UK population in 10 or fewer sites).

9. Puffin *Fratercula arctica.* This species qualifies Skokholm and Skomer for SPA status under Article 4.2 of the EC Birds Directive. In 2002 there was a peak spring count of 4,115 individuals. It is on the Amber List of the Birds of Conservation Concern (> 50 percent of UK population in 10 or fewer sites) and is a Species of European Conservation Concern.

Assemblages

10. The assemblage of saxicolous lichens which are influenced by guano.

11. The assemblage of guano-influenced terricolous lichens.

12. The seabird assemblage defined as those species already identified (features 4 - 9) and also:

Fulmar *Fulmarus glacialis* – there were 176 Apparently Occupied Sites in 2002, and there seems to be a continuous steady increase.

Herring Gull *Larus argentatus argenteus* – maximum 1,400 pairs in the mid-1970's (278 Apparently Occupied Nests in 2003). On the Amber List of Birds of Conservation Concern (25 - 49 percent 25 year decline in UK).

Great Black-backed Gull *Larus marinus* – highest count of 72 pairs in 1949 (71 AONs in 2004).

B: Secondary features (features/assemblages/species of interest but that do not qualify the site for SSSI status):

13. Peregrine *Falco peregrinus.* A pair bred in 1930 and 1932, then virtually annually from 1988. It is an Amber-listed species in the Red Data Book and is a Species of European Conservation Concern.

14. Chough *Pyrrhocorax pyrrhocorax.* One pair bred annually on Skokholm 1992 - 1999 and 2001 - 2004, and two pairs in 2000. Previously bred only in 1928, but was suspected in 1965. On the Amber List of the Birds of Conservation Concern (> 50 percent of UK population in 10 or fewer sites) and is a Species of European Conservation Concern.

15. The invertebrate assemblage "especially of the orders Coleoptera and Lepidoptera" (a qualifying feature in 1954 and 1986, but no longer deemed so because surveying of many other areas in the UK has revealed lots of the same species). The site is nationally important for the conservation of harvestmen (Opiliones).

16. *Calluna* heathland. Area <1 ha. (this was formerly 5 ha; removed from SSSI notification in 1994).

17. Bluebell *Hyacinthoides non-scriptus* – restricted to countries with a European Atlantic coastline.

18. Three-lobed crowfoot *Ranunculus tripartitus*. UK status: Red Data Book vulnerable; a Pink List species for which CCW has an Action Plan.

19. The assemblage of ground-nesting birds, defined as:

    Oystercatcher *Haematopus ostralegus* – around 40 pairs on average each year.
    Lapwing *Vanellus vanellus* – maximum 27 pairs in 1966. None bred 2001 - 2005.
    Skylark *Alauda arvensis* – maximum of 48 pairs in 1966.
    Wheatear *Oenanthe oenanthe* – maximum of 38 pairs in 1951 and 1952.

20. House Mouse *Mus musculus*. A genetically-isolated and hence unique population of up to 6,000 individuals.

21. Rabbit *Oryctolagus cuniculus*. A maximum of (an estimated) 10,000 individuals, that maintain a relatively flower-rich turf and provide nest burrows for Manx shearwaters. Numbers greatly reduced in recent years to about 1,000 (Viral Haemorrhagic Disease and *Myxomatosis* both present, probably the cause of decline).

22. Grey Seal *Halichoerus grypus*. In 2004, there were 6 pups born on Skokholm beaches, approximately one percent of the Pembrokeshire population. The population is close to the southern limit for this species.

Chapter 2: The Physical Environment

Section 2.1. Climate

Skokholm was a Climatological Station from 1950 until 2003, with recording equipment supplied by H.M. Meteorological Office. For two summers prior to 1950, "private" instruments were used to record weather conditions. In 1950, in addition to the new official station on Northern Plain (with "average exposure" and from which the monthly weather report was compiled), two others were established, one situated in a more exposed situation, the other at a sheltered site. Measurements of wind speed (estimated using Beaufort scale) and direction, visibility, cloud cover, humidity, daily maximum and minimum temperatures, grass minimum and total rainfall were taken daily whilst the Wardens were in residence (normally March to October or November inclusive). In addition, a weather diary was maintained, noting general changes throughout the day, the time of the onset or cessation of rain, and so on. There is a more comprehensive recording station at Dale Fort Field Centre (Field Studies Council), which is operated throughout the year. Previous to the Climatological Station being established on Skokholm, and before a long run of data was obtained, figures obtained from St. Ann's Head were used to describe the climate on the island, and wind records obtained at the Skokholm lighthouse have also been used (Goodman & Gillham, 1954). Data concerning wind speed and its direction is currently also available from CCW at the Skomer Marine Nature Reserve (MNR), which has recording equipment at the former Coastguard lookout station on the Deer Park above Martin's Haven. Unfortunately, 2003 was the final year of weather recording on the island, because the incomplete recording (i.e. taken over just 8 or 9 months each year) meant that it did not conform to a British Standard, and the Meteorological Office was not willing to provide funds or equipment (the Stephenson screen was badly in need of replacement that year). All of the thermometers were removed in 2004.

Skokholm is situated directly in the track of the Gulf Stream. As a consequence, the climate is described as "hyper-oceanic", being "slightly moist" and "slightly cool", with the mean annual range and diurnal fluctuation of temperature being small; there are mild winters and cool summers (Bendelow & Hartnup, 1980). Consequently frosts are fairly infrequent and snow is far less common, with any that falls lying for only a very short time. Annual precipitation is comparatively low. The growing season is long but not intense. Insolation has been estimated as being about 36 percent of possible sunshine, and is at its maximum in June. Because there is a clear stretch of sea to the west of Skokholm (South America being the closest land in a direct line to the south-west), it receives the full force of Atlantic westerlies. Even though the stretches of sea to the north and east are miniscule by comparison, the island is still very much exposed to winds from these directions and is therefore one of the windiest places in Britain. Thus gales, storms and strong winds are characteristic of Skokholm, and are very important factors contributing to the degree of exposure and widespread damage to the vegetation due to the blown salt-spray (Goodman & Gillham, 1954).

A report from Her Majesty's Meteorological Office summarizing climate estimates for the island between 1961 and 1990 is found in Appendix I and is summarized below.

Opposite: Figure 6. The author standing beside Little Bay Wall (which bisects the rabbit-grazed turf of Northern Plain), enjoying snow on Skokholm in late-February 2004, the first time he'd witnessed such an event there in 9 years as Warden (a covering of hail – not quite as rare – does not count!). The buildings are seen nestling beside The Knoll, with the dark shape of Spy Rock in view beyond the cottage roof. To the right is West Knoll, and South Crags is beyond.

Note that because the island isn't occupied year-round, these are estimates interpolated from values on a 5 km grid (analysed from station values) taking into account the altitude of the location, and effectively representing typical values over a flat area of about one square kilometre centred on Skokholm.

Temperature

From 1961 to 1990, mean daily temperatures ranged from 5.7°C (February) to 15.8°C (August), i.e. summers are warm and winters mild. The lowest minimum temperature was minus 8°C (January) and the lowest maximum was minus 2°C (January). The highest minimum was 20°C (August), and highest maximum 29°C (June, July, August).

In summer when the ambient moisture content is high, south-facing aspects may reach high temperatures.

Relative humidity

In summer, the maximum hourly relative humidity was about 90 percent (June), the minimum 76 percent (April to August).

Sunshine.

The area is one of the sunniest in Britain, having an average of 4.79 hours each day during the period 1961 - 90, or over 1700 hours of sunshine each year.

Rainfall.

On average, 849 mm of rain fell in a year, the wettest months being December (100mm) and January (90mm). On average, 45 mm of rain fell in July, the driest month. Hail was recorded on an average of 18 days per annum.

Wind.

The mean wind speed (at 10m height) is estimated at 13.2 knots or 6.78m/second. The island is therefore classed as "very exposed", i.e. with wind speed greater than 6.6 metres per second. Data is also collected locally by the Skomer Marine Nature Reserve, and it is seen that the island is subject to frequent strong winds, with gales on an average of 31.5 days each year, the majority from the south and west.

Frost

Snowfall is very rare (4.5 days/year 1961 - 90) and it quickly melts when it does occur. Grass frost averages 32 days in a year, and air frost 9.4 days. Most of these are not actually observed because the island is not occupied during the period mid-December to late February.

It is notable that even in mid-summer, most visitors find the climate rather cool, but the proliferation of central-heating in modern day housing probably accentuates the coolness experienced on the island.

Section 2.2. Hydrology

A number of springs, flushes and ponds are found on the island. Normally only one area, North Pond, retains open water throughout the summer months (though it is reduced in size to a small pool, with a firm sand and stone bed). When full, it is the largest area of standing water, of almost 1 ha in size, and is fully exposed to sun and wind. From October to May there is an inflow of surface water through several channels from "The Bog" in the centre of the island (to the south). At other times of year, rainfall is insufficient to raise the water table and cause the streams to flow at the surface. When the pond water level is sufficiently high there is an outflow via North Gully stream, into an area of damp grassland where sand sedge *Carex arenaria* is dominant, and which retains pools – previously ancient "turbaries" from which "peat" was dug for burning – through the wetter part of the year. Another stream flows to the west, through Long Low (another temporary pool), terminating in a waterfall over the cliffs at Twinlet Bay.

Surface drainage also accumulates to the south, forming two other relatively-large ponds (Winter Pond and South Pond), but much of this water quickly runs off in streams and cliff-flushes and seepages, and so they dry up entirely during the summer months, despite attempts at simple dam construction. However, periods of continuous or heavy rainfall may have the upper reaches of the streams flowing for a short time even in midsummer. The temporary ponds are both shallow and exposed, used by gulls for bathing and drinking, and in the spring and early summer a flora of algae soon develops in the warm and highly-eutrophicated water.

Springs and flushes located on a fault-line orientated approximately N-S from Orchid Bog/ North Haven to East Bog/Crab Bay produce areas of open water during the winter months, but otherwise disappear beneath mats of vegetation. One of these is tapped in order to supply drinking water ("the well") and the supply from this is quite reliable. A number of other wet flushes rise to the cliffs, particularly along the south coast, and in particular at The Dip, where a shallow pool persists through much of the year.

The quality of ground-water is undoubtedly modified by nutrients from bird- and animal-droppings, and salty sea-spray. In 1998, a chemical analysis was carried out on the water issuing from the kitchen tap (direct from "the well") in addition to the bacterial check. The observations were reported by Pembrokeshire County Council's Environmental Health Department as follows: "*This sample of private water was acidic in reaction, and exhibited an intermediate level of corrosivity, as demonstrated by the Langelier Index. The water was odourless and of a satisfactory appearance, including freedom from turbidity and sediment, with a reasonable taste. Traces of metallic impurities were present in the water with their concentrations contained within the respective maximum admissible limits for a potable supply. The level of zinc was very marginally elevated, suggesting contact of the water with a galvanised surface at some stage. This has not, however, altered the potability of the water. The nitrate concentration was at an acceptable level, amounting to some 41 percent of the maximum limit.*"

The zinc had undoubtedly originated from the galvanized storage tank. Skokholm waters, draining through sandstone, are relatively soft; there has been no fertilization of much of the land for at least 80 years, though it was once limed.

Davis (1956a) detailed the results of chemical measurements made in the island ponds and streams in September. Blown sea-spray renders North, South and Winter Ponds distinctly brackish at times, with the concentrations of dissolved salts increasing with evaporation of water.

Section 2.3. Geology and geomorphology

The following is based on a report by E. Jones (1949), a hand-drawn map and report by Barbara Whitaker (date unknown) and another by Sid Howells, Area Earth Scientist with the Countryside Council for Wales.

Skokholm is composed of sedimentary rocks that form part of the sequence commonly referred to as the "Old Red Sandstone" and they are mainly of Devonian age. Those on the island belong to the Moor Cliffs Formation of the Milford Haven Group. They are predominantly bright-red calcareous mudstones (marls), siltstones and fine sandstones together with subordinate, but prominent, medium-to-coarse-grained micaceous and/or feldspathic sandstones. The last-named are generally purple in colour but are occasionally green and sometimes display lenses of conglomerate. In places, particularly on the north coast, edges of layers of more resistant sandstones are exposed, forming ledges that are suitable for cliff-nesting seabirds, and some caves have resulted from marine erosion of the softer material once sandwiched between two resistant layers (see Figure 7). Within the marls there are numerous well-developed calcrete horizons. These are characterised by an abundance of calcium carbonate nodules which, by interaction with rain and salt-spray, have resulted in the development of shallow solution pits. The sequence also includes a series of magenta-coloured tuff beds (volcanic ashes) of varying thickness up to about 1.5m, including the Townsend Tuff Bed and Pickard Bay Tuff Bed, exposed in the cliffs along the south coast and at the western end of the island. The Townsend Tuff is an important stratigraphic marker horizon, which is locally taken as the base of the Devonian Series. The lowest part of the sequence on Skokholm, lying below this horizon, and to the north of a line between Crab Bay and Mad Bay, is of Silurian age.

The sedimentary sequence was deposited on a low-lying coastal plain approximately 410 to 395 million years ago. The sandstones represent deposits of broad and shallow river channels, whilst the silts and muds were deposited in times of flood, with possible brackish marine incursions. On the mainland this sequence has yielded fossil remains of some of the earliest land plants and primitive fish. Infilled burrows are common and are generally thought to be the burrows of arthropods or possibly amphibians. There is a "Fossil Bay" on the island, so presumably some have been discovered in the past.

The rocks were affected by the Variscan Orogeny which imposed a fairly well-developed slaty cleavage in the mudstones and tuffs at 30° - 35° to the bedding plane. At Spy Rock this is at an angle of 80° to the horizontal. Some of these rocks have previously been utilised as roofing materials for some of the buildings, whilst flagstones and walling materials have perhaps been derived from the micaceous siltstone/sandstone beds. The bedding generally dips southwards at an angle of between 40° and 50°, but there are several fold axes which traverse the island from WNW to ESE. The most prominent of these is the asymmetric syncline which affects the rocks of the southern cliffs and at the south-western end of the island in the vicinity of "The Quarry" (see Figure 4, page 21). The southern limb of the syncline dips towards the north at about 45° (in places the angle of dip is far greater, to between 65° and 85° - see Figure 25, page 140), but to the north the beds generally dip southwards at about 45° (see Figure 7), except in an anticline-syncline fold pair, the axes of which cross the island near the old farmhouse. A dextral wrench fault cuts across the eastern part of the island from Crab Bay to North Haven and there are a number of minor faults which show up well on the southern coastline. This also explains the existence of a line of springs that are drained away to the east coast by small streams (see Section 2.2. Hydrology). Jointing is also well developed, particularly in the sandstone beds, where the joints and en-echelon tension gashes are often filled by quartz veins. The general direction of strike is from east to west, with a pitch of 10° to 15° towards the west, clearly seen between Frank's Point and the lighthouse.

Figure 7: A cave in Calf Bay on the north side of The Neck, formed by the erosion (by the sea) of a layer of soft mudstone between more-resistant sandstones. In places a layer of quartz also affords further protection to soft beds of rock, and these are most easily observed at Twinlet Bay.

All rocks are generally impermeable, but seepages occur on the fault- and joint-planes. The main subsurface movements of water are confined to gradient controlled through-flow in the soils, except where there are impermeable till deposits.

The island has a gently-sloping surface that rises from 25m OD at the northern end to 50m OD in the south. This is due to the bevelling of the rock (cut by marine erosion during the Cretaceous and uplifted during the Tertiary) by southwards movements of the Irish Sea Ice Sheet during the Pleistocene. There are two small areas of glacial till on the island. South Pond is situated on one of these whilst the other lies near North Haven on the line of the fault mentioned previously. Numerous glacial erratics are present including an augite granophyre thought to have been derived from the Isle of Mull, all originally identified by T.C. Cantrill in 1909. There is a map showing the location and composition of those that are still known, located in the island files (some of the smaller rocks have been moved since 1909).

Skokholm provides an opportunity to study many sedimentological and palaeontological features of the most westerly exposure of the Old Red Sandstone outcrops south of the Ritec Fault, together with structural, geomorphological and glaciological interest. It has been recommended that Skokholm be recognised as a Regionally Important Geological Site (RIGS).

Section 2.4. Soils and substrates

With the exception of patches of clay, the soil is a uniform friable, reddish, sandy loam of the Brown Earth type. Ploughing and liming in the past has previously enriched a considerable portion of it, but since it has been left undisturbed for some time it has been suggested that it is developing the incipient podsol characteristics of a degraded Brown Earth. Its depth and stoniness show considerable variation (Goodman & Gillham, 1954). The proportions of the chief constituents of the soil may vary, depending chiefly upon the proximity of the underlying rock, local biotic activity and the nature of the plant community supported.

The pH of the soil has frequently been recorded being between 6.0 and 6.8, somewhat higher than usual for this type of soil, mainly due to the contribution of weathered marls and calcretes together with calcareous Irish Sea Till.

The chemical composition of the soils beneath the various plant communities is sufficiently similar to suggest that the edaphic factor is unimportant in determining the type of flora supported, but rather that it is the influence of grazing and exposure to salty sea-spray and wind. Indeed, Skomer has very similar vegetation despite a very different geology. The vegetation of Grassholm is, however, very different, and although exposure is generally greater, there are parts of Skokholm with comparable exposure, and Gillham (1953a) found that the factors governing the difference in vegetation between the two sites were biotic – grazing is completely absent on Grassholm – and not edaphic.

It was long thought that a sheet of boulder clay was present across much of the centre of the island, resulting in the impeded drainage of water and hence "the bog" and some ponds. In September 1954, W. Bishop sank several shafts in this area and found no definite boulder clay and he concluded that the Geological Survey map that existed at that time had perhaps over-estimated the extent of its distribution (Skokholm Bird Observatory Report for 1955). However, in September of 2003, CCW Earth scientist S. Howells took a small sample from the bed of Winter Pond during a deepening operation, and described a mottled clay (stagno-gley), containing fragments of the red siltstone and grey sandstone that are so typical of Skokholm's geology.

Digging and trampling by seabirds exacerbate erosion of the topsoil. Human pressure, through walking, accelerates the rate of soil loss, as demonstrated by many of the coastal footpaths being deeply eroded in places.

Chapter 3: Biology

Introduction

In the 1950's, Skokholm was probably the most intensively-studied nature reserve in the country. In general, much of the work carried out has been purely descriptive, often nothing more than annotated lists of species, albeit produced by specialists in a particular field of biology and thus forming the proper foundation for subsequent work. However, there have also been some more detailed studies, the island forming a virtually closed system in the case of less mobile or flightless species. However, it has always been the seabirds that have been the greatest attraction, luring naturalists and scientists from across Britain.

Section 3.1. FLORA – an introduction

The vegetation of the island plateau consists of a mosaic of herbaceous stands with bracken, affected to various degrees by the effects of exposure to salt-laden winds and to grazing by rabbits. These factors do not encourage a luxuriant plant growth, but the impressions of relative barrenness that are gained at first glance in mid-summer can be deceptive. The grazing has resulted in the development of a species-rich turf in the fields, most noticeable in spring and summer when flowers are produced, whilst vast swathes of sea campion *Silene maritima* and scurvygrass *Cochlearia* spp. cause the island perimeter to be brilliant white in colour in early-summer. The many acres of bracken require closer inspection to discover that they too hide many secrets, including large expanses of withering bluebells *Hyacinthoides non-scripta*, that flower profusely each year in late-May and early-June. These bluebells and a few cliff-inhabiting shrubs are perhaps relics of a woodland flora. Given that several cliff-top sites on the nearby mainland currently support a woodland flora – albeit somewhat stunted – it is reasonable to suggest that the island once had some tree or scrub cover. The introduction of rabbits (see page 90) would have led to the cessation of any natural regeneration of these plants, and their use as firewood and as building materials would have quickened the loss. The rock outcrops, meanwhile, are ablaze with the many riotous colours of the thalli of a multitude of lichens whatever the time of year.

There is only one indigenous "tree" on the island, this being creeping willow *Salix repens*, of which there is a thriving population at East Bog, mainly within the rabbit exclosure there (the fence was erected specifically to protect it, though it seems to grow quite happily outside). Growing low to the ground, it is hardly affected by the occasional summer gale. The most obvious woody plants on the island are rather stunted specimens of sycamore *Acer pseudoplatanus*. Some of these have been present since before 1947 (E. Gynn, 1985), presumably planted in the gardens and other sheltered areas to provide cover for birds. Much more planting was done in the late 1980's and early 1990's, as new rabbit-proof areas were set up alongside some of the farmyard walls. The result has been the formation of a narrow "copse", much favoured by migrant insectivorous birds. Although some of the older specimens are occasionally prolific seed-producers, very few of the seedlings survive unless protected against grazing.

There are many specimens of elder *Sambucus nigra* scattered here and there on the relatively sheltered eastern side of the island, and around the buildings and in gardens. The island "Chatty Log" of 1948 notes that ash *Fraxinus excelsior*, sycamore, *Fuchsia* and elder were planted in 1935 - 36. Many elders were also planted in the Observatory gardens in 1951, and subsequently in the Heligoland trap that was beside the Well. After the removal of goats in 1981, numerous bushes appeared in the bracken to the east of the Observatory (Gynn &

Gynn, 1982) and continue to do so. They were accurately mapped, and height and diameter measured in 1995 (report in island files). Those in the more sheltered locations do produce berries that are obviously relished by the island's blackbirds *Turdus merula* and occasionally migrants such as blackcap *Sylvia atricapilla* and garden warbler *Sylvia borin*, plus some of the hundreds of juvenile starlings *Sturnus vulgaris* that appear in late-summer.

Various plant species have been introduced to the island, particularly in the gardens, but with many quickly becoming extinct, e.g. pine *Pinus muricata* and Norway spruce *Picea abies* (Gynn, 1982). In fact, of the 270 or so species listed by Gillham, about 5 percent were deliberate introductions (Gillham, 1953b and 1956a, Goodman & Gillham, 1954). One species that is thriving around the observatory buildings is the extremely fragrant bunch-flowered daffodil *Narcissus tazetta*, but because this species flowers in March and April, it is usually only ever seen by the Island Wardens.

Also in the gardens and in the rabbit-exclosure at The Well are specimens of goat willow *Salix caprea*, cuttings having been planted in 1980 - 81. Cuttings of buddleia *Buddleia davidii* were introduced into the gardens in 1981. These died, but others replaced them in 1988, and in addition, 50 willow cuttings were planted in and around the Well Rabbit Exclosure. Also planted in 1982 were old man's beard *Clematis vitalba* and hawthorn *Crataegus monogyna* (Wardens Annual Report, 1982), none of which survived. There is also some blackthorn *Prunus spinosa* in the cottage garden – which is often heavily grazed by rabbits that reach the twigs by sitting on the tops of the adjacent walls – and hazel *Corylus avellana*. A few specimens of privet *Ligustrum vulgare* and blackthorn *Prunus spinosa* survive on a relatively sheltered cliff-face in North Haven. Rhizomes of yellow flag *Iris pseudacorus* taken from Skomer were planted in the Heligoland trap beside the spring (now known as "The Well" or "Well Pool") in 1956. Some have since been transplanted to North Pond and they continue to flourish, requiring a degree of control in the original site to prevent it from becoming a monoculture (they were also planted in Winter Pond in recent years, from where they were quickly removed when they began to spread too quickly).

The only nationally rare plant (listed in the Red Data Book) on the island is three-lobed crowfoot *Ranunculus tripartitus*, subject of a U.K. Biodiversity Action Plan, and which is generally restricted to just one shallow, ephemeral, spring-fed pool at The Dip and the stream which flows away from it. It is an Atlantic species, restricted to the western Palaearctic from Morocco to north Germany, and is declining throughout its range. Britain has a core group of populations on the Lizard in Cornwall, a number in Wales, and a scattering of old records across southern England to Kent. So Britain arguably has an international responsibility to conserve the plant for biodiversity. Described as a "winter annual", and normally flowering in March and April, it has defied this description on Skokholm by flowering throughout wet summers in the late 1990's and more recently, sometimes right through until December. Genetical investigation is perhaps warranted. It was first recorded in June 1949, and has remained in the same wet hollow ever since. The pool is situated in an area with a low density of breeding gulls, so it is infrequently visited by these birds, and nutrient enrichment is unlikely. This is despite it sometimes being littered with shearwater carcasses that are brought to the water by great black-backed gulls *Larus marinus* for "cleaning". The continuous flow of spring-water perhaps flushes nutrients through. The Skokholm population of *R. tripartitus* may have greater significance nationally than was previously thought, as it has recently been found that it hybridises "promiscuously" with round-leaved crowfoot *Ranunculus omiophyllus*, to produce the highly fertile hybrid *R. x novae-forestae*, so it is becoming even more rare where the two species coexist (FitzGerald, 1999). Thankfully *R. omiophyllus* is not found on Skokholm. The ivy-leaved crowfoot *R. hederaceus* is present, but this is not known to hybridise with *R. tripartitus*.

In 1997, a "nationally-scarce" species was discovered on the island. A single specimen of divided sedge *Carex divisa* was collected from amongst the sand sedge *C. arenaria* to the north of North Pond, between the outflow stream and Halfway Wall. It is only the second known site in Pembrokeshire, the other being at Dale on the nearby mainland. Mr. A. Chater of the Botanical Society of the British Isles (BSBI) confirmed its identity, and it was deposited in the herbarium of the National Museum of Wales. A search for this species was initiated by Dr. Pat Doody, an ecologist with the Nature Conservancy Council who, in 1982, was astonished that there was so much *C. arenaria* growing in wet hollows and suggested that a different species might be present, but it was not until S.B. Evans of CCW recalled that day in 1982 and made the request to the author (in 1997) to search for "etiolated" specimens of sedge. The sample site has subsequently been relocated, where the two sedge species coexist and look very similar to the untrained eye.

A succulent variety of buck's-horn plantain *Plantago coronopus* is found on Skokholm, variety *maritimus*. Upon inspection of the sea-cliffs and stacks, this fleshy form – superficially resembling a cabbage and growing up to 35 cm in height – is very obvious and would undoubtedly be considered to be growing in such a manner because of the absence of grazing. The plants on the main island are usually just one or two centimeters across where soils are thin and grazing is heavy, forming the dominant part of a biotic community brought about by a combination of intensive grazing by rabbits, burrowing, trampling and manuring. However, transfer of plants, and germination of seeds under laboratory conditions revealed that these are indeed two separate types, breeding true for several generations and not producing intermediate forms when grown in close proximity to the usual type (Gillham 1953? - unpublished). The succulent variety is intolerant of grazing, hence its distribution.

Another species that had its autecology closely studied on the island by Gillham was shoreweed *Littorella uniflora*. This unspectacular, grass-like plant is abundant in shallow water of all depression pans and seasonal ponds, and in some of the streams and ditches. It prolifically produces flowers and fruits as the ponds dry up, but is heavily grazed and adopts a rosette form, from which the stamens and carpels emerge. It also exists as a submerged, non-flowering form, with each changing to the other with transfer from one habitat to the other (Gillham, 1953?).

Other locally-scarce plants recorded on Skokholm include sea storks-bill *Erodium maritimum*, wild pansy *Viola tricolor* ssp. *tricolor* (at one of very few sites in Pembrokeshire), red goosefoot *Chenopodium rubrum*, nettle-leaved goosefoot *C. murale*, lesser water plantain *Baldellia ranunculoides* (though this species has not been recorded for several years now), tree mallow *Lavatera arborea*, adder's-tongue fern *Ophioglossum vulgatum*, chaffweed *Anagallis minima* and lesser marshwort *Apium inundatum*. A number of agricultural weeds that are now rare on mainland Britain were formerly found on Skokholm, namely field poppy *Papaver rhoeas*, Fluellen *Kicksia elatine* and field woundwort *Stachys arvensis*, but these are unfortunately now extinct on the island following the cessation of agricultural practises. Also, two calcicoles, cowslip *Primula veris* and thyme-leaved sandwort *Arenaria serpyllifolia* have also disappeared, undoubtedly as a result of the cessation of liming of the soil.

Overleaf: Figure 8. The main courtyard, seen from the roof of the "Middle Block", looking north-east. The sycamore tree in the foreground is actually comprised of three individual plants, and is a valuable source of cover for passerines on migration, and for the few breeding species (blackbird, wren). Also in the foreground, right, is a shed that is used as the island shop. The far block comprises (left to right) Wardens' quarters, kitchen, pantry, dining room ("Wheelhouse", where the wheel , figurehead, life-rings and nameplate of the wrecked topsail schooner *Alice Williams* currently reside). Note the water butts. To the right is a tiny, two-roomed building, part being the Warden's office, the other a storeroom or very small bedroom. Behind the wall, on the sheltered eastern side, are lines of sycamore saplings. More have been planted on the western side, within the yard (in 1997-98).

A herbarium was put together by Mary Gillham in the 1950's. Concern over its condition led to its removal from the island in 1988, and it was donated to the National Museum of Wales. Photocopies of the specimen sheets are, however, kept on the island but these generally show only silhouettes of the plants.

An attempt was made to improve about ten acres of pasture on the western half of Northern Plain in 1962 - 63 by the spreading of fertilizer (Lloyd, 1964). This was in an effort to assess whether the quality and abundance of food has an affect upon reproduction in rabbits. It is unlikely that there were any long-lasting effects upon the vegetation, and certainly nothing is obvious today – thrift *Armeria maritima* has been ousted by sea campion *Silene maritima* over much of the area, in a similar fashion to that of the cliff-top zones right around the island's perimeter.

Some aspects of the flora are reminiscent of those more typical in a woodland habitat, and it could be that the island was once wooded, but the absence of peat deposits precludes any pollen analysis. The Danes invaded Dyfed in 878 AD; the "Skok" part of the name "Skokholm" is possibly from the Norse "hulk of wood", which might imply that it was indeed wooded, since there were no rabbits to destroy such vegetation at that time.

Record cards have been completed since the 1950's, though the standard and degree of record keeping has varied over the years subsequently, depending a great deal on the interest in plants possessed by the Warden at the time and of the visitors on the island. A complete up-to-date species list with location details is included in Appendix II.

Subsection 3.1.1. Vegetation studies

The vegetation has been described in some detail by various authors, as follows:

- Lockley (1947) – a list of species, and a description of them and their locations.
- Gillham (1948) – a 25" map.
- Gillham (1953b) – an annotated list of the flowering plants and ferns.
- Goodman & Gillham (1954) – a description and map of the vegetation.
- Gillham (1956a). Plant notes 1954 - 56. New species not recorded in the 1953 plant list.
- Brooke (1964) – a 1:2500 map.
- Lawman (1976) – a 1:2500 map.
- Gynn (1982) – a 1:2500 map based on an early draft of the National Vegetation Classification (NVC).
- SSSI evaluation in 1986 – a description of the vegetation
- Ninnes (1989) – a 1:2500 map.
- Ninnes (1998) – a classification of the vegetation based on data from the monitoring programme.

Though much of R.M. Lockley's work involved birds, he had a great interest in all aspects of the island's natural history, and listed 185 plants that he found on Skokholm between 1927 and 1940 (Lockley, 1947).

In 1947, commencing with the involvement of the Council for the Promotion of Field Studies (now the Field Studies Council), there was a broadening of the range of studies carried out on Skokholm, to include far more than the ornithological work that had become well-established since 1933. With plants being the basis of all food chains, it was thought necessary to carry out a detailed survey of the botanical aspects of the island. In order to facilitate this work, in April 1948 a party of students from the University College of Wales at Aberystwyth laid a half-furlong grid on the island (using a baseline that ran from somewhere on The Head to somewhere on The Neck) and began to map the vegetation in September of that year. It provided a quality baseline map allowing later comparisons. In addition, M. Gillham established a number of "permanent" quadrats (which enable a very small sample area to be monitored in detail), but these and the grid-points were all subsequently lost, along with the data generated from them. Gillham (1953b) listed all of the species of flowering plants and ferns recorded during 1947 - 53, and this was subsequently considered to be an appendix to the general account of the vegetation of Skokholm that was published in 1954 (Goodman & Gillham, 1954).

In 1981 and 1982 another quadrat-monitoring programme was begun by Island Warden Elizabeth Gynn. She established 93 permanent quadrats, each with sides of 2 metres, where the percentage cover of plant species was recorded, plus one smaller 1m x 1m square situated at the south-western corner of the large square and further subdivided into 9 smaller squares for very detailed monitoring (see Figure 9). They are located so that they sample all of the main plant communities. Gynn also compiled a vegetation map in 1982, produced with the aid of a 1980 aerial photograph. Difficulties were encountered when trying to assign the vegetation to categories of the National Vegetation Classification (NVC*), thought to be due to the effects of the heavy grazing by rabbits. Full surveys of the quadrats were carried out in 1982, 1988 - 89 and 1997, with smaller selections surveyed at other times. The 1988 - 89 survey was initiated as a result of an outbreak of *Myxomatosis* in the rabbit population, when dramatic changes were expected to follow in the composition of the vegetation. Photographs were taken of all 2m x 2m quadrats in 1984 and both 1 sq m and 2 sq m in 1988. Subsequently, they were photographed whenever they were surveyed except in 1995 and 1996. In addition to the quadrats, 9 belt transects of lengths up to 70 metres were established and recorded by Gynn in 1982. Two of them, running through bracken fronts, were lost before a re-survey of 5 of the remaining 7 was carried out in 1990. A few have been surveyed on occasion since. They are designed to monitor in detail any movement of vegetation boundaries, and require up to 25 hours of time in order to survey each one. Photographs were taken during surveys, including annotated ones showing the beginning and end of each transect.

Another map, painstakingly drawn by R. Ninnes, (1989) was compiled from a ground survey in 1988 and 1989, with the aid of a 1984 aerial photograph. The base map was drawn as an overlay to Ordnance Survey maps, so ensuring accurate scaling. Ninnes did not attempt to assign the NVC classification to communities, and did not use the same classification as E. Gynn, so he did produce a report to compare and contrast the two. This was preliminary to him examining changes in the vegetation, and to attempt to assign NVC communities. In 2000, bracken *Pteridium aquilinum* was remapped using an aerial photograph combined with ground survey (figure in Thompson, 2000), and then sea campion *Silene maritima* in 2002 (figure in Thompson, 2002).

* The National Vegetation Classification (NVC) is a system based on natural habitat types according to the species they contain. It is published in 5 volumes by Cambridge University Press titled *British Plant Communities*.

Opposite: Figure 9. Theresa Thompson carrying out vegetation monitoring in one of the many quadrats, this one (number 56) located on The Neck and dominated by sea campion and ground ivy. The bay behind is Dumbbell Bay, and the jagged rocks are a few of the Devil's Teeth. Beyond lies the "mainland" in the form of the Dale Peninsular (ends at St. Ann's Head), and just visible further right is Linney Head.

Subsection 3.1.2. The results of the studies – the vegetation described in detail

Skokholm's vegetation communities are possibly unique. They do not seem to match completely with any previously-described NVC community, thought to be due to one or a combination of factors. The maritime grassland of the plateau is certainly a rare example of rabbit-maintained vegetation.

Goodman & Gillham (1954) were the first to show the strong effects that wind, sea-spray, rabbits and seabirds have on the vegetation, bringing about varying degrees of complexity and leading to an abundance of species that possess one or more of the following attributes: are able to tolerate grazing and sea spray; are unpalatable to rabbits; grow well with extra nutrients from seabird guano; or tolerate (or are even encouraged by) the burrowing activities of rabbits and birds. They described the vegetation as a complex mosaic of herbaceous stands, and divided it into six major communities and a number of minor associates, as follows:

1. *Armerietum maritimae*
2. *Caricetum arenariae*
3. Grasslands - *Holcetum; Agrostidetum; Festucetum*
4. *Callunetum vulgaris*
5. *Pteridietum aquilini*
6. Wet heath
7. *Erodietum maritimi*
8. *Plantaginetum coronopi*
9. *Silenetum maritimae*
10. *Cochlearietum*
11. *Rumicetum*
12. Aspect societies of *Senecio jacobaea*
13. Freshwater communities

It was found that these communities are distributed across the island in accordance with their ability to tolerate exposure to salt-laden winds, which mainly emanate from the westerly quarter. A degree of shelter is also afforded as a result of the island's plateau sloping down towards the east, where local wind velocities are lessened due to friction and turbulence. Thus the Armerietum (thrift community) is found mainly in the west, the Pteridietum (bracken community) in the east. Richard Ninnes' 1989 map is shown in Figure 11 (page 63).

M.E. Gillham (1955) published a detailed prediction of what might happen to the flora if Skokholm's rabbits were eliminated (thoughts that were undoubtedly prompted by the spread of *Myxomatosis* through Britain at that time). The various "rabbit exclosures" (constructed with rabbit-proof mesh) on the island today demonstrate some aspects dramatically – in the absence of grazing, red fescue grass *Festuca rubra* becomes completely dominant. That the decline of *Calluna* heathland on Skokholm is at least partly attributable to rabbits is also shown by the erection of rabbit-proof fencing on Green Heath in 1991 (and greatly extended in 1997), which has encouraged the heather to flourish within (see Figure 10). Plant species unpalatable to rabbits include Yorkshire fog grass *Holcus lanatus*, bracken *Pteridium aquilinum* and wood sage *Teucrium scorodonia*. In drought years, they have taken to eating creeping thistle *Cirsium arvense*, sow-thistles *Sonchus* sp., and sand sedge *Carex arenaria* (Gynn, 1984). Although Rabbit Viral Haemorrhagic Disease and low levels of *Myxomatosis* have intermittently affected the rabbit population in recent years, the only effect recorded so far has been a slightly greater degree of flowering of false oat-grass *Arrhenatherum elatius* (growing amongst bracken) in 1988, though it has since been suspected that the growth and flowering of this grass fluctuates from year to year anyway, perhaps due to the level of rainfall (both views are very subjective "observations").

Opposite: Figure 10. The rabbit exclosure on Green Heath (right hand side of the photograph). Erected in 1997, it clearly demonstrates how grazing pressure affects the vegetation. Outside the fenced area, only those plants that are able to withstand or avoid being grazed (most noticeably thistles here), manage to thrive. Inside, there is a lush growth of grass and heather.

After careful analysis of the various maps and especially the quadrat data from 1982 - 88, Ninnes (1998) summarized the changes recorded between 1948 and 1997, as follows:

- A spread of sea campion *Silene maritima*, increasing from 1 percent to 15 percent cover, a change apparently linked to the removal of Soay sheep in the 1960's and of goats in 1981, which previously grazed it (the combined stocking rate was about 1/ha).
- A 50 percent decline in the amount of thrift *Armeria maritima*, which had either been overgrown by *Silene maritima*, or become grassland (although thrift had become established in some new areas).
- The general spread of bracken, but decline in some areas.
- The substantial decline of Yorkshire fog grass *Holcus lanatus* and red fescue *Festuca rubra* in dry grassland.
- The almost complete loss of ling *Calluna vulgaris* heath.
- Eutrophication of wetlands due to gulls.

The changes all seem to be related to one or more of the following three factors: grazing by rabbits, past land use and changes in the abundance and distribution of seabirds. From the quadrat study, Ninnes also described three broad vegetation types comprising 10 sub-groups, as follows:

a) Maritime types: thrift-dominated turf; sea campion-dominated turf; dry short grassland (maritime); dry short grassland (ex-heathland); ling *Calluna vulgaris* heathland.
b) Bracken *Pteridium aquilinum*.
c) Wetland types: Yorkshire fog grass-dominated; *Potentilla anserina* / *Polygonum* dominated; *Carex arenaria* swards; spring-line mires.

Cliff vegetation was not included in the quadrat study.

Ninnes (1998) used the multivariate statistical analyses Detrended Correspondence Analysis (DCA) and TWINSPAN to demonstrate the main variation present on the island. He compared the grassland and maritime vegetation types found on Skokholm with communities described in the National Vegetation Classification. None of the NVC communities could be matched exactly, for two reasons: 1). The Skokholm vegetation lacked several constants of the NVC and; 2). The Skokholm vegetation has an abundance and constancy of species that do not appear in the NVC communities.

Ninnes described the Skokholm vegetation types as being almost within the range encompassed by the following NVC communities:

MC5	*Armeria maritima - Cerastium diffusum diffusum* maritime therophyte community.
MC8g	*Armeria maritima*-dominated sub-community of the *Festuca rubra - Armeria maritima* maritime grassland.
MC12b	*Silene maritima* sub-community of the *Festuca rubra - Hyacinthoides non-scripta* bluebell community.
U1f	*Hypochaeris radicata* sub-community of the *Festuca ovina - Agrostis capillaris - Rumex acetosella* grassland.
H7	*Calluna vulgaris* sub-community of *Calluna vulgaris - Scilla verna* heath.
MC7	*Stellaria media - Rumex acetosa* seabird cliff community.

The *Armeria maritima* type has the greatest affinities with MC8g. The perched grassland containing *Armeria maritima* and a lot of bare ground has affinities with MC5. The *Silene maritima*-dominated types have the greatest affinities with MC12b. The dry short grassland types are variations on U1f. The acidic maritime grassland group is U1f, but includes elements of the H7 heathland community. The maritime grassland group has mild affinities with MC8g. The dry short grassland / *Pteridium* mixes proved difficult to place, but have affinities with U1f and 12b, especially where *Armeria maritima* or *Silene maritima* appear. These are relatively poor "fits", with the community possibly tending towards U4b, the *Holcus lanatus - Festuca ovina - Agrostis capillaris - Galium saxatile* grassland.

The biggest obstacles to matching Skokholm data to NVC communities are: the abundance of *Agrostis capillaris* and sorrel *Rumex* species; the absence of creeping bent grass *Agrostis stolonifera*; and the rarity of sheep's fescue *Festuca ovina*. Several unusual factors go some way to explain the differences:

a) The long history of grazing by rabbits, which has produced vegetation dominated by relatively few species that are either tolerant of grazing or unpalatable to rabbits. This appears to have suppressed *Festuca rubra* and enabled the dominance of *Armeria maritima* and *Silene maritima*.

b) The abundance of seabird burrows, with consequent physical pressure and manuring effects on the vegetation. This may account for the abundance of *Agrostis capillaris*, *Festuca rubra* and *Rumex* species in place of *Festuca ovina*, which features more commonly as an associate of *Armeria maritima* in some Maritime Cliff NVC communities.

c) The manuring and trampling effects of roosting gulls on the main grassland areas. This may account for the abundance of *Agrostis capillaris* and *Festuca rubra* in the acidic maritime grassland, which would normally have *Festuca ovina* in the U1 community.

d) The recent decline of heathland, which left traces of a heathland community within the acidic maritime grassland.

e) The spring-time presence of *Hyacinthoides non-scripta* and *Scilla verna* means that they have not appeared in the late-summer surveys of the permanent quadrats. Adding these species to many Skokholm quadrats would provide a good match with MC12b, especially on the sheltered cliff-slopes (all from Ninnes, 1998).

The wetter areas on the island are, by intention, poorly represented in the permanent quadrat series. They are mostly very diverse and all different, but only occupy very small areas and so are of relatively little significance concerning the overall vegetation dynamics. The results of the detailed monitoring of the vegetation in quadrats show that these small samples are indicative of the main trends identified from study of the aerial photographs and maps. In addition, the quadrat monitoring revealed stable community composition within the maritime vegetation types dominated by *Armeria maritima* and *Silene uniflora*. Also, except for a change in grass species (from areas dominated by *Festuca rubra* and *Holcus lanatus* to *Agrostis capillaris*) the composition of Dry Short Grassland has been relatively stable. So, maritime communities may have replaced each other, but the species assemblages have remained fairly constant within each community.

The combined effects of the physical and biotic factors are further explained in Chapter 4.

The SSSI notification groups the Festucetum, Armerietum and Silenetum described by the authors named above as "coastal grassland". (Also see NVC Maritime Cliffs and Communities in Rodwell, 2000). The notification also lists the following qualifying habitats and mixture components, which are now described further:

Main habitats:
1. Coastal grassland. Area 55 ha.
2. Maritime cliff and associates. Area 26 ha.

Mixture components:
3. Flushes, springs and standing water. Area 6.5 ha.
4. Bracken and acid grassland. Area 16 ha.
5. Marshy grassland. Area 1 ha.

1. Coastal grassland.

The relatively flat plateau of Skokholm supports a range of sub-maritime grassland communities which are strongly influenced by the joint effects of heavy grazing by rabbits and manuring by the extensive seabird colonies. The combination of grazing and extreme salt/wind exposure allows a greater diversity in the sward than would occur where only one of these factors was present. In the absence of grazing pressure *Festuca rubra* would become dominant, but on Skokholm less-palatable species – notably *Holcus lanatus* and *Armeria maritima* – have tended to dominate all but the most-sheltered parts of the island that have not succumbed to *Pteridium* invasion.

There are numerous communities contained within the umbrella title of coastal grassland, with the main three described thus:

a. Despite the lack of a complete match, there is a close resemblance to NVC community Maritime Cliff 8 (MC8), the Red Fescue *Festuca rubra* – Thrift *Armeria maritima* maritime grassland. This community is grassland with a generally-closed sward, and of the grasslands occurring in coastal areas, it occupies the most maritime position. There are various sub-communities, of which the following are found on Skokholm:

• The typical Red Fescue *Festuca rubra* sub-community, where the *Festuca* is overwhelmingly dominant as a thick mattress. This is synonymous with the "Festucetum rubrae" of Goodman & Gillham (1954).

Opposite: Figure 11. Richard Ninnes' map of the vegetation, 1989. The scale of the reproduction makes it impossible to read the key to the vegetation. However, as a rough guide: the yellow areas consist of dry grassland; the pale blue as bog communities (with dominant species being Yorkshire fog grass *Holcus lanatus*, silverweed *Potentilla anserina*, marsh pennywort *Hydrocotyle vulgaris* and *Polgonum* species); the pinkish-red as thrift *Armeria maritima*; the paler pink as *Holcus lanatus*; the green that occupies most of the central zone (but is also near cliff edges in places, e.g. North Haven) as bracken *Pteridium vulgaris*; the mint green as sea campion *Silene maritima*; white patches are wood sage *Teucrium scorodonia*; the brown is "thin soil" grassland, comprised of *Festuca rubra* and *Plantago coronopus*. Bracken has since spread further into most areas, whilst thrift has been replaced by sea campion in many areas.

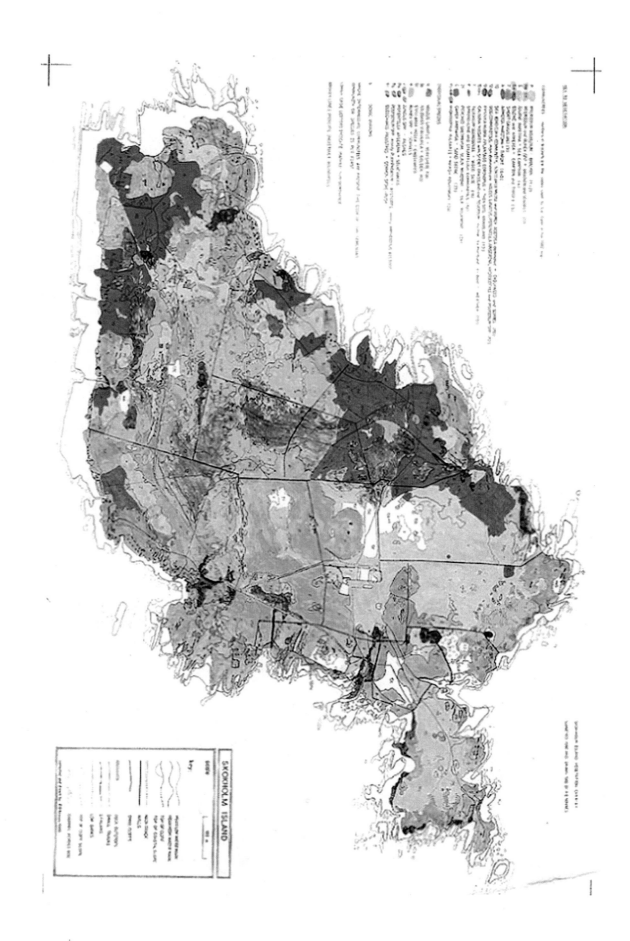

- The Yorkshire Fog *Holcus lanatus* sub-community. As above, there is a thick mattress of *Festuca*, with scattered *Armeria*, but here there is a prominent contribution by species that are characteristic of inland neutral grasslands. *Holcus* is constant and tends to make a substantial contribution to the grassy cover. This is synonymous with the "inland Armerietum" of Goodman & Gillham (1954).

- The Buck's-horn Plantain *Plantago coronopus* sub-community where, in stark contrast to the above, there is a short, tight sward, still generally dominated by *Festuca rubra* with scattered *Armeria*, but here with constant Creeping Bent *Agrostis stolonifera* and *Plantago coronopus*. This tends to dominate the thinner soils on some coastal slopes.

- The thrift-dominated sub-community, where *Armeria* and *Festuca rubra* are the sole constituents in this, the most open and species-poor of the sub-communities. The thrift dominates, with *Festuca* rarely attaining over 10 percent cover. Rock Sea-spurrey *Spergularia rupicola* is the only other frequent species. It is synonymous with the "coastal Armerietum" of Goodman & Gillham (1954). Of the island's plant communities, the Armerietum was once of primary importance, particularly on the south and west coasts. Thrift forms a deep bed of stems and leaves which birds such as puffins and shearwaters find relatively east to burrow into. It is very tolerant of exposure and grazing, although burrowing leads to erosion and tussock formation and perhaps the eventual death of the original plant. One effect of this on Skokholm has been the increase of sea campion *Silene maritima*, which is also resistant to grazing by rabbits and soon colonises the bare soil around burrows. Frequent associates in the Armerietum are *Festuca rubra*, sea mayweed *Matricaria maritima* and sea storks-bill *Erodium maritimum*; in addition, extensive patches of spring squill *Scilla verna* occur on the exposed north-west coast. The presence of *Rumex acetosa*, *R. acetosella* and *Stellaria media* is closely linked with sea-bird manuring and these nitrophilous species often clearly indicate the line taken by burrows underground. Further inland, away from the greatest influence of salt-spray, *Holcus lanatus*, *Viola riviniana*, *Radiola linoides*, *Anagallis arvensis*, *Lotus corniculatus* and others contribute to the floristic diversity of the sward.

Some of the floristic variation within this community can be understood in relation to a gradient of maritime influence and topography. Where site drainage becomes excessive, *Armeria* tends to become dominant over *Festuca*. Also, *Armeria* is able to root itself deeply on cliff edges prone to erosion, whereas *Festuca* is lost. Grazing produces and maintains the short sward of the *Plantago coronopus* sub-community, which is (not surprisingly) extremely widespread on Skokholm.

b. Also represented is a close resemblance to NVC community MC9, the *Festuca rubra – Holcus lanatus* maritime grassland. This is synonymous with the "Holcetum lanati" of Gillham (1953b) and Goodman & Gillham (1954). It has a rather rank and tussocky sward, classified as almost always being dominated by *Festuca rubra*, but *Holcus lanatus* is often abundant. It occupies a less maritime position on sea-cliffs, in somewhat sheltered positions. It is generally ungrazed on Skokholm, for *Holcus* is not favoured by rabbits, and grows best in damp places. This accounts for its widespread occurrence in the very centre of the island ("The Bog"). Gillham & Goodman (1954) suggest that its tussocky growth form protects it from exposure to some extent, allowing it to grow in places which it would not otherwise tolerate. In addition, the hairs on the leaves may intercept much of the salty sea-spray and so the leaf surface is protected.

c. The bluebell-dominated areas so admired by visitors to Skokholm are, as we have seen above, included in NVC vegetation type MC12, the *Festuca rubra – Hyacinthoides non-scripta* maritime bluebell community. Constant species are *Festuca*, *Hyacinthoides*, *Rumex acetosa* and *Holcus lanatus*, though grazing by rabbits modifies the vegetation to some degree by restricting growth of grasses. The *Silene maritima* sub-community is represented. It is most characteristic of situations where deep, moist and fertile soils develop. It is apparently synonymous with the "Pteridietum aquilini" of Goodman & Gillham (1954), although they gave no detailed account of this vegetation.

2. Maritime cliff and associated crevice habitat and communities.

The general prevalence of south-westerly winds over the British Isles, and the substantial fetch along the Atlantic coast, means that there is a far richer development of maritime vegetation on the west coast of Britain. The exposed nature of Skokholm is reflected in the vegetation, and particularly that of the cliff-face, of which there is approximately 8 km. The coastline is very indented, due to erosion of the fairly-soft mudstones along the many joints and faults. The highest cliffs are found to the west, in the face of the prevailing winds. The island plateau slopes gradually downward to the east, resulting in a degree of shelter being afforded to the cliffs of the eastern end and thus giving two widely divergent types of cliff habitat. In some bays on the northern side of *The Neck*, following differential erosion, spits of the harder rock afford some protection to the bays themselves (comprised of softer sandstones or mudstones) and have resulted in south-facing cliffs. The outcome is two-fold: firstly, the north-facing cliffs are sheltered from the main onslaught of the sea that is impeded as it enters the bay through the fairly narrow opening; and secondly, the southerly aspect of the cliff on the inside of the spit means that it is sunny, but relatively sheltered from the wind. Thus the microclimate is probably altered, although the higher plants do not seem different at first glance, but the lichen flora and the invertebrate fauna have not yet been investigated there.

The salty sea-spray, correlated with degree of exposure, is the primary factor influencing the distribution of plants. It is difficult to estimate the amount of salt commonly occurring in cliff-face soils, for it fluctuates markedly from season-to-season and even from day-to-day. Windy conditions prevail in the autumn and winter, therefore salt levels increase, but frequent rainfall then results in salts being washed away. In summer, hot weather results in evaporation of soil water and salts are left behind. This variability may cause problems for seedlings, but generally the mature halophytic plants have deep tap-roots and/or are succulent. The maritime influence means that climatic factors, other than spray-bearing winds, have a negligible effect. For example, frosts are rare, and long periods of hot weather are uncommon. Other factors influencing the floristic composition include: the presence or absence of grazing; seabird guano; nesting material; food remains and so on. But, as with salt levels, amounts of nutrients deposited in guano also decline from time to time, in this case overwinter when the vast majority of the seabirds are absent, so the maritime influence again predominates.

On the westernmost cliffs, where there is very extreme exposure to wind and salt-spray, plants are unable to survive and it is only in sheltered conditions that thrift *Armeria maritima* and rock sea-spurrey *Spergularia rupicola* can find a toe-hold. The less-hostile environment that prevails on the eastern and southern cliffs allows the establishment of a richer flora containing rock samphire *Crithmum maritimum*, rock sea-spurrey *Spergularia rupicola*, *Festuca rubra*, *Armeria maritima*, *Plantago maritima*, *Silene maritima* and common scurvygrass *Cochlearia officinalis*. In relatively-sheltered inlets along the cliff are to be found two of the islands rarer species – tree mallow *Lavatera arborea* and sea purslane *Halimione portulacoides* (at one of only seven cliff sites in west Wales – see below).

Crevices and inaccessible ledges provide a niche for plants which would otherwise succumb to the incessant grazing pressure of the island's rabbit population. In addition to the cliff species mentioned above, crevices also support sea beet *Beta vulgaris*, and where there is a freshwater influence from streams and flushes, sea spleenwort *Asplenium marinum* occurs commonly.

Sea purslane *Halimione portulacoides* is characteristically a salt-marsh plant in Britain and Ireland, where it grows at all levels of the marsh, but rarely it occurs on sea-cliffs (Akeroyd & Preston, 1984). On Skokholm, Gillham (1953b) mentions it being present from 1947 to 1953 "on the tops of small sea stacks in the north-east". On 14th August 1973 it was seen by S. B. Evans "north of East Bay on a rock in the *Crithmum* zone". It persists there to this day, actually situated on the top of a steep-sided and sharply-pointed rock in Obione Bay (the northernmost inlet of East Bay), just a metre or so above the high-tide sea-level. Two plants continue to thrive, at one of only seven cliff sites in Wales. No other vascular plants grow with it. There is no evidence of any consistent morphological differences between rupestral and salt marsh populations of *Halimione*. They do show great variation even within salt-marsh populations, presumably genotypic rather than phenotypic variation, and a large scale genecological experiment would be needed to test for genetic differences between populations from different habitats (Akeroyd & Preston, 1984). A pair of herring gulls *Larus argentatus* has taken to nesting on the top of the plants (from 2001 onwards), but no long-term detrimental effects have yet been observed despite a yellowing of some of the foliage (presumably as a result of guano deposits).

Fowles (1986) identified the following NVC maritime cliff communities: MC1, MC6 and MC7.

a. MC1 is the Rock Samphire *Crithmum maritimum* – Rock Sea-spurrey *Spergularia rupicola* maritime rock-crevice community. Constant species are *Crithmum maritimum, Spergularia rupicola, Festuca rubra* and *Armeria maritima*. It consists of a low-growing, very open "cover" of scattered vascular perennials rooted in rock crevices. This, the "Crithmo-Spergularietum", occupies the most maritime zone of vascular plant vegetation on rocky cliffs, where there is the largest input of salt from sea-spray and onshore winds and the highest salt content in the soil (Malloch & Okusanya, 1979). Seeds of *Crithmum* and *Spergularia* germinate adequately at high salinities (Okusanya, 1979). Within this extreme maritime zone, the occurrence of the association is limited mainly by the availability of crevices, narrow ledges and friable rock surfaces. It is rarely grazed by rabbits, being generally inaccessible, but the vegetation is sometimes disturbed and manured by seabirds. The Crithmo-Spergularietum is restricted in Britain to the south and west coasts. It seems that it was not identified by M. Gillham in the 1950's.

b. MC6 is the Spear-leaved Orache *Atriplex prostrata* – Sea Beet *Beta vulgaris* ssp. *maritima* seabird cliff community, synonymous with the "Atriplicetum" and "ornithocoprophilous vegetation" of Gillham (1953b and 1956c respectively). Constant species are *Atriplex prostrata, Beta maritima* ssp. *maritima, Festuca rubra* and sea mayweed *Matricaria maritima*. This community is very variable in its floristics and appearance. Usually one or more of *Atriplex, Beta* and tree mallow *Lavatera arborea* dominate in an open or closed cover, sometimes with abundant *Matricaria*. It is most characteristic of rocky coastal sites where there is a combination of strong maritime influence and intense disturbance by seabirds, notably gulls *Larus* spp., razorbill *Alca torda* and guillemot *Uria aalge*. The community usually represents the most maritime vegetation where it occurs, replacing the Crithmo-Spergularietum. It occurs patchily around the coastal cliffs of the south and west of Britain. The finest examples are found where there is little disturbance of nesting seabirds, such as on Skokholm. MC6 reaches its best condition in August, just as the majority of gulls are leaving or have left the cliffs.

It was generally assumed that the major influence of the birds is to enrich the soils with nutrients through their guano. But, in a study of herring gull *Larus argentatus* colonies on the east coast of Scotland, Sobey and Kenworthy (1979) demonstrated that physical disturbance in treading, nest-building and particularly in boundary-clashes ("grass-pulling") is also of considerable importance. Such disturbance fragments and may even destroy the existing vegetation, both directly and by making it susceptible to wind erosion, but the rate of seed germination is high in late-summer to immediately replace such losses (pers. obs.).

c. MC7 is the Common Chickweed *Stellaria media* – Common Sorrel *Rumex acetosa* seabird cliff community, synonymous with the "Cochlearietum" of Goodman & Gillham (1954). It has a scruffy but generally closed cover of *Stellaria media* with some *Festuca rubra*, *Agrostis stolonifera* and *Holcus lanatus* (each of which may be abundant) and a little *Rumex acetosa* and *Armeria maritima*. The abundance of these grasses suggests an affinity with the vegetation of enriched and disturbed inland habitats. Common scurvygrass *Cochlearia officinalis* is abundant only early in the spring. The community is always associated with disturbance and manuring by colonial seabirds, particularly where there is considerable excavation of soil, e.g. in the vicinity of puffin *Fratercula arctica* burrows.

As with the *Atriplex* – *Beta* community, this vegetation forms a mosaic with the surrounding maritime crevice communities and grasslands, and its spatial and temporal relationships with these is likely to be governed by the intensity of seabird activity and the maritime influence. This vegetation has been recorded from scattered sites form Pembrokeshire round to the Firth of Forth, and is at its finest in August and September on Skokholm (pers. obs.).

Generally, these community divisions are difficult to observe, particularly those of the rock crevices, since they are not pure and the classification should be viewed with a degree of flexibility in mind.

3. Flushes, springs and standing water.

The location of some of the streams, temporary and permanent pools can be found in the aerial photographs (Figures 3 and 4), whilst others will be locatable via the descriptions below.

Gillham described the freshwater communities in some detail. A brief summary of the various habitats and species as they existed in 2004 follows:

Ponds, temporary pools and associated streams.

Three relatively-large ponds exist on the island, these being North, South and Winter Ponds. They are much used by bathing gulls, and so manuring and consequently eutrophication occur.

Only a small proportion (around 5 to 10 percent) of North Pond regularly remains wet throughout the summer, to a maximum depth of about 70 centimetres. This is on average about 75 centimetres shallower than the deepest part of the full pond in winter/early spring. The vegetation here mainly consists of amphibious bistort *Persicaria amphibia*, with common spike-rush *Eleocharis palustris* and marsh pennywort *Hydrocotyle vulgaris* towards the shallower margins. Yellow iris *Iris pseudacorus* has been planted along a wall at the eastern edge. The open water is frequently covered with duckweed *Lemna minor*. Pond water-crowfoot *Ranunculus peltatus* and alternate water-milfoil *Myriophyllum alterniflorum* both flourish, although the former has been known to virtually disappear in some years (pers. obs.). Damp mud at the edges of a number of "summer pools" situated at various places within the winter boundary of North Pond has much lesser marshwort *Apium inundatum*. Others nearby tend to be dominated by *Myriophyllum alterniflorum* at this time. The outlet stream that runs directly to the north has plentiful creeping forget-me-not *Myosotis secunda* and blinks *Montia fontana*. In stream-pools where the water flows more slowly, water starwort *Callitriche* agg. is present along with small patches of fool's water-cress *Apium nodiflorum*.

Surrounding North Pond are numerous small hollows where there is impeded drainage. These "depression pans" have a relatively rich flora when they eventually dry out in late-spring and into summer, including much lesser water-plantain *Baldellia ranunculoides*, red goosefoot *Chenopodium rubrum*, water purslane *Lythrum portula*, shoreweed *Littorella uniflora* and marsh cudweed *Filaginella uliginosa*. They include "Long Low", which carries much water from the overflowing pond towards the cliff at Twinlet Bay during the wetter periods of the year.

South Pond is much shallower, normally drying up in May, the majority of water having flowed away via the outlet stream into Crab Bay. It generally has a similar floristic composition to North Pond when wet, except that soft rush *Juncus effusus* is present and very common. Red goosefoot *Chenopodium rubrum* flourishes on the dry pond bed throughout the summer, as do toad rushes *Juncus ambiguus* and *J. bufonius*, curled dock *Rumex crispus* and shoreweed *Littorella uniflora*. The outlet ditch (Half Way Dyke) to the south-east is dominated in its upper, and wetter, regions by water pepper *Polygonum hydropiper*. Further down towards the cliffs, the bed is most often dry except in periods of frequent rainfall; digging and manuring by rabbits is frequent, and so here stinging nettle *Urtica dioica* and ragwort *Senecio vulgaris* are common.

Winter Pond is more exposed, and is shallow (no more than 30 cm deep) with no tall growth of macrophytes, nor *Polygonum* nor *Juncus*. A stream drains it when its level is sufficiently deep, via its south-western corner through an area of sea mayweed and over the cliff. Water starwort *Callitriche* agg. is present in small amounts. Shoreweed *Littorella uniflora* becomes dominant as the pond dries out (usually in May), then *Chenopodium rubrum* dominates the remainder of the dry phase, fruiting freely from July to October. It becomes extremely eutrophicated during the early-summer as it becomes shallower, well-supplied with guano from bathing gulls, and warmed by the sun's rays. When any of the ponds show signs of silting up, they are excavated, though usually most of the material in them is organic and disappears once it is exposed.

A small seasonal pool in The Dip is the site of three-lobed crowfoot *Ranunculus tripartitus*, a rare species in Britain (see Section 3.1 – introduction). In addition, blinks *Montia fontana*, brookweed *Samolus valeriandi* and creeping forget-me-not *Myosotis secunda* are common. The outlet stream also contains these species, before it disappears underground in an area of burrowed thrift, and reappears as a wet flush close to the cliff-top, where again *Montia fontana* is common.

A number of rainwater-fed streams and rivulets arise in the centre of the island, in the "Holcetum lanati" of The Bog, and these drain into North Pond via some tortuous routes reminiscent of a river meandering across its floodplain. Their flora is dominated by creeping forget-me-not *Myosotis secunda*.

Springs, flushes and associated streams.

There are eight small streams on Skokholm, all but three of which (North, South and Winter Pond streams – see previously) drain from springs on the east and south coasts and terminate in species-rich flushes on the cliff-tops. The species of the streams draining the ponds (previously) also occur widely in the spring-fed ones, along with watercress *Rorippa nasturtium-aquaticum*, water pepper *Polygonum hydropiper*, brookweed *Samolus valerandi* and bog pondweed *Potamogeton polygonifolius*, although lesser marshwort *Apium inundatum* is replaced by fool's water-cress *A. nodiflorum*.

The occurrence of springs at various locations along the eastern end of the island results in a number of permanently-wet areas, these being known as Orchid Bog, The Well Pool (formerly known as Heligoland Marsh on account of the presence of a Heligoland-type bird trap there in the past) and East Bog. East Bog is floristically the richest area on Skokholm. Marsh St. John's wort *Hypericum elodes*, water mint *Mentha aquatica* and bog pondweed *Potamogeton polygonifolius* are dominant in a waterlogged mat of vegetation with a depth of about 0.7 metres. This was occasionally excavated in the past, but in 1981 it was decided that open water would encourage gulls (then experiencing a population increase) to bathe and possibly lead to eutrophication. A pair of Canada geese *Branta canadensis* has recently taken to nesting nearby, and the birds frequently graze the marsh plants and create open water. Both the *Potomogeton* and *Hypericum* require acid conditions if they are to grow, a factor that could possibly be neutralized by excessive manuring by birds. Two streams drain this area, joining to become one in East Stream, the gently-sloping banks of which have shoreweed *Littorella uniflora* and brookweed *Samolus valeriandi*, whilst the water itself contains some water-cress *Rorippa nasturtium-aquaticum*. This stream – which terminates in a waterfall at Hog Bay – was previously dammed in order to form a pond for livestock that is situated on the western-side of the main track that runs through the area. Creeping willow *Salix repens* also grows here, mostly in a rabbit-exclosure, along with rushes *Juncus* spp, lady fern *Athyrium felix-femina* and a few patches of purple moor-grass *Molinia caerulea*. On the higher marshland to the southwest, from which spring-fed water drains across towards the waterlogged soil, once grew adder's tongue fern *Ophioglossum vulgatum* (not recorded there since 1996); there still exists an attractive carpet of marsh pennywort *Hydrocotyle vulgaris*, lesser spearwort *Ranunculus flammula*, bog pimpernel *Anagallis tenella* and lesser skullcap *Scutellaria minor*. Due to the extensive cover of aquatic plants over the pools, there is very little in the way of surface-breathing insect life. Small ponds are maintained (by excavation of silt) in the vicinity of the springs at both Orchid Bog and the Well, and previously at East Bog (see above).

At the Well Pool, hemlock water-dropwort *Oenanthe crocata* and yellow flag *Iris pseudacorus* completely dominate, requiring frequent digging of rhizomes to prevent the area from silting-up completely. In recent years, another macrophyte in the form of common reed *Phragmites communis* has appeared, presumably by way of seed produced by plants on the cliff in South Haven, and is spreading rapidly. It required annual management, but does add some much-needed diversity to the pool. Where there is open water, ivy-leaved crowfoot *Ranunculus hederaceus* is abundant, where it competes with a spreading mat of fool's water-cress *Apium nodiflorum*, water starwort *Callitriche* agg., and two grasses, floating reed-sweet *Glyceria fluitans* and creeping bent *Agrostis stolonifera*. Bog stitchwort *Stellaria alsine* is also present, but only occasionally seen because of its small size. Small pools become covered in blinks *Montia fontana*. Marshy areas to the immediate north have a carpet of marsh pennywort *Hydocotyle vulgaris*, creeping bent grass *Agrostis stolonifera*, lesser spearwort *Ranunculus flammula* and occasional hybrid marsh orchid *D.* x *grandis* (cross between *Dactylorhiza praetermissa* and *D. fuchsii*) was described, though none have been seen since 1998. The stream draining into South Haven also has *Ranunculus hederaceus*.

The pool at Orchid Bog is dominated by hemlock water-dropwort *Oenanthe crocata* during the summer, with spike rush *Eleocharis palustris* and water mint *Mentha aquatica* in shallow water. *Hydrocotyle vulgaris*, *Agrostis stolonifera* and *Juncus effusus* dominate the marshy areas that surround the pool.

In addition to the springs, a number of flushes occur where drainage water flows from the island plateau towards the cliffs, and infrequently appear at or just beneath the surface. These are particularly frequent along the south-west coast, in the vicinity of The Dip. Green algae are frequent, along with blinks *Montia fontana*. Three-lobed crowfoot is also present in a flush to the south-east of The Dip, in the vicinity of the pool which also has this plant.

There are frequently large numbers of bird corpses in the pools, thought to result from great black-backed gulls *Larus marinus* bringing them to water for "cleaning". Therefore there is probably considerable nutrient input. However, Gillham (1952) carried out various physical and chemical tests on water samples from various sites on Skokholm, including pH, temperature, oxygen and chloride content, and of exchangeable calcium, sesquioxides and nitrates in the mud substrates. No high nitrate content of substrate was recorded, despite bird activity in the ponds, and this was attributed to their high solubility and resultant leaching.

Davis (1956a) carried out tests on water samples from all wet areas, including those for dissolved oxygen, chloride, and alkalinity. Water samples were taken on a warm September day in 1956. It was shown that blown salty sea-spray renders the three main ponds distinctly brackish at times. Levels of dissolved oxygen on the day of sampling were high due to the rising temperature and sunny conditions leading to rapid photosynthesis by various plants. Other wet areas were distinctly less oxygenated, particularly at depth, i.e. the flowing waters of the springs where there was relatively little plant life, and in the deeper areas of East Bog where light is unable to penetrate due to the thick mat of vegetation at the surface.

4. Bracken *Pteridium aquilinum*

Of all the major plant communities on Skokholm, the Pteridietum is the least tolerant of wind and salt-spray, as its distribution shows – in the sheltered east, its growth is luxuriant, casting deep shade in summer and so preventing the development of a varied ground flora. (However, once the fronds begin to die back in late summer, a flush of growth occurs in the common sorrel *Rumex acetosa* and ground ivy *Glechoma hederacea*). In the west, the increased exposure ensures that the fronds are sparsely distributed and stunted (except where they are afforded a degree of shelter by a rock outcrop), so the ground flora is typical of the surroundings, i.e. dominated by sea campion *Silene uniflora*, Danish scurvygrass *Cochlearia danica* and sea mayweed *Tripleurospermum maritimum*. Elsewhere, the canopy is sufficiently open to allow the development of a varied ground flora, with ground ivy *Glechoma hederacea*, goldenrod *Solidago virgaurea*, common sorrel *Rumex acetosa* and wood sage *Teucrium scorodonia* locally dominant. The most common situation is for *Pteridium aquilinum* to form a sparse canopy of less than 30 percent cover, with an understorey dominated by *Rumex acetosella* and *Agrostis capillaris*. These are joined by *Stellaria media* and *Holcus lanatus* where gulls nest among the *Pteridium*. Bracken is unable to invade shallow or waterlogged soils, and frequently the former are dominated by sorrels *Rumex* spp. and bent grass *Agrostis capillaris*. A fine example of this vegetation is found in a strip of land running approximately east-to-west to the northeast of Gull Rocks, near South Bog.

Stands of bracken are the main home of bluebells *Hyacinthoides non-scriptus*. The delightfully-scented flowers form carpets in the east in late-May. In the area at the head of South Haven this has become mixed with red campion *Silene dioica* in the past decade as this species has suddenly (and inexplicably) spread from just a few tiny patches. Bluebells do also grow amongst sparse *Pteridium* and extend into maritime grassland at the western end of the island, creating a community that corresponds reasonably well to the NVC's *Festuca rubra - Hyacinthoides non-scripta* bluebell community.

The mixes of Dry Short Grassland and *Pteridium* have proved difficult to place in the NVC, but have affinities with Uf1 and 12b, especially where *Armeria maritima* or *Silene maritima* appear. These are relatively poor fits, with the community possibly tending towards U4b, the *Holcus lanatus - Trifolium repens* sub-community of *Festuca ovina - Agrostis capillaris - Galium saxatile* grassland.

The cover of *Pteridium* varies spatially from year to year, especially in the less-sheltered areas and alongside seasonal ponds. This suggests that the underground distribution of *Pteridium aquilinum* is much greater than is apparent above ground in any one year (Ninnes, 1998).

Previously, bracken was held in check by agricultural practises and trampling by livestock, but the removal of the flock of Soay sheep in the 1960's has allowed invasion into the old field system around the farmstead and into the areas of previously-declining *Calluna* heath. Lesser black-backed gulls prefer to nest in the bracken, once amongst the stunted fronds at the western end of the island, but in recent times the birds have taken to nesting in the tall stands in the east (see Section 3.2.2: Birds).

In 1983, it was decided that efforts to control bracken should be instigated, and that its distribution be reduced to the situation known in the early 1950's, as shown by M. Gillham's vegetation map. To this end, an Assistant Warden was employed for six weeks in the summer with the sole purpose of destroying bracken. However, by the early 1990's the "bracken basher" had become a more general assistant, and volunteers were (and still are) relied upon to continue the control programme. This of course varies from year to year, depending upon the availability of accommodation for volunteers, who pay a considerably reduced fee for their stay when compared to other visitors. Spraying of the herbicide Asulam has been employed from time to time. This is extremely effective, killing the buds on the rhizome that would ultimately produce the following year's fronds, but there are very specific conditions which suit its application – a light breeze and dry weather but not too hot – and these are rarely encountered for suitable lengths of time on the island. In addition, much of the terrain is peppered with fragile burrows containing Manx shearwaters, and many can be collapsed underfoot, so the area where treatment is possible is also limited. So treatment is generally infrequent, often restricted to the edges of the central fields, and on the coastal slopes where bracken encroachment affects breeding puffins (herbicide has been sprayed in Crab Bay and between South Haven and The Anticline in recent years). Thus bracken continues to spread. A map produced by Thompson (2000) shows how bracken increased its cover by about 40 percent between 1989 and 2001. In Figures 1, 3 and 4 (aerial photographs), the bracken is clearly seen as the darkest areas.

The presence of several woodland plants, notably the fine vernal display of *Hyacinthoides non-scripta*, suggests that *Pteridium* was a relic from the island's former woodland cover. The occurrence of the fungus *Mycena filopes* supports this.

5. Marshy grassland.

This is characterised as containing significant areas of purple moor-grass *Molinia caerulea* without ericaceous components.

Once fairly widespread in the central "Bog", the largest existing patches of *Molinia* are found in the Caricetum arenariae (sand sedge *Carex arenaria*) to the north and south of North Pond, though these are somewhat fragmented, with *Holcus lanatus* also frequent. A few clumps are also found within the fenced rabbit-exclosure at Orchid Bog, and a fairly extensive stand within the confines of a rabbit-exclosure at East Bog.

6. Intertidal.

In 1954, Gillham reported on the marine algae to be found around Skokholm's shores, by way of descending the cliffs where possible, and most of the coastline was visited (Gillham, 1954a). Exposure to wave action is considerable on the western-most shores due to the huge distance of open water to the west and south-west that, when combined with the prevailing westerly winds, results in a huge fetch. The lively conditions mean that although there is a small shell-sand beach exposed at low water at North Haven, elsewhere – with the exception of a few small eastern bays – all of the finer particles are scoured away by wave action, small rocks are extremely mobile and only very large boulders remain *in situ* at the foot of the cliffs.

The Scottish Marine Biological Association survey of 1979 indicated that Skokholm may have some of the more unusual sub-littoral species already found around Skomer, within the Marine Nature Reserve there. A "phase 1" (preliminary) survey was carried out in the summers of 1998 and 1999 by the Countryside Council for Wales (CCW), with the surveyors travelling around the island by boat during a period of spring tides, and also carrying out SCUBA diving. Excursions ashore were not made in many places due to the presence of cliff-nesting seabirds, so that disturbance was avoided.

The Phase 1 survey identified 29 different "biotopes", where a biotope is defined as the physical environment of a community of organisms. Various factors are analysed, including: 1. substratum; 2. salinity; 3. strength of tidal stream; 4. wave exposure; 5. shore zone occupied (from the splash zone down to greater than 50m depth). The biotope is thus identified using a combination of parameters. For details on this classification (that has been altered since the CCW survey) see Connor *et al.* (2004). The following descriptions are based upon the three reports outlined above, and some personal observations.

The southern and western shores between Frank's Point and Short Nose are very exposed. The cliffs are near-vertical in places and have the typical yellow and grey lichen bands of up to 30 metres in width. Below this there is a distinct band of the black tar lichen *Verrucaria maura*, over which lies the laver bread seaweed *Porphyra* sp. The upper and mid-eulittoral zone is characterized by a faunal encrustation of barnacles *Semibalanus balanoides* and limpets *Patella* sp. (biotope LR.HLR.MusB.Sem). There are few other species, though the pygmy lichen *Lichina pygmaea* occurs in the upper limits. The non-vesiculate form of bladder wrack *Fucus vesiculosus* var. *linearis* occurs at the lower limits of this encrustation on sloping and horizontal areas of bedrock (biotope LR.HLR.MusB.Sem.FvesR). The lower eulittoral has a faunal encrustation of the mussel *Mytilus edulis* and *Semibalanus balanoides* with a high abundance of encrusting coralline algae including *Corallina officinalis* (biotope LR.HLR.MusB.MytB). The sublittoral fringe is dominated by dense stands of dabberlocks *Alaria esculenta* with an understorey of coralline algae and the mussel *Mytilus edulis* is plentiful (biotope EIR.KFaR.Ala.Myt).

Cliffs in Mad Bay on the north-west side of the island reach up to 20m in height and are slightly less-exposed. Zonation differs here, due to a noticeable absence of *L. pygmaea*. Also, the lower eulittoral has thongweed *Himanthalia elongata* over encrusting coralline algae and additional red algae (biotope LR.HLR.FR.Him). The sublittoral fringe contains both *A. esculenta* and the kelp *Laminaria digitata* over a similar assemblage of coralline algae and additional red algae.

The east side of the island between Little Bay Point and Crab Bay Rocks does not receive the prevailing (south-westerly) winds and is consequently less-exposed and the zonation here reflects this. Below the yellow and grey lichens, there is a band of *V. maura* on both vertical and sloping bedrock, lacking *Porphyra* spp. The upper eulittoral is characterized by the presence of channel wrack *Pelvetia canaliculata*, some spiral wrack *Fucus spiralis*, and *L. pygmaea* growing over a barnacle and limpet encrustation. Below there is a band of barnacles and limpets, with either the vesiculate or non-vesiculate form of *Fucus vesiculosus* at their lower limits. The lower eulittoral contains *H. elongata* over encrusting coralline and red algae (biotope LR.HLR.FR.Him). The dominant kelp in the sublittoral fringe is *Laminaria digitata*. The sublittoral fringes between the islet of The Stack and the main island contain interesting tide-swept *L. digitata* communities (biotope MIR.Ldig.T). The movement of water encourages various filter-feeding animal species that here include the anemone *Actinothoe sphyrodeta*, the purse sponge *Grantia compressa*, the bryozoan *Alcyonidium gelatinosum*, the gooseberry seasquirt *Dendrodoa grossularia* and numerous other seasquirts of the family Polyclinidae. Beaches on the eastern side of the island contain large boulders and areas of bedrock. Zonation reflects the reduced exposure, with *Fucus serratus* and red algae present (and replacing *H. elongata*) and with wider bands of the fucoids *P. canaliculata* and *F. spiralis*. In Peter's Bay, rock-pools with sediment floors occur between large boulders, and contain a diverse range of sand-tolerant algae such as *Ahnfeltia plicata*, *Cystoclonium purpureum*, *Dumontia contorta*, *Polyides rotundus* and *Porphyra* spp. (biotope LR.FLR.Rkp.SwSed). Large boulders in North Haven and Peter's Bay support animal- and plant-dominated overhangs. Shaded sides of these boulders also support the red alga *Catenella caespitosa*.

Gillham (1954a) made a study of the various rock-pools around the island's rocky shore. The water in these shows wide fluctuations in physical and chemical properties over a short period of time – particularly those not reached by neap tides – and the flora able to survive such changes is limited. Low spring tides occur at about midday on Skokholm, and thus heating and evaporation of water, with the consequent result of increasing concentrations of salts, is significant. Temperatures as high as 27°C have been recorded in pools on the south coast on sunny afternoons, whereas those on the north side would be no higher than 18°C. Hydrogen ion concentrations (pH - a measure of acidity) show similar variation – values of pH are closely correlated with the amount of photosynthesis, respiration and decomposition that is occurring in each pool, and the absorption of carbon dioxide (which produces a weak acid in solution) by photosynthesizing plants can significantly reduce the acidity of the water. The dominant species in pools showing the greatest fluctuations are of the genera *Ulva*, *Enteromorpha*, *Corallina* and *Lithothamnion*. By the end of the summer the only surviving algae will be the calcareous *Corallina* spp., and limpet-dominated pools result.

Other plant communities

Sea Cliff Heath

The *Calluna vulgaris* heath on Skokholm in the 1940's occupied many of the fields in the vicinity of the Observatory buildings, but was in steady decline subsequently, being damaged by grazing and digging by rabbits, and subsequent invasion by bracken. There was still some hope for it, for in the early 1980's the area of heath in the field north-west of the house had substantially increased since the survey of 1948. Bracken had been unable to reach this field, presumably because of the presence of the metre-thick walls. But by 1989 the *Calluna* remained only as small shoots within a single area of short grassland.

The *Calluna* has been reportedly suppressed by rabbits since at least 1948 (Goodman & Gillham, 1954), when it exhibited various growth forms depending upon the degree of exposure and grazing pressure, from loose bushy mats up to 12 centimetres high in more sheltered areas, to prostrate branches no more than two centimetres or so high in more exposed sites. That heavy grazing was the dominant factor affecting *Calluna* was demonstrated by the fact that even species considered to be unpalatable to rabbits were virtually absent from the heath. Removal of goats in 1981 (see Section 1.3: Archaeology and past land use) led to the establishment of numerous heather seedlings on Middle Heath and Northern Plain (Gynn, 1982), but these did not escape the attentions of rabbits and thus failed to develop into flowering plants.

E. Gynn (1985) suggests that successive strong storms (resulting in salty sea-spray) may have contributed to the decline of the already-weakened plants in the early 1980's. This would be particularly destructive in mid-summer, since sunshine would cause rapid evaporation of the water from the salty spray, leaving concentrated salt behind that would quickly cause harm to plants. This would be compounded since rainfall is at its lowest at this time, and there would be little chance of it being washed off before it could do considerable damage to the plant tissues.

Skokholm's heather (with perhaps a unique genetic make-up) was thought worthy of conserving, and so in 1991 a small area of moribund heath was fenced to prevent grazing by rabbits. The heather soon began to flourish, and a further extension to the exclosure in 1997 has since led to further spread. An interesting and attractive early succession was observed, with herbs such as heath bedstraw *Galium saxatile*, common dog-violet *Viola riviniana* and tormentil *Potentilla erecta* becoming dominant for a few seasons and forming a carpet of flowers, until the red fescue grass, common bent grass and heather began to assert themselves. The smaller herbs are, however, still abundant today, and also in places outside the exclosure. Collection of seed and its subsequent sowing onto specially prepared areas of soil could easily encourage the spread of heath, as long as grazing was prevented, but this would have to be balanced against the killing of nocturnal birds (Manx shearwaters and storm petrels) that would certainly result as they flew into the fences at night (personal observations).

Walls

The boundaries of the former field-system are stone-lined earth banks which provide sites for squirrel-tail fescue *Vulpia bromoides* and sea fern-grass *Catapodium marinum*. The latter is also found on the lime kiln in South Haven. Various lichens and English stonecrop *Sedum anglicum* also thrive. Planting of shrubs and trees in the shelter afforded by the taller walls around the buildings has caused the loss of *Vulpia* from much of its former habitat. The lighthouse boundary walls once held a small population of ivy-leaved goosefoot *Chenopodium murale*, but this has sadly since been removed during the process of repainting.

Ruderal communities: i.e. those found in "waste places" near human habitation. These form one of the visually "most lush" and seemingly most invertebrate-rich habitats on Skokholm, consisting of rank vegetation in the form of coarse grasses such as cock's-foot *Dactylis glomerata*, hogweed *Heracleum sphondylium*, various thistles *Cirsium* spp., ragwort *Senecio vulgaris* and stinging nettles *Urtica dioica* and *U. urens* (see Figure 12, below).

Figure 12: The author standing beside the "Wall Garden". The tallest plants behind are planted shrubs and trees (Buddleja, Willow, Sycamore), situated in a rabbit-exclosure on the east-side of the easternmost (sheltered) wall next to The Wheelhouse. The tall, pale plant in the middle-distance is Tree Mallow. Ragwort and Spear Thistle dominate the foreground.

Subsection 3.1.3. LOWER PLANTS

Bryophytes – mosses and liverworts

There has never been a detailed study of Skokholm's bryophyte flora, though Gillham (1954b) published a "preliminary list" of species with mention of their typical habitats, in the hope that others might use this as a basis for further work. Salty sea-spray prevents all but a few species growing in the west and south-west coastal regions, and grazing by rabbits perhaps limits some species, but a greater number may be found near to the sheltered streams and flushes in the east. Gillham lists just less than 60 mosses and 30 liverworts, but subsequently Smith (1995) and then Johnson (2002) carried out surveys during a week-long stay on the island and both found the same single additional species (i.e. new to the island list) of liverwort. The mosses of the grasslands and shallow soils around rock outcrops are most obvious during the winter months, when the frequent rains encourage their rejuvenation and growth, whilst other plants are moribund. Digging and scratching by rabbits seems to produce much in the way of suitable habitat for mosses. In addition, man-made structures, such as walls and buildings, provide shelter for a number of species. A complete list is included in Appendix III.

Lichens

Skokholm is listed in a report to the Nature Conservancy Council as a site of national/international importance for lichens (James & Rose, 1978). This is despite a lack of trees, limiting the lichen flora somewhat in numerical terms, though heavy grazing, scratching and digging by rabbits does result in a fairly rich terricolous (ground) flora. It is however the rock-loving (saxicolous) species of the cliffs and rocky outcrops that are best represented. Even some of these, such as the fruiticose *Ramalina* species, were heavily grazed by goats until late in 1981, when the animals were removed from the island.

There are a number of recognized bands of lichens on the maritime cliffs, which can be conveniently described as three main zones, as follows:

1. The black zone, which is found just above the high-water mark and is characterized on Skokholm by the crustose species *Verrucaria maura* and *V. mucosa*, and the fruiticose species *Lichina pygmaea* and *L. confinis*.

2. The orange zone, typically composed of various *Caloplaca* species and a number of grey species such as *Lecanora dispersa*, *L. actophila*, *L. helicopsis* and *L. leprosescens*.

3. The grey zone, comprised of the fruiticose *Ramalina* species. The rocky outcrops in the centre of the island exhibit a similar flora to the grey zone of the sea cliffs.

Gillham (1954b) carried out a basic survey over a number of years whilst studying all aspects of Skokholm's botany, and made a list of species along with a mention of the habitat each was found in. They were included in the publication *Lichens of Pembrokeshire* (Wade, 1954).

Opposite: Figure 13. Lichens smother virtually every square millimetre of rock on Skokholm, producing a mass of colour and pattern at all times of year.

The rock structure undoubtedly plays a fundamental part in determining the distribution of saxicolous lichen species. Sheard & Ferry (1964) described this aspect and also the lichen flora in some detail following their visit in March 1964, when they set up a number of transects on various rocks and sampled both north and south sides (they were oriented with their long axis running East-West). Unfortunately these are not relocatable today. However, approximate locations of all species were recorded using a 4-figure map reference taken from a 1:2500 half-furlong gridded map of the island (this map is something of a rarity today). Their reference collection for the island contains 113 species and/or varieties, and is housed at the National Museum of Wales in Cardiff. Another 7 species previously recorded by Gillham (1954b) were not found by Sheard and Ferry but were considered by them as "likely to be present". Thirty-eight of the species were new vice-county records. *Rocella fusiformis* is currently regarded as a "Near Threatened" species (occurring in 15 or fewer 10km x 10km squares in GB), whilst *Rocella phycopsis* and *Rinodina confragosa* are nationally scarce (occurring in 16 to 100 of the 10km x 10km squares in GB).

In recent years, studies have been initiated by Tranter (1994), and Fox (1995), which resulted in the identification of species new to the island list, including some that are, perhaps strangely, extremely widespread there today. It is unlikely that they were simply overlooked in previous surveys, suggesting that their spread has been rapid, a fact that surely warrants further investigation. These authors also drew simple distribution maps of some of the commoner species. These demonstrated, for example, that *Parmelia caperata* cannot tolerate extreme exposure to the sea spray, being found only on the central and eastern rock outcrops, but able to tolerate either sunny or shady conditions (south and north-facing rocks); the map lichen *Rhizocarpon geographicum* is mainly found on the south side of rocks and walls in central localities; *Caloplaca verrucilifera* is found on cliffs in the north and west, where seabird activity is great and exposure to the maritime environment is extreme. *Xanthoria candellaria* was first found in 1994, another species that was surely not overlooked previously. This rather diminutive but brightly-coloured lichen is widely found in crevices on the tops of rocks that are used as perches by gulls. Numbers of these birds have increased dramatically in recent years (although are in rapid decline again now), and it could be that it has only just become established on Skokholm.

Further mapping in 2002 demonstrated that *R. phycopsis* is currently widespread on the island, with over 5,400 thalli counted (Purcell & Thompson, 2002), including many small ones which, when combined with the knowledge that the species was found only in one locality in 1994 - 95, perhaps indicates that it too is spreading fast. There is undoubtedly much to be discovered about the ecology of this species, but it clearly prefers north or north-west-facing rocks (usually co-dominant with or subordinate to *Ramalina siliquosa*), and in particular the many crevices aligned from east to west – and formed by the slaty cleavage of the mudstones – that are a feature of the Skokholm rock outcrops.

The Golden Hair Lichen *Teloschistes flavicans* is the only specially-protected species on Skokholm, being named in Schedule 8 of the Wildlife and Countryside Act 1981, and it is included on the IUCN (World Conservation Union) Global Red List. It is classified as being either regionally extinct or else endangered within the European Community (Sérusiaux, 1989), and is one of the most pollution-sensitive lichens in the British flora (Gilbert & Purvis, 1996). Until recently, there were 7 well-separated populations on the island, the largest consisting of about 200 thalli (in North Haven), the smallest of just a few thalli, six of which were found on rock outcrops, the other on moribund heather. Unfortunately it seems to have been obliterated at one of its sites, on the flat top of a large rock at the base of the western end of Spy Rock, perhaps due to rabbit activity. It seems generally dependent on a number of other lichen species for anchorage. It is also present on Skomer and Ramsey islands, and the three populations are regarded as "core" sites by Gilbert and Purvis. Purvis and James (1995) describe the status of this species in Pembrokeshire.

Lichens are generally dependant on an unpolluted atmosphere and can be affected even by a short-term deterioration in air quality (*Teloschistes flavicans* is particularly sensitive, for example). Some important species on Skokholm are associated with seabird guano (e.g. *Rocella* spp.) and so significant changes in the status of seabirds may affect these lichen assemblages. Those species at the edge of their range may be particularly vulnerable to small environmental changes. Of the current management procedures carried out on the island, spraying of bracken with herbicide could threaten them. Lichens are known to suffer from thallus breakdown if emulsifying or detergent agents are added to the pesticide to assist with its distribution, so the current practise on Skokholm is to mix the asulam with water.

A complete species list is included in Appendix IV.

Fungi

Skokholm's fungi have been intensively studied by Dr. A.F. Parker-Rhodes, who visited the island on numerous occasions between 1947 and 1954, and subsequently had numerous papers published about them. These included a series of thirteen titled "The Basidiomycetes of Skokholm Island", all but three of which were published in the journal *New Phytologist* (with others in *Transactions of the British Mycological Society*). The first of this series is an annotated species list (Parker-Rhodes, 1954), while the others deal with aspects concerned mainly with genetics and population structure. There were also reports in various Skokholm Bird Observatory Reports (1949 - 50, 1952 and 1954). A hand-written "Identification key to basidiomycetes of Skokholm", with illustrations, was produced by Dr. Parker-Rhodes and presented to the island laboratory in 1949.

The island has an <u>estimated</u> total of over 400 species of macroscopic fungi. It is virtually impossible to discover the total number due to the infrequent nature in which many species fruit, so statistical methods are generally applied, utilizing knowledge of the propensity of different species to fructify. Also, some idea of the number can be obtained by the rate of increase in the cumulative number of species discovered over a number of years.

Of the 400 or so species estimated, 225 would be higher Basidiomycetes, and 17 of those actually found were considered unusual enough to warrant publication of reports of ecological studies carried out on them. Theoretical consideration of airborne dissemination of fungi led Parker-Rhodes to suggest that Skokholm is far enough from the mainland for gene flow to be minimal and thus allow "incipient speciation", and this was then supported by genetical studies and microscopic observations of spores. Inbreeding too was found to be common, further supporting his theory that a barrier existed to gene flow. He described a new species of *Psilocybe* (*P. scocholmica*), and a new species (and genus, though it is not currently in use) *Echinotrema clanculare* (now *Trechispora clancularis*) of the Basidiomycete family Sistotremataceae (it was found in puffin burrows). The *Psilocybe* was described as being partly intermediate between *P. bullacea* and *P. coprophila*, with many of the "intermediate" specimens being of hybrid origin. However, others had formed a population that was genetically stable, persisting long enough as a breeding population to have formed a new species. It was shown to compete successfully with the "parent" species, and he suspected that it might exterminate them from the island (one of these, *P. bullacea*, inhabited Pony dung, an animal that was last on Skokholm in 1957, so is unlikely to exist there today). In fact, during the study period, it was estimated that there might have been 10,000 mycelia of it present on the island at any one time, making it by far the most abundant coprophilous agaric on Skokholm.

The community structure of the island's Basidiomycetes is controlled largely by the distribution of "higher plant" communities. The lack of cover, particularly during the winter months, imposes a severe microclimate, thus limiting many species to those plant communities that produce a thick leaf litter. Of these, the bracken *Pteridium aquilinum* and rushes *Juncus* spp. are the most obvious, and the fungi inhabiting them pass their dormant and non-fruiting stages in scraps of vegetable matter, and produce fruit when the cover afforded them is the best that the island possesses. Given these factors, it is therefore not surprising that the majority of the fungi are found in the sheltered east. Various puffballs are found even in the west in short grass, presumably because they are the most xerophytic of the higher fungi. The Skokholm study gave a "higher fungus" to higher plant ratio of 1.6 to one.

Many of the lignicolous fungi (those that live upon lignin in wood) that are found on Skokholm are probably not part of the natural flora, but have arrived there courtesy of the regular importation of timber for use in buildings and fencing. Few, if any, species would arrive on driftwood – once collected with relish for the Cottage fire – since immersion in salt-water would certainly kill all fungal mycelia. Parker-Rhodes identified a number of natural sources of lignin on the island, including heather *Calluna vulgaris,* which had a fungus flora associated with it (presumably it still exists today to a degree, despite the paucity of aged and dead woody material at present). Also, the mass of dead "woody" stems of bracken and the humus its breakdown produces provide a habitat for a number of fungi, and in fact, Parker-Rhodes identified this medium as the place where a considerable proportion of the Skokholm fungus flora would be found.

Many invertebrates depend on fungi during part of their life cycle, with some feeding on the fruiting bodies in the autumn and others feeding selectively on the mycelium, whilst those that feed on dead wood and detritus benefit from the fungi producing many enzymes that break down the substrate into digestible particles or compounds.

Some of Skokholm's Basidiomycetes occur in habitats that are not considered to be their "normal" preference. For example, *Mycena sanguinolenta, Leucoagaricus georginae* and *Hygrophoropsis aurantiaca* are more usually associated with coniferous woodland while *Mycena filopes* is generally found in deciduous woods. On Skokholm these species were found in bracken-dominated communities, and support the view that the island was perhaps once wooded.

From mid-September onwards, the fruiting bodies of one species of fungi are particularly conspicuous: the parasol *Macrolepiota procera* appears amongst bracken and in grasslands, and these are relished by the island Wardens at this time of year, particularly when a supply boat with food isn't due to arrive until some weeks later. There is a particular flush of relatively small "higher" fungi each autumn/early winter, many of which have probably not been recorded until recently because of the longer period that the island was occupied each year by the author, compared with the past. Fungi of the type generally known as "waxcaps" are particularly well-represented, with 14 species recorded so far; these are generally associated with unimproved grasslands, with coastal grassland being of particular importance.

In addition to the work of Parker-Rhodes, G. Pugh (1965) reported on the keratinophilic fungi recorded on birds on Skokholm. Able to utilize keratin – the substance composing feathers and skin – as a food source, these fungi are microscopic and some species have strong associations with any one particular bird genus. Many are common in the soil and on plant debris, and undoubtedly picked up from the ground by birds such as pipits and larks, whereas others are found in tree foliage and thus more commonly found on leaf warblers *Phylloscopus* spp. Among the species recorded, the commonest was the soil species *Paecilomyces lilacinus*. The causal agent of the lung disease Aspergillosis, *Aspergillus fumigatus*, was found on 7 percent of the total number of birds examined, but it was not known if the birds were actually diseased because they were quickly released and continued their migration. A similar study on Bardsey, North Wales, produced a similar flora, qualitatively, to the Skokholm list. It was hoped that such studies would assist in the plotting of bird migration routes, but the ubiquity of most of the fungi appeared to preclude the possibility. It does, however, demonstrate the potential for transportation of various species onto and off of the island.

A complete species list of fungi is included in Appendix V. Considerable changes in nomenclature over the years since Parker-Rhodes' work has meant that a few of the species (and especially "forms" or varieties of species) that he named have been difficult or even impossible to trace. In these cases, they are not included in the updated list, for fear of errors on the part of the author.

Section 3.2. FAUNA

Subsection 3.2.1: Mammals

Introduction.

Just two species of land mammal are found on Skokholm – the house mouse *Mus musculus* and the rabbit *Oryctolagus cuniculus*. Both were undoubtedly introduced to the island by Man, the former presumably by mistake! Skokholm is considered to be sufficiently isolated from the mainland so that genetic isolation has resulted in a unique variety of House Mouse. The Skokholm rabbits have a very interesting history, particularly where persecution has been concerned (see below).

Seabird islands and mammalian ground-predators do not mix, and it is fortunate that none of the latter have ever been recorded on Skokholm, with the exception of a fleeting visit by an otter *Lutra lutra* on 6th November 2003, which was observed by the author with delight and not the trepidation that might have been expected were it an American mink *Mustela vison*! This is in stark contrast to many other islands, the result of the (albeit accidental) introduction of species such as the brown rat *Rattus norvegicus* leading to the virtual extinction of ground-nesting birds. There have been occasional scares though – in the summer of 1995, a number of "strange-looking" droppings were discovered on Skokholm, and taken off for analysis. The conclusion was what everyone involved with Skokholm and seabirds everywhere were dreading – that a rat was present on the island! This news came late into the autumn, the Warden not having been informed with any hurry for some reason. A few "live" traps were put out, and the island vacated for the winter. These traps were not selective, and any bird or rabbit could have been captured, thereby rendering the trap ineffective from that point on. The author returned to Skokholm the following spring, but thankfully the traps were empty, and there never was any sign of rats subsequently. The droppings were probably those of a rabbit suffering with a bowel problem, since numerous other "strangely-shaped" droppings are seen frequently (pers. obs.).

It is thought that a small number of bank voles *Clethrionomys glareolus* were introduced in 1950 or 1951. One female was trapped on 14th August 1951 and sent to the British Museum to have its identity confirmed. It was of the typical mainland race and not that of *C. g. skomerensis*, the subspecies found only on neighbouring Skomer Island. Another was sighted almost exactly one year later (Skokholm Bird Observatory Report (SBOR) 1951 and 1952). There have been no records since, despite intensive trapping of house mice from 1956 onwards. In 1957, the upper and lower dentaries of a hedgehog *Erinaceus europaeus* were found on a cliff at Mad Bay, from an animal that was almost certainly transported across by a bird.

Small numbers of the grey seal *Halichoerus grypus* breed on the few suitable beaches and in sea caves, and up to 30 are currently seen throughout the summer months in the waters around the island, and basking on the rocks of the middle shore.

Two species of bat have been recorded: pipistrelle *Pipistrellus pipistrellus* (one seen in April 1949, again in 1988, and many other single bats thought to be this species more frequently since) and noctule *Nyctalus noctula* (one was caught in a mist-net in September 1968 and other singles were occasionally seen in the late 1980's, and one thought to be this species in 2002). The droppings of a third, one of the horseshoe bats *Rhinolophus sp.*, were found in a sea cave in 1993 (Betts, 1993).

Cetaceans are seen close inshore, including daily sightings of harbour porpoise *Phocoena phocoena*, often foraging in a tide race of the south-western tip of the island (Purcell & Thompson, 1997), and infrequent sightings of common dolphins *Delphinus delphis*, bottlenosed dolphin *Tursiops truncatus* and Risso's dolphin *Grampus griseus*. A complete list is included as an appendix to this subsection.

There are no domestic animals on the island at present, and the SPA and SSSI status makes it very unlikely that they will be reintroduced (for a brief historical account, see Section 1.3: Archaeology and Past Land Use).

SPECIES ACCOUNTS

Atlantic Grey Seal *Halichoerus grypus*

This species is cited in the Pembrokeshire Marine Special Area of Conservation documentation, and is a feature of European Importance.

Grey seals are present in the waters around the island throughout the year, apparently comprising a resident group, and seen basking on rocks at low water whenever they are exposed sufficiently by the tide. They are a great favourite amongst the island's human visitors, who like to sit quietly on the cliff-top and watch the animals' antics below. Conversely, the seals seem to enjoy watching people, as long as no noises or sudden movements are made. The most favoured locations are South Bay and Crab Bay Rocks. In the autumn there are seldom more than 2 or 3 bulls present, patrolling the few suitable pupping sites for females. Lockley (1947) states that "most autumns a young seal is dropped in North Haven", but between 1939 and 1987 there are very few records of pups, presumably in part because the island was usually vacated by mid-October during this period. In recent years, however, more observations have been made through to the end of November and pups have been recorded, albeit in small numbers. These appear mainly on the North Haven beaches, but also in Seal Cave, Peter's Bay, Peter's Cave, Hog Bay and Crab Bay. Rough seas coinciding with spring tides often brings about the death of pups by way of drowning or battering on the rocks, or at the very least are caused to leave the relative safety of the pupping site. At least with such a small breeding population there is a smaller chance of confusion with regard to which pup belongs to which parent, a factor very important in larger colonies (Davis & Davis, 1975). They are poor swimmers at a young age, and many are washed away.

A very recent increase is presumably an aspect of an upward population trend for grey seals in Pembrokeshire (Baines, 1993), while the shortage of suitable boulder beaches above the high water mark is an obvious limiting factor on the island. These animals are part of a localized population which breeds on the islands of Skomer, Ramsey, Caldey and Skokholm, in addition to sites along the north and west coasts of Pembrokeshire. In 1994, Baines *et al.* (1995) assessed the population and estimated that it consisted of about 4,700 individuals.

Being Britain's largest mammal, and easily viewed from the cliff-tops on Skokholm, it is undoubtedly a major attraction bringing visitors to the island.

Opposite: Figure 14. A bull Grey Seal. One or two patrol the few suitable pupping beaches around Skokholm in the autumn, waiting for a chance to mate with the small number of cow seals present.

Factors affecting Grey Seals on and around Skokholm

Sadly, the few boulder beaches on Skokholm have also proved to be lethal for pups. The interstices between the huge rocks have frequently been known to trap animals that slip down into them. Wedged fast, they usually drown (pers. obs.), unless they are fortunate enough to be seen and then rescued by a passing Warden.

There is always the threat of oil spillages in the vicinity of the island, given its proximity to the shipping lanes and oil refineries of Milford Haven. Observations made by Davis & Anderson (1976) following an oiling incident on the pupping beaches of Skomer island revealed that the behaviour of oiled seals did not appear to differ from unoiled animals, but that peak weights of unoiled pups were significantly greater than oiled ones, ultimately giving the unaffected individuals a greater chance of survival.

A new threat to seals has come about with the dramatic increase in the amount of boating activity around the islands, particularly those vessels carrying SCUBA divers, but also the advent of the "sea safari" where particularly fast, noisy craft with a shallow draught are able to get close to beaches. Both types of user target seals and attempt to get close to them, ultimately resulting in disturbance, and most harrowing is the blatant advertising by some dive schools informing potential clients that they will be able to "swim with the seals". The author personally witnessed instructors on their boats shouting to divers in the water, informing them of the location of seals, and encouraging them to swim towards the animals. At low tide, when the seals are hauled out on the rocks, the only way the divers can swim with them is by scaring them into the water, so that is exactly what they do (pers. obs.). As the animals panic, they risk injury on the jagged sandstone rocks over which they must clamber, not just to themselves, but to the unborn pups that they are carrying. Despite the pupping season being late in the year, it is becoming more likely that they will be disturbed at such a critical time, as people have more and more leisure time and boats become more able to cope with the rough seas that are frequently encountered at this time. The positioning of a replica of the figurehead of the wrecked ship *Alice Williams* on a clifftop in South Bay (where the original sat for many years, but which now resides in The Wheelhouse alongside other items from the wreck) is foolhardy, encouraging boat owners close inshore to where the seals prefer to haul out, resulting in their frequent disturbance.

The demands for management of seal populations in order to minimise either genuine or perceived interaction with commercial fisheries could be a significant issue in the near future, as seal populations continue to grow, for the time being, alongside those of a significantly less-restricted one – that of mankind.

House Mouse *Mus musculus* L.

Many aspects (including the ecology, genetics and physiology) of Skokholm's mice have been intensively studied, mainly by Professor R.J. Berry (formerly of the Royal Free Hospital School of Medicine, London, and more recently of the Department of Animal Genetics/Biology, University College, London). The initial purpose of Berry's study was to collect animals for genetical characterization. He produced a paper on the ecology of the island mice (Berry, 1968), and went on to summarize the ecology and genetics (Berry, 1977). It is from these and other papers (including those by R.A. Davies, 1957 b and c) that much of the information below has been gleaned.

Virtually every mouse population is unique, since each tends to be founded by a small group of animals (or even one pregnant female) originating from a genetically-variable ancestral population. The main factor in differentiating island races from their mainland ancestors is the chance genetic composition of the founding animal(s), and subsequent change (both genotypic and phenotypic) based on the genes and frequencies carried by these colonizers (Berry, 1996). The species is apparently an ideal one for the general biological task of "dissecting" the traits that contribute to its incredible adaptability; the material is largely available for such a task in the diversity of local forms established in different habitats and characterized genetical varieties maintained in the laboratory. The complete barrier to the immigration of other small mammals made Skokholm the ideal location for an ecological-genetical study.

The founder mice are thought to have been accidentally introduced to Skokholm from the nearby mainland at Dale (to which they are most similar when compared to all other populations, with 10 percent of these also affected by spina bifida – see below), probably in the mid-1890s, and colonized all parts of the island (Berry, 1964).

From 1960 to 1963, Berry collected mice annually for determination of changes in inherited skeletal characteristics. The Skokholm house mice show a high degree of variance from mainland populations. There is a high frequency of midline skeletal defect (*spina bifida occulta*), which is rare in most wild-living mice. They are also, on average, about 14 percent heavier and 5 percent longer than mainland mice, changes that are common to all island populations of British small mammals and that presumably represent adaptation to island conditions by way of reducing the surface area to volume ratio (hence animals lose body heat more slowly). But how well-adapted are the Skokholm mice to their island environment? It is better to say that only some of the individuals are "adapted", i.e. by possessing traits that may be advantageous to them and that many of their fellow mice do not have. In this case, how much variation is there? The skeletal variation mentioned previously actually increases as the summer goes on; the average variance of those animals that survive the winter is much less than this. Hence it applies that natural selection is operating through some of the over-wintering mortality. It is perhaps unusual that the population as a whole has not become less sensitive to adverse environmental conditions.

Berry also noted the varying density of mice across the island. In the summers of 1964 to 1966, and the winter of 1965/66, he undertook mark-and-recapture experiments to supplement the information gained on density. Traps were set in groups where previous experience indicated that mice occurred, mostly in the vicinity of the buildings and on the cliffs, but also on the walls and rock-outcrops in the centre of the island. A large effort was put into studying The Neck, because it is easily defined, of small size, and hence can be studied in its entirety. The greatest densities of mice were found to be around the observatory buildings (inside them during the winter months) and at the lighthouse. Elsewhere, the greatest concentrations were found on the cliffs, where mice were also found throughout the year. There was no obvious association between mice and rabbits or birds. Individual mice were found to wander widely, some regularly caught 27 metres from where they were found most frequently, males more so than females, and up to 47m distance on The Neck, a situation far more flat and open than elsewhere on the island. Larger movements, referred to as "dispersal", occurred more frequently in the early-spring, some the whole length of the island (1.5 km in distance).

Population growth is quite slow until the first-born young of the year begin to breed themselves. Using data on survival collected from the mark-and-recapture experiments, and on litter size derived from *post mortem* examination, Berry & Jakobsen (1971) constructed a composite life-table for the island population. They discovered that in the period 1964 - 69, the mean two-monthly death rate was 40 percent between April and November, and that the winter death rate varied according to the severity of the weather, but generally 55 - 60 percent for animals in their first winter and a rate much higher in their second winter (no animal was ever found that had survived two winters, and in fact at the end of the winter period many animals simply died of "shock" as a result of being handled). It was also estimated that the population in the period 1960 - 69 fluctuated from winter-low values of about 150 individuals to a late-summer peak of around 6,000, and generally increased ten-fold during each breeding season. The ten-fold increase made it possible to estimate the average post-natal mortality of young mice: it was assumed that each pair of mice produces a litter every 4 weeks (this was tested in the laboratory) and that a pair will give rise to around 40 young in seven litters. The first-born may themselves produce a first litter in July, and these youngsters then reproduce in mid-August, and so on. With no mortality (and assuming an equal sex-ratio), a pair could give rise to 300 young in a season, that is a 150-fold increase in population size. However, the rate of animals trapped was shown to decrease by 15 - 20 percent, and taking this into account, it is necessary to assume an average pre-weaning death-rate of half of each litter to limit the population to a ten-fold increase. It is amazing to think that, at the beginning of the 21st Century, the original founders of the population have given rise to something not far short of half-a-million descendants.

The massive winter mortality of mice is most marked in the wetter central areas of the island and it appears that these regions are re-colonized by survivors from the sheltered cliff areas in the spring. Mild winters lead to an increased over-winter survival and mice are far more numerous in some years than in others, but no mice were found breeding during the winter. It seems that, by chance, the month of February in the years immediately following the arrival of the first mice on Skokholm (1896 - 1899) were mild ones, allowing the founders to survive and multiply to such a degree that they were able to establish themselves as a viable population.

Diet studies (R.A. Davis, 1957b) by way of stomach content and dropping analyses, revealed that the Skokholm mice are omnivorous, with arthropods – and in particular members of the order Lepidoptera – being of greatest importance. Other foodstuffs included mites, centipedes, spiders, woodlice, ants and bees, flies, and various bits of plants.

Seasonal changes in the physiology and ecology of a number of other rodents have been demonstrated (e.g. Hart & Heroux, 1953), and this led Jakobsen (1971) to investigate the nature of adjustment to cold in the Skokholm population. Mice were captured in samples from both inside and outside the buildings at varying times in the autumn and winter and kept in the island laboratory, where they were exposed to cold (5°C) for 225 minutes and their thermoregulation monitored by way of oxygen consumption. Their colonic temperature was measured before and after the experiment by way of a thermocouple inserted into the anus to a depth of 2.5 cm. Mean oxygen consumption was shown to drop by between 6 and 10 percent during the exposure to the lower temperatures, as was total heat loss (also partly due to a thickening of the pelage, and vasoconstriction of peripheral blood vessels), resulting in a reduction in heat production and hence energy consumption – obvious physiological changes. However, not all of the mice managed to cope with the suddenly-imposed cold – some became hypothermic and were removed from the experiment. These had exhibited higher-than-average rates of oxygen consumption (i.e. metabolic rate) beforehand, and were obviously less-resistant to cold stress as a result. This variation in resistance could indicate a survival characteristic upon which natural selection is operating.

The owner of the island put a stop to trapping of mice for study purposes in 1969, having apparently been upset by the experiments being carried out on the mice (and at how birds were reportedly being handled and "stored" during the ringing programme), but trapping of those entering the buildings continued to be carried out. In recent years, "permission" for this has had to be sought from The Countryside Council for Wales – the trapping of any animal is seen as a "potentially damaging operation" on the SSSI. Unless great care is taken with closing of doors of "mouse-proof" rooms (it is extremely doubtful that these really exist at the bird observatory), the animals can quickly cause vast amounts of damage to various materials – particularly those suitable for use as nest bedding – though foodstuffs generally seem to be their target. They have been known to eat their way through rotten door jambs and even tunnel through concrete floors in order to affect entry into buildings (personal observations). Their droppings and urine cause yet further discomfort to human residents, but thankfully they are less likely to inhabit the buildings during the summer months when paying visitors are present, so it is usually only staff members who suffer. Unlike the observatory buildings, the lighthouse is of solid construction, and is most certainly "mouse proof", but only when the doors aren't left wide open!

There exists a myth that the house mouse *Mus musculus* is an obligate commensal, yet there have been many populations known to live separately from human dwellings. The lighthouse has been unmanned (apart from occasional brief visits) since 1984, and the observatory buildings – empty at least from early-December to mid-February – are little-used by mice except during the autumn and winter, so the population is almost entirely non-commensal with man. Where a population has become extinct following the evacuation of people from an area, it has most certainly been due to competition from other rodents, e.g. the St. Kilda field mouse *Apodemus sylvaticus hirtensis* on St. Kilda, west of the Outer Hebrides, Scotland. There is no such competition on Skokholm. The mice nest in burrow-systems in the ground and in old walls and feed upon a variety of plant and animal foods. They do not appear to interact strongly with any other element of the island's fauna, though in the autumn kestrels *Falco tinnunculus* and short-eared owls *Asio flammeus* are not uncommon and these take mice, as do gulls and corvids (pers. obs.).

Three species of flea have been found on Skokholm's mice (Davis, R.A., 1956 and 1957a), on individuals in all habitats and at all times of year, but these have not been implicated in the transmission of disease and it seems that Skokholm's mice are not infected with leptospirosis, a common disease of mainland small mammals (Twigg & Cuerden, 1967). The harvest mite *Neotrombicula autumnalis* was commonly found, but no ticks. One gut parasite was discovered, the coccidian *Eimeria* sp., but no other, which is quite astonishing. Around 5 percent of the mice had disease of the liver, containing the helminth worm *Capillaria hepatica*.

Their unique genetic make-up suggests that all efforts should be made to ensure their isolation and thus the survival of this particular population. There has recently been a new application from the Royal School of Medicine to recommence the study of the genetics of the House Mouse, but this was declined due to the restrictions in force at the time. Also declined was a proposal to investigate salt-tasting in mice, or more specifically whether mice living near to the sea liked the taste of salty water more than those in populations away from the coast. One has to ask the question, do we really need to know that? Until recently, such pointless experiments have been forbidden by the previous landowner, but this could all change in the very near future.

Rabbit *Oryctolagus cuniculus*

Skokholm is probably the best place in Britain to observe rabbits. The large population has relatively little fear of man, and there are no ground-predators, with the result that some are extremely approachable (and some virtually tame – pers. obs.). In sunny weather large numbers can be seen sunbathing around the warrens, or even sleeping out in the little available shade that exists in summer. Sunning is also particularly common during the cooler days of the autumn and winter, when large numbers bask and groom themselves in the early-morning sunshine. Slater (1995) made observations of the daily rhythm of rabbits on Skomer Island, and discovered that this was far more relaxed than in mainland populations, and that there was increased daytime activity, though the main peak of emergence was at dusk. This is indeed the case on Skokholm, particularly away from footpaths (i.e. where there is no disturbance by people), and more so during the winter months when it seems that the majority of rabbits completely abandon their crepuscular-dominated existence and are seen throughout the day in all but the worst weather conditions (pers. obs.). A sharp shower of rain during the summer will cause rabbits to run for cover, whereas they will remain out in the open during prolonged, steady rain, particularly so during the winter, when they cannot afford the luxury of a cessation of foraging.

Rabbits were probably introduced into Britain by the Normans, and are first recorded from Skokholm in a document of 1324, but it is thought that they were probably introduced at around 1180 (Stanbury, 1997). Rabbit colonies were established in special enclosures where they were protected. In the Middle Ages, Skokholm was run as a successful warren and two ferreters were employed to supply rabbits to the mainland for fur and meat. The oldest wall present on the island is thought to be the one that separates the 15 hectares of an area called The Neck from the bulk of the island, and it is feasible that this was built with rabbits in mind, behind which the animals could be easily confined, accessed and captured or killed.

Lockley (1947) wrote that in order to increase the vigour of the Skokholm rabbits – which, unlike mainland ones, were easily caught by dogs – occasional introductions of tame varieties and from wild mainland stock were made, to bring new genetic material into the population. Lockley (1947) also surmised that when farming was abandoned in the early 1900's, rabbit-catchers tore holes in the stone-faced banks that were built to keep them out in order to give the conies dry breeding and sleeping dens, and so that their numbers would increase across the island. Personal experience in recent years has demonstrated that rabbits will soon get through these walls and beneath "rabbit-proof" fences without any encouragement whatsoever.

Upon R.M. Lockley's arrival on Skokholm in 1927 one of his main aims was to replace the existing wild rabbit population with chinchilla rabbits and to achieve this he employed two trappers using 144 steel gin-traps in the winter of 1927 - 28 and 288 similar traps supplemented 120 snares in the winter of 1928 - 29 (Lockley, 1947). An estimated two-thirds of the winter population was caught, but because of the large number of birds incidentally killed in the traps the attempt was abandoned, and after unsuccessful endeavors with ferrets the rabbits were allowed to return to previous levels between 1931 and 1936.

In September 1936, Lockley was approached by Sir Charles Martin, a Fellow of the Royal Society, London, about the possibility of carrying out a large scale test on the spread of the *Myxomatosis* virus, which was seen as a method of reducing the numbers of rabbits in the British countryside because of the economic effects they were having on farming. Lockley agreed and the attempt to introduce the virus to the island was made by releasing rabbits that had been inoculated with the disease. This failed, as did similar attempts in 1937 and 1938 (Lockley, 1940b). Sir Charles had been totally successful in wiping out rabbits in enclosures in Cambridgeshire and was baffled by this failure. Much later it was learned that the virus is not transmitted by <u>contact</u> between rabbits, as was supposed, but by a vector in the form of the rabbit flea *Spilopsyllus cuniculi*, which has not been found on Skokholm despite numerous searches. This absence had been noticed by Sir Charles, but its significance was overlooked (Lockley, 1955). Many other fleas have been found on the island, including three species on the house mouse (R.A. Davis, 1957a) – see previous page and the list in Section XX, "Invertebrates".

Another, and most successful, attempt at extermination was conducted in the winter of 1938 - 39 using a calcium cyanide dust marketed under the name of "Cyanogas". This was placed into burrows, where it released hydrogen cyanide gas, so causing the rapid death of any animal within the treated burrow. After three treatments, Lockley (1947) estimated that the method was 96 percent successful and that only about 400 rabbits had survived, mainly at inaccessible cliff-sites. Three-quarters of these were subsequently shot (Lockley, 1940c). The Second World War intervened, gassing was not continued (Lockley vacated the island, although the lighthouse remained manned) and numbers must have quickly recovered.

Myxomatosis reached south-east Britain in the autumn of 1953, and spread rapidly across the country following the deliberate movement of infected animals. On Skomer, the disease hit hard in 1954, reducing the rabbit population to an estimated 20 animals by August 1955. In early-January 1955, the Advisory Committee on *Myxomatosis* recommended that every advantage should be taken of the outbreaks of the disease in an attempt to eliminate all survivors to prevent them from building up in number again. However, the great interest in rabbits at this time led to Skokholm becoming the ideal location for a study into the relationship between fecundity, fertility, survival rate and population density in an expanding, insular, predator-free population, <u>without</u> *Myxomatosis*, and the results were to astonish all of those who had made similar studies of populations on mainland Britain. Previously it had been known that the peak of rabbit breeding activity occurred in June. As a result, a visit was made to the island in June 1958, mainly to analyse the incidence of prenatal mortality of litters, but it was discovered that the breeding season on Skokholm was already over! These observations led to further studies being initiated, and Lloyd (1964) carried out extensive work between 1960 and 1963 on the island, using a programme of trapping, marking and releasing of rabbits of all ages. A map of the distribution of rabbit warrens was produced by Lloyd (in Berry, 1968), showing that they were distributed island-wide, a situation that remains the same today except that there are a number presently unoccupied. Some warrens are extremely complex and occupy an area as large as 30m x 100m (Lloyd & McCowan, 1968).

The summer of 1959 was exceptionally hot and dry, rabbits were struggling to find food on the island and the mortality rate was unusually high for the time of year. A noticeable "crash" occurred during the winter months that followed, and it was estimated that only 150 animals survived by the following spring, of which all were adults (Lloyd, 1964). Thus Lloyd was afforded another opportunity, to study the effects of low population density on fecundity. He found that once the pastures had recovered in the following summer, breeding recommenced in September and continued until December. Conversely, when numbers were high again, he found that increasing population density exerted a depressing action upon ovulation rates and actually restricted the breeding season. So the species is one of few animals that can alter their selectivity with regard to breeding. It is well-adapted to rapid colonization, i.e. is highly r-selective, with a gestation period of 28 days; the does can mate again within 24 hours of giving birth, and can produce up to 7 kittens per litter and 8 litters per year, with young capable of breeding within 4 months. By contrast, in areas of high density with high population pressure (k-selection), the rabbit's ability to reduce its breeding is also highly effective in ensuring the survival of the species (Slater, 1995). A number of stops were excavated in 1964 that revealed the effects of heavy rainfall during the early part of the breeding season – a large proportion contained drowned litters (Lloyd & McCowan, 1968).

There were very occasional records of Skokholm rabbits with *Myxomatosis* in the 1960's and blood samples confirmed that the population does carry antibodies to the virus, i.e. a degree of immunity. This was a surprise, since it was thought that the Skokholm rabbits had never had the disease. This afforded another unique opportunity to the Ministry of Agriculture, of studying the epidemiology of the disease in a large population of rabbits in the absence of the vectors which are known to be important in its dissemination, but an outbreak of the disease did not materialize. In 1988 - 89 there were numerous outbreaks, apparently leading to a growth of vegetation which had not been recorded since 1939, though far less dramatically. Again, searches for the rabbit flea proved fruitless.

Skokholm's rabbits were less fortunate with regard to Rabbit Viral Haemorrhagic Disease (RVHD), which arrived in Europe (via Asia) in 1988, where there was a 70 to 90 percent decline in rabbit populations following initial contact. Symptoms of the disease may include lack of coordination, difficulties breathing and a lack of response to stimuli, and it eventually causes death by bringing about pulmonary haemorrhaging. It is highly contagious, spread by direct contact between infected rabbits and by mechanical transmission (e.g. on a person's clothing). It was first recorded from the south-east of England in 1992 (from pet and show rabbits), and there immediately followed a programme of obtaining blood samples from rabbits on sites of nature conservation importance where the animals were known to a crucial element of the ecosystem, in order to analyse serum for antibody as evidence of immunity to the disease (Trout, 1995). In the spring of 1995, blood was taken from 20 freshly-killed Skokholm rabbits in order to test for resistance to RVHD, this following its discovery on nearby Ramsey Island in 1994. The MAFF tests showed that 50 percent of the Skokholm population had resistance to it (though the test sample of 20 animals was very small).

RVHD struck Skokholm's rabbits in the autumn of 1995, and counts of individuals were quickly initiated in order to monitor the progress of the disease, undertaken from a fixed-point on the Knoll and overlooking two fields on Northern Plain (approximately 7 ha in size). In the spring of 1996, further counts revealed a significant decrease in number, but the change could have been due to normal rates of winter mortality. However, diseased rabbits were seen throughout the summer, and autumn counts revealed that numbers within the study-plots were indeed way down, by about 70 percent compared with the 1995 average of 55 animals/ha. Rabbit numbers in study-plots remained at less than 40 percent of the October 1995 number until 1998, when there was a steady increase, and a peak in spring of year 2000 with 53 rabbits/ha (includes kittens). Another large outbreak of RVHD in July 2000 only temporarily reduced numbers, the October 2000 figure being 41/ha. But disease has continued to affect them, and the density in 2003 was on average just 28/ha. *Myxomatosis* has also been in evidence since 1995, albeit in a small way, and the impact of these diseases on the island population in the long-term remains uncertain, although with hindsight it is interesting that in 1948 many young rabbits were reported as being in a semi-comatose state, a condition that can be likened to RVHD.

Prior to the outbreaks of the two diseases, Skokholm supported a very high density of rabbits, with a typical autumn population of about 10,000 individuals, giving a density of 40 per acre, or 100 per hectare. In spring, following winter mortality, numbers had diminished to about 5,000 adults (Lloyd, 1970), although in hard years the residual population was considerably lower. In the spring of 1960, following drought the previous year, there were only an estimated 150 animals on the island and by September of 1962 the breeding population had still only climbed to 5,500, to be halved again by the harsh winter that followed, but then reached 7,500 the following autumn. In October 2003, rabbits were counted on many days right across the island, from various vantage points that did not result in them being disturbed. Their diurnal habits, the identification of certain well-marked individuals, and the ease of separating count areas due to stands of bracken, wall and cliff, and the knowledge that individuals remain faithful to an area gave the distinct impression that very few, if any, animals were being missed or counted twice, and the approximate population was found to be around 1,080 individuals. This was some way down on previous estimates of 6,000 (maximum 10,000), but not unexpected given study-plot results. Closer inspection of these study-plot counts – a mean of 28/ha in 2003 – tallies extremely well given that, approximately, less than half of the island consists of suitable rabbit habitat, i.e. less than 40 ha of habitable surface, with 28 animals per hectare, equals 1,120 rabbits, very close to that number actually counted, and suggesting that such counts are possible thanks to the rabbits' diurnal habits on the island.

Lloyd's long-term study of the population ecology of the rabbit on Skokholm included observations on the number of breeding burrows or "stops" used by subordinate females (the dominant ones give birth in the main warrens), their construction and distribution, and the frequency of visits by nursing does. Significant differences were discovered for these factors between mainland and Skokholm populations (Lloyd & McCowan 1968).

Fluctuations in the rabbit population will clearly affect grazing pressure and long-term changes will give rise to cyclical variation in the floristic structure of the vegetation. Complete exclusion or extermination of rabbits from parts of the island results in dramatic plant growth, as described by R.M. Lockley (1947). He reports that after Cyanogas treatment (see above), he managed to crop hay from the island "for the first time in living memory." The maritime grassland of Skokholm is a rare example of rabbit-maintained vegetation, these animals clearly playing a vital role in maintaining Skokholm's vegetation in its present state, and any protracted reduction in the population would carry serious implications for the vegetation and for several bird species that require open areas for nesting and feeding, i.e. oystercatcher and wheatear. Manx shearwaters, puffins and wheatears use rabbit burrows as nest-sites (Brooke, 1990; Harris, 1984; Conder, 1980 respectively).

Skokholm's rabbits are smaller and darker than their mainland counterparts and varieties such as black (normally 1 percent of the population), long-haired and "Dutch" marked (white collar and face) occur at frequencies that are thought to be higher than normal, although little is known about the distribution of these so-called "sports" in Britain. It is believed, however, that they are more common in isolated populations, perhaps due to the lack of genetic variability in times of low density. They also exhibit an abnormal condition of adipose tissue described as "yellow fat" (Jones et al., 1965), only known from Skokholm and Skomer and possibly caused by a virus. The drought conditions in the summer of 1959 caused an unusually heavy mortality of adult rabbits, and Lloyd (1960) suspected that the "yellow fat virus" caused the deaths at a time when the rabbits were at a period of low resistance due to malnutrition. In 1984, a summer drought resulted in rabbits being forced to graze sand sedge *Carex arenaria* and various thistles, and numbers dropped dramatically in the following winter.

Overleaf: Figure 15. A rabbit *Oryctolagus cuniculus* on Skokholm. This one (individuals located in certain areas were often easily identified by their behaviour, markings, and other features) inhabited the main yard, and frequently sat alongside the wheels and section of rail that were once part of the system that ran from South Haven to the lighthouse. These were retrieved by the Warden in the late 1990's from where they were disposed: the wheels from The Quarry, the track-way from in The Well Pool.

Berry (1977) suggested that atypical colour morphs, and in particular black rabbits, suffer greater predation by buzzards and great black-backed gulls, but that they persist in the population due to their less timid nature and greater use of daylight hours for feeding. This does not seem to be the case in recent years, as black rabbits seem particularly numerous and distribution and numbers do not change much at all, with predated black rabbits reported only rarely (pers. obs.).

Thus, the Skokholm rabbits have had a particularly interesting, and especially challenging, history. It is to be hoped that the island's rabbit population never succumbs completely to any disease, not only because of its success in maintaining a flower-rich turf and suitable nesting and feeding sites for a variety of special birds, but because they are, to quote the words of H.G. Lloyd, "part of the Skokholm scene".

CETACEANS

Throughout the life of the Bird Observatory, resident Wardens have maintained notes of observations of whales, dolphins and porpoises witnessed during sea-watches for birds, and although not strictly a part of the natural history of the island itself, it would be remiss to not make mention of them here.

In 1973, the Cetacean Group was established within the Mammal Society of the British Isles, and a national observer network set up. Skokholm has always contributed records to the scheme. For a précis of the history of cetacean recording in Wales, see Evans, P.G.H. (1998).

Cetacean sightings records fall into two main categories: 1) Incidental sightings for which there was no account of observer effort; and 2) sightings collected using protocols that do record observer effort. Skokholm is a participating "coastal study site" where regular quantified effort watches have been carried out (for further details see Baines *et al.*, 1997).

Harbour Porpoise *Phocoena phocoena*

Incidental sightings show that the Harbour Porpoise is the most widely distributed cetacean in the Irish and Celtic Seas (Baines *et al.*, 1997). Animals are sighted on a daily basis around Skokholm, particularly where strong tidal currents can be seen as surface upwellings and fronts between moving streams of water, where they seem to be exploiting foraging opportunities created by such currents (Thompson & Purcell, 1997). They are frequently joined by plunging gannets *Morus bassanus* and even Manx shearwaters *Puffinus puffinus*. Observations of porpoises in the waters around Ramsey island ascertained that there was a strong tidal influence on the foraging behaviour and movements of these mammals (Pierpoint, 1998), and so watches in a tide race off Skokholm's southwestern most point were carried out. The race in question is easily identified by two parallel strips of water with contrasting appearance – one a smooth upwelling, the other of a choppy nature. There is a distinct link between the state of the tide and sightings, and from observations of behaviour it appears that the animals find good foraging opportunities in the tide race around the low-water period when it is flowing south past the island.

Interestingly, there seem to have been relatively few sightings in the 1970's (Lawman, 2000) and 1980's (G. & E. Gynn, 1982), but many throughout the 1990's and in these early years of the 21st Century.

<u>Threats to the Harbour Porpoise</u>

The Harbour Porpoise is a coastal species ranging over a rather restricted geographical area. It is therefore very unlikely to escape an oil-pollution incident in the immediate locality, and so would probably suffer long-term exposure to contaminants. Potential direct impacts of an oil spillage include damage to the respiratory tract by the inhalation of light oil fractions; digestive tract and liver damage through ingestion of oil; and damage to eyes and mouth through direct contact. Potential indirect impacts include the damage through the bioaccumulation of toxins through feeding, and starvation or insufficient amounts of food due to prey-depletion by the pollution. Thanks to regular monitoring of porpoise sightings, comparisons could be made of the number of animals recorded before and after the spillage by the *Sea Empress* in 1996, and there was no numerical evidence that they had been affected by the oil on that occasion (Baines *et al.*, 1997; SEEEC, 1998).

Other threats include fisheries interactions and noise. Entanglement and death in fishing nets is a problem affecting many species of cetaceans. A review of cetacean by-catch mortality world-wide indicates that whilst most fisheries had some effect, those employing the use of gill-nets had the greatest impact (Northridge, 1991). The harbour porpoise appears to be one of the most vulnerable species to capture in fishing nets, and there is some speculation that this vulnerability may partly reflect the nature of their echolocatory abilities when compared to dolphins (International Whaling Commission, 1994). A 1988 IUCN (World Conservation Union) action plan identified the incidental killing of harbour porpoises in gill-nets in the eastern North Atlantic as a priority for monitoring (for further discussion, see Chapter 4, Section 4 – fishing and fisheries). The recent appearance of the all-to-frequent and ridiculously loud and fast "sea safari" boats is also considered to be a threat (see *Grey Seal* above).

For a clear and concise account of the threats to cetaceans in UK waters, readers are referred to *The Dolphin Agenda* by Simmonds *et al.* (1997), published by The Whale & Dolphin Conservation Society.

Other cetaceans

Although there are records for all months May to November, the period August to September has produced most. The following have been confidently identified:

Common Dolphin *Delphinus delphis*:   This is predominately an offshore species, but pods are frequently encountered passing Skokholm. Large schools are sometimes recorded, e.g. 50 on 5th July 1948, 40 on 20th September 1992 and an estimated 250 on two dates in mid-September 2003.

"Small dolphin" species: Dolphin sightings are much less frequent than of Harbour Porpoise and the species is often not determined unless experienced observers are present.

Bottle-nosed Dolphin *Tursiops truncatus*: Very much an inshore species, but with only occasional records around Skokholm, usually of between 1 and 5 individuals. There have been a few exceptions: a pod of 50 animals which cavorted in the mouth of South Haven for one hour on 21st August 1950 (Skokholm Bird Observatory Report, 1950); another similarly-sized pod (probably the same) off the south-western tip of the island on the same day; and an estimated 40 performing acrobatics to the north of the island on 22nd September 1996.

Risso's Dolphin *Grampus griseus*: Once probably the most regularly recorded dolphin, in singles or small parties, usually July - August, but currently only very infrequent, with just one sighting (of two animals) in the nine years from 1996 - 2004.

Killer Whale *Orcinus orca*: There are records of brief sightings of singles on 8th and 11th September 1989, and 20th October 1989. Super views of a pod of about 5 animals were obtained by a group of lucky observers (including the author) on 14th May 2003, as they milled about in an area of water just about a mile from the south-western tip of the island for almost two hours duration.

Minke Whale *Balaenoptera acutorostrata*: Predominately an offshore species and generally found in deeper waters, it is not surprising that there is only one record, of a single animal on 21st August 1994.

Pilot Whale *Globicephala melaena*: Infrequently encountered in Welsh waters, and thus few Skokholm records: a single on 29th October 1992; and a "probable" on 29th September 1991.

Bottle-nosed Whale *Hyperoodon ampullatus*: Up to 40 were recorded on several dates in August and September 1960.

Subsection 3.2.2: BIRDS

Introduction

Skokholm is of international importance for its colonies of breeding seabirds, and this is recognized by its SSSI and SPA notification. In addition, there are other breeding birds of particular importance, included in the Red Data Book (Batten *et al.*, 1990) or that are regionally important. Some species are included in the Red and Amber Lists of Birds of Conservation Concern in the UK (Gibbons *et al.*, 1996) and some are Species of European Conservation Concern (Tucker & Heath, 1994).

The suitability of the island to breeding seabirds is largely due to the lack of mammalian ground-predators. The birds which do nest on Skokholm are, of course, subject to influences that are not under the control of island managers whilst they are not breeding, and also whilst they are making excursions away from their nests to their feeding grounds and while travelling between these sites. So the influence of island managers is restricted to proper maintenance of the breeding habitat and the prevention of disturbance. However, there is some knowledge of the location of feeding areas (e.g. Stone *et al.*, 1992), which could perhaps be used to influence government with regard to fisheries management for seabirds and – necessary in recent years – the control of boat operators who seem to have little regard for the birds and other wildlife that they speed past or travel out to observe for financial gain.

All breeding birds are censused annually and location maps drawn. A daily log of migrant and resident birds seen on (or from) the island is kept. This has been maintained since 1928 and, with the exception of the war years 1940 - 1945, is complete for those months when a warden is resident (has usually been March to October inclusive, but in the last decade has included the latter half of February and the whole of November and the first few days of December, and also for most of January in 1998). All of the logs dating from 1946 are kept on the island, with photocopies kept on the mainland by the Wildlife Trust of South and West Wales. Descriptions of nationally- and locally-rare birds are sent to the British Birds Rarities Committee (BBRC) and Pembrokeshire Records Committee (PRC, of the Pembrokeshire Bird Group) respectively for scrutiny. These organisations produce annual reports in their journals, *British Birds* and *Pembrokeshire Bird Report* respectively. The secretary of the latter forwards the records it accepts to the Welsh Rarities Advisory Group for inclusion in publications including *Welsh Birds*.

There is a large diversity of migrant birds recorded on Skokholm, but generally they are present in small numbers, unlike the masses encountered at those observatories on the east coast of Britain (thanks to their closer proximity to mainland Europe). Conversely, there is a slightly greater chance of seeing American passerines on Skokholm, given its location on the eastern seaboard of the Atlantic, but such birds arrive only rarely in Britain. Many of the scarce and rare species that have been frequently recorded on Skokholm are referred to as "island specialities" in Wales, being found also on Bardsey – where ringing operations using mist nets helps substantially in their location – and on Skomer, but with very few mainland records. These include Richard's pipit *Anthus novaseelandiae*, icterine warbler *Hippolais icterina*, melodious warbler *H. polyglotta*, subalpine warbler *Sylvia cantillans*, barred warbler *Sylvia nisoria*, greenish warbler *Phylloscopus trochiloides*, red-breasted flycatcher *Ficedula parva*, woodchat shrike *Lanius senator*, common rosefinch *Carpodacus erythrinus*, and rustic bunting *Emberiza rustica*.

There are, to date, three species of which the first records for Britain were made on Skokholm: olive-backed pipit *A. hodgsoni*, Swainson's thrush *Catharus ustulatus*, and western Bonelli's warbler *Phylloscopus bonelli*. A complete list of first records for the UK, for Wales and for Pembrokeshire is found in Appendix VI.

For every year up to and including 1972, the data was summarized in the Skokholm Bird Observatory Report (SBOR) which, in addition to a systematic list of birds, contained occasional accounts of other research that had been carried out on the island during that year. From 1973 to 1976, the Skokholm report was jointly produced with one from Skomer. In the period 1977 to 1980, only systematic lists, in loose-leaf form, were produced. From 1981 to the present, the systematic list, together with Warden's report and ornithological summary has been published in the "Journal of the Friends of Skokholm and Skomer", currently known as "The Island Naturalist" (although there were no issues produced in 2005 or 2006). The bird report makes a significant contribution to the annual "Bird Report" of the Pembrokeshire Bird Group, and the "Welsh Bird Report" of the Welsh Ornithological Society. Formerly the log data was summarized monthly and the information distributed among observatories participating in the Bird Observatories Council 'grapevine' scheme, but this was not strictly applicable due to the lack of Bird Observatory status post-1976. A general account of many of the common migrants and their time of appearance is given in Appendix VII: The Island Year.

In 1979, a considerable volume of data was extracted from old logs and was used alongside data from other observatories in "Seasonal Movements of Summer Migrants" (British Trust for Ornithology, Guide no. 18). More recently, with concerns over global warming there has been interest in phenological phenomena such as the timing of bird migration. Loxton & Sparks (1999) analysed the spring arrival dates of 24 species of migrant birds recorded by four Bird Observatories – Bardsey, Calf of Man, Portland and Skokholm – and also the relationship between the yearly totals for each species and the arrival date. The data revealed that fewer birds meant a later "first arrival" date, and the expected earlier arrival at the more southerly sites. However, with many species their arrival at Bardsey – some 123 km further south on a bearing of 195° – **preceded** that at Skokholm and it is suggested that the small size of Skokholm and the general lack of cover is not conducive to "holding" migrants for long (no trapping or ringing since 1976 has undoubtedly meant that many have been overlooked). Loxton & Sparks also surmised that Skokholm is perhaps situated a little to the west of the main migration route taken by most birds. They also found that the warmer spring weather recently encountered is significantly correlated with earlier arrival. Unfortunately some species' data could not be used, because the lateness of the start of the recording season on Skokholm and Bardsey in the past would have meant that it was uncertain whether the first records really were of the first birds to arrive in any particular spring. Thankfully, in recent years (until 2005) the Wardens have been in occupation earlier, from the last week in February on Skokholm, but if spring temperatures continue to rise at an earlier date, even this will be too late to record the first migrants.

The same study also highlighted the importance of the observatory data, which had been put to very little use prior to this, particularly since radar studies of migration in the 1960's discovered that bird movements observed on the ground were by no means representative of the whole (e.g. Lack, 1962; Lack & Parslow, 1962). Successful birds were shown to migrate at high altitude, out of view of persons manning the observatories, which led to the suggestion that data obtained from the Bird Observatory network was of little use, that generally those individuals seen on the ground in the autumn are inexperienced immature birds and not representative of a species' main movements. However, there have been efforts recently to re-investigate the validity of data obtained by observations made at ground level, with a great many uses proposed, including analysis of population trends and of the median arrival date as opposed to the first arrival date (Loxton, 2002). There remains an urgent need to transcribe the Skokholm data onto a computerized system for ease of access, but considerable funding is required in order to allow this to take place unless a very-willing volunteer can be found with much time to spare.

Synopses of all of the log data has led to the production of numerous summaries all titled 'Birds of Skokholm', by Lockley (1936), Conder (1953), Barrett (1959), Chambers (1971a), G. Gynn & E. Gynn (1985) and Betts (1992). The last-named summarizes the status of all species recorded, presents graphs of breeding histories, and histograms to show patterns of occurrence of around 60 commoner migrants. An up-dated list is given in this book in Appendix VIII.

Annual counts of all breeding species (except those difficult-to-census burrow-nesters, i.e. Manx shearwater, storm petrel and puffin) are carried out according to established methods and, in the case of seabirds, follow national guidelines (see Walsh *et al.*, 1995). The cessation of ringing presented problems for censuses of the burrow-nesting species, but these were certainly not insurmountable – puffins were censused in 1990, storm petrels in 1995 and again in 2001 and 2003, and Manx shearwaters in 1998, using new methods (see species accounts for more details). In addition to annual whole-island counts of all other species, Annual Seabird Census counts have been carried out at two sites (consisting of four study-plots) since 1981, with figures sent to The Seabird Group.

R.M. Lockley pioneered the study of seabirds with his programme of catching and ringing Manx shearwaters, which continued until ringing ceased in late-1976; between 1936 and 1976, a total of 169,895 of these were ringed on Skokholm. Studies of storm petrels were also initiated by Lockley and continued by Peter Davis in the 1950's and Derek Scott in the late 1960's. Ultimately 18,528 storm petrels were ringed as well as very large number of auks and gulls, and the results of "ground-breaking" work was published on these and a number of other species in many scientific journals. Peter J. Conder, Skokholm Warden from 1947 - 54, wrote the monograph *The Wheatear* following his studies of this species on the island and then elsewhere (Conder, 1990).

The building of Heligoland-type traps in 1933 and August of 1935 made it possible to catch considerable numbers of passerine birds (the 1935 addition was full-size and funded by a donation following an appeal for "The Skokholm Bird Observatory Fund" in *The Spectator* magazine). Among those caught were migrants, both common and rare, which were ringed as they passed through Skokholm on spring and autumn passage. Retrap data provided valuable information on bird movements, and Skokholm became the model for subsequent bird observatories, providing the impetus in Britain for the study of migration. In addition, observations were carried out on many aspects of bird behaviour, for example the distance defended by an individual bird (Conder, 1949a).

The introduction of mist nets in 1956 made it possible to catch large numbers of many species that would not have been trapped by other methods such as the use of Heligoland traps. One problem that was not solved, however, was the need for visitors to the island to use their own rings at this time (the observatory could not afford them), and as a result many recoveries would probably not have been reported back to the Bird Observatory and there is undoubtedly much information still to be retrieved. There has been no detailed review of the ringing work carried out on Skokholm, although Harris (1963) outlined the history up to that year, and some of the particularly interesting recoveries are mentioned in the complete bird list in Appendix VIII.

The trapping of birds for ringing purposes also provided an opportunity to observe the many aspects of identification, and important notes were produced. For example, as a result of trapping a total of 362 willow warblers *Phylloscopus trochilus* and chiffchaffs *P. collybita* in 1947 and 1949, Conder & Keighley (1950) discovered that there was a considerable range of leg colouration within each species and even overlap between the two species, thus effectively precluding leg colour from being a diagnostic field character when used alone. Sadly, Britain's first Bonelli's warbler *P. bonelli* (on Skokholm in 1948) could not be identified (suitable literature to facilitate identification was not widely available at the time), so it was killed and sent to the Director of the Yorkshire Museum, who identified it (Sharrock & Grant, 1982).

The weather greatly influences the appearance and number of many migrant birds, and is a complex subject. Situated at the maritime edge of a continental landmass, the island is strongly affected by two main types of weather system. One is created out in the western Atlantic along the boundary of the cold polar air masses and warm, subtropical ones and consists of depressions with their associated wind and rain, hitting the west coast of Britain with their greatest ferocity. The other is by way of anticyclones formed over the continent of Europe, which bring settled weather with light winds. Then of course there is weather that can be described anywhere within these two extremes, thus it is extremely varied and changeable. It is for this reason that a great variety of birds have been recorded on the island, including some from North America, others from Asia, and many more from all locations in between. Winds from the east frequently bring red-breasted flycatcher *Ficedula parva* and icterine warbler *Hippolais icterina*; those from the south bring melodious warbler *Hippolais polyglotta* and subalpine warbler *Sylvia cantillans*; from the north come snow bunting *Plectrophenax nivalis* and Lapland bunting *Calcarius lapponicus*; and from the west a multitude of seabirds and the occasional North American duck, wader or passerine. Annual bird reports have occasionally made reference to weather conditions, but this is a vast subject beyond the scope of this book, and readers are referred to *Birds and Weather – A Birdwatchers' Guide* by Stephen Moss (1995), and *Weather and Bird Behaviour* by Norman Elkins (2004).

In addition to publishing details of Manx shearwater breeding biology, Lockley, and later Matthews, conducted experiments to investigate the homing ability of shearwaters (see Matthews, 1953 and 1954) and gulls (Matthews, 1950). Many of these experiments involved the release of Skokholm birds from distant locations and analysis of the time and, if possible, the route of the return trip. Conclusive proof was produced that birds really can locate themselves accurately enough to perform return flights to their breeding grounds in a remarkably short time, even from points considered far removed from a species' normal range. The mechanism of location was not discovered during these experiments and it still has to be fully explained.

Between 1963 and 1976, under the scientific guidance of the Edward Grey Institute (EGI) of Ornithology at Oxford University, a large number of people carried out an immense amount of work on the avifauna as well as carrying out the routine ringing programme at an even greater rate than before. Ringing effort was concentrated on Skokholm's seabirds, and in particular large numbers of fledgling Manx Shearwaters in order to allow the discovery of various factors of their natural history. Perrins (1972) summarized the work carried out, that included studies on the breeding success, age of first breeding, and mortality rates. Even large numbers of eggs of various species were measured (Diamond, 1963). Among the many notable results of the EGI programme is the monographic work on the Manx shearwater (Brooke, 1990). The programme for 1973 lists the following opportunities for field work: 1) Recapture of Manx shearwaters; 2) Ringing of young shearwaters; 3) Finding nests of the birds of cliff and maritime heath; 4) Ringing of razorbills and gulls; 5) Trapping of storm petrels.

The banning of the capture of animals in the early autumn of 1976 included the trapping of birds, and so abruptly terminated a number of long-term studies, and the EGI promptly withdrew from Skokholm. The insistence of the landlord that ringing be ended was brought about by numerous disagreements between him and the Wildlife Trust about how it was being carried out. Stories abound that birds were being poorly treated in the quest to ring more and more in even shorter periods of time; "incidental" problems included the collapse underfoot of large numbers of nesting burrows, and the "storage" (in woefully poor conditions) of birds that were awaiting the attention of the ringer, which included piling shearwaters into a lobster pot until no more could be fitted into it (of course, the first put in was one of the last to be subsequently removed). Lawman (2000) describes how up to 30 Manx shearwaters could be stuffed into an oversized woolly jumper – being worn at the time, tied tight around the collector's waist with string to prevent the birds from escaping – for transporting to the ringer. It is not surprising that some regurgitated (and thus lost) their hard-earned food that was destined for a hungry chick. And also how torchlight was used to dazzle wading birds on the margins of North Pond on wet and very windy nights, with the theory that they would remain still and be easily captured by a ringer: "It does not take flight for fear of being driven down wind to… it knows not where." (Brooke, 1983). Often however the reality was surely very different, as the birds would have indeed taken to the wing, to be carried off to oblivion by the very strong winds. Lawman herself now openly admits that the intensity of the ringing caused her to be concerned for the birds' welfare. The author has personal experience of the seabird ringing programme on Skomer – when, for example, gull chicks are crushed underfoot whilst dense bracken is being walked through in a hurried fashion; razorbill chicks are seen leaping to their deaths on the rocks below in a desperate attempt to escape the grasp of an insensitive "ringer" aiming to band a certain number before the day is over; and shearwater nesting burrows being collapsed underfoot and the occupants crushed. It seems that there is still a great deal to fret about even today, and it is worrying that ringing might again one day soon recommence on Skokholm, for although some ringers would undoubtedly intend to adhere to accepted practises at first, bad habits inevitably creep in, particularly when the powerful desire to ring more birds ever more quickly (and add species to their "ringed it" list) takes hold.

A recently-developed branch of bird-watching is that of "sea-watching" – the searching for, and identification of seabirds that are passing a watch point on the land, usually at some distance away – and which is a popular pastime with visitors on Skokholm. The weather greatly affects the species seen, with strong westerly or south-westerly winds most productive for those sea-watching on the island, as they drive ocean-going or pelagic species closer to the shore. For this reason a stone shelter was built immediately to the south of the lighthouse in the early 1990's to facilitate more comfortable viewing. A number of timed sea-watches have been carried out over the years, with all species seen logged, although such systematic recording has been rare. Sea-watching is carried out virtually full-time by some dedicated observers at nearby Strumble Head in North Pembrokeshire, where large numbers of various species are seen each year. Although the observer effort put in on Skokholm is far less, it is clear that the passage of seabirds witnessed from the island does not compare with that seen from Strumble Head. It is thought that many of the birds seen there are those that have entered the Irish Sea during periods of rough weather, and are making their way back out into the open ocean again. This means that they do not pass close to Skokholm. Lockley (1932a) referred to the status of the various shearwater species off the west coast of Britain, and it is clear that, as today, in the late 1920's species such as great shearwater *Puffinus gravis* and sooty shearwater *P. griseus* were rarely seen from land but were frequent further offshore (although sustained effort by observers at sites such as Strumble Head have shown that large numbers can be seen in some years).

A number of PhD. studies have been carried out on the island up to 1976, as follows:

Brooke, M de L. (1977).   The breeding biology of the Manx shearwater. D. Phil. thesis, Oxford.

Davis, J.W.F. (1973a).   Aspects of the breeding ecology and feeding of certain gulls. D. Phil. thesis, Oxford.

Lloyd, C.S. (1976).   The breeding biology and survival of the razorbill *Alca torda*. D. Phil. thesis, Oxford.

Safriel, U. (1967).   Population and food study of the oystercatcher. D. Phil. thesis, Oxford.

Scott, D.A. (1970).   The breeding biology of the storm petrel *Hydrobates pelagicus*. D. Phil. thesis, Oxford.

The total number of birds ringed between 1936 and 1976 by Skokholm Bird Observatory is listed below, taken from the Bird Observatory Report for 1976. Note that some species were ringed on visits to other islands, e.g. Gannets were caught on Grassholm.

Fulmar (34); Manx Shearwater (169,895); Storm Petrel (18,526); Leach's Petrel (1); Gannet (5,750); Cormorant (295); Shag (178); Mallard (10); Teal (16); Wigeon (1); Common Scoter (11); Buzzard (11); Sparrowhawk (10); Montagu's Harrier (2); Merlin (9); Kestrel (8); Quail (1); Water Rail (19); Spotted Crake (1); Corncrake (10); Moorhen (10); Coot (2); Oystercatcher (1,882); Lapwing (694); Ringed Plover(3); Golden Plover (1); Dotterel (1); Turnstone (12); Snipe (54); Jack Snipe (8); Woodcock (3); Curlew (141); Whimbrel (30);Black-tailed Godwit (1); Bar tailed Godwit (8); Wood Sandpiper (2); Common Sandpiper (23); Redshank (4); Knot (8); Purple Sandpiper (8); Little Stint (9); pectoral Sandpiper (5); Dunlin (181); Curlew Sandpiper (2); Semi-palmated Sandpiper (1); Sanderling (2); Ruff (7); Great Black-backed Gull (219); Lesser Black-backed Gull (12,085); Herring Gull (13,164); Larus fuscus/argentatus (38); Common Gull (12); Kittiwake (379); Common Tern (1); Arctic Tern (3); Razorbill (9,220); Little Auk (1); Guillemot (1,023); Puffin (5,411); Stock Dove (28); Woodpigeon (3); Turtle Dove (36); Collared Dove (36); Cuckoo (82); Scops Owl (1); Little Owl (9); Long-eared Owl (2); Short-eared Owl (5); Nightjar (4); Swift (12); Kingfisher (1); Hoopoe (1); Wryneck (11); Short-toed Lark (1); Skylark (299); Swallow (238); House Martin (17); Sand Martin (8); Raven (67); Carrion Crow (152); Jackdaw (83); Magpie (1); Chough (1); Great Tit (36); Blue Tit (186); Coal Tit (10); Long-tailed Tit (1); Wren (876); Treecreeper (1); Mistle Thrush (3); Fieldfare (7); Song Thrush (465); Redwing (157); Ring Ouzel (51); Blackbird (1,718); Olive-backed Thrush (1); Northern Wheatear (3,578); Pied Wheatear (1); Stonechat (336); Whinchat (326); Redstart (394); Black Redstart (100); Nightingale (5); Bluethroat (6); Robin (717); Grasshopper Warbler (298); Great Reed Warbler (2); Reed Warbler (15); Sedge Warbler (1,977); Aquatic Warbler (3); Melodious Warbler (37); Icterine Warbler (7); Olivaceous Warbler (1); Blackcap (211); Barred Warbler (3); Garden Warbler (172); Whitethroat (5,898); Lesser Whitethroat (31); Sardinian Warbler (1); Subalpine Warbler (3); Willow Warbler (11,665); Greenish Warbler (3); Wood Warbler (5); Yellow-browed Warbler (2); Radde's Warbler (1); Goldcrest (438); Firecrest (23); Spotted Flycatcher (1,613); Pied Flycatcher (393); Red-breasted Flycatcher (9); Dunnock (304); Tawny Pipit (1); Meadow Pipit (4,102); Tree Pipit (122); Rock Pipit (2,593); *alba* wagtail (349); Grey Wagtail (8); *flava* wagtail (79); Woodchat Shrike (16); Red-backed Shrike (10); Starling (1,082); Red-eyed Vireo (1); Baltimore Oriole (1); Hawfinch (1); Greenfinch (93); Goldfinch (65); Siskin (37); Linnet (63); Redpoll (16); Serin (1); Bullfinch (10); Scarlet Rosefinch (4); Crossbill (7); Chaffinch (255); Brambling (5); Yellowhammer (28); Ortolan Bunting (6); Rustic Bunting (2); Reed Bunting (174); Lapland Bunting (1); Snow Bunting (6); Rose-breasted Grosbeak (1); House Sparrow (20); Tree Sparrow (7).

TOTAL = 284,655 birds.

FEATURE SPECIES OF THE SEABIRD ASSEMBLAGE

Details relevant to the important breeding species follow.

Notes:

SPA = Special Protection Area, designated under the provisions of the European Community Directive 79/409/EEC on the Conservation of Wild Birds.

RDB = listed in the **Red Data Book**.

BCC = Birds of Conservation Concern. A revised RDB, with prioritization for species into three categories: **red** (demonstrably threatened), **amber** (rare, localized, internationally important or less threatened) or **green**.

SPEC = Species of European Conservation Concern. SPEC 1 includes species of global conservation concern; SPEC 2 includes species of unfavourable status and concentrated in Europe (more than 50 percent of world population or range in Europe); SPEC 3 species are of unfavourable status, but not concentrated in Europe.

<u>Manx Shearwater</u> *Puffinus puffinus* **SPA, RDB, BCC Amber, SPEC 2**

The Manx shearwater is a member of the Order Procellariiformes, otherwise known as the "tubenoses", a group that contains a number of highly-pelagic birds including the fulmar, albatrosses and petrels. It is the island's *cause celebre*, the bird that attracts visitors to Skokholm like no other. Being nocturnal on land, an overnight stay on the island is required to see them properly. Most birdwatchers that have seen this species have done so from a considerable distance, whilst sea-watching from land, when they will have witnessed its habit of gliding just above the surface of the sea, intermixed with short periods of flapping, one moment showing its white underparts, the next its blackish upperparts as it twists to change direction. This flight action, utilising the air currents amongst troughs and peaks of the waves, is called "dynamic soaring", and is quite mesmerising to watch, particularly if there are thousands of birds together.

Adults of breeding age return to Skokholm on dark nights in late-February after a winter at sea (in the South Atlantic Ocean), the long-established pairs taking possession of their nesting burrow on the island plateau. These adults have generally departed before the end of September. Late youngsters are still present in the first half of October. However, in recent years adult birds have regularly been heard calling at night in late-October and even mid-November, as they flew over the island during the period around the new moon (pers obs.).

The island is at all times littered with their corpses, a sign that these birds face a daunting prospect whenever they venture out onto the plateau. Once witnessed at close quarters, it is clear why they are so vulnerable. The species is completely adapted for a life at sea, over which birds fly with unrivalled speed and grace, surely the envy of all other seabirds except, perhaps, for the albatrosses. It is the necessity to come to land to breed that is their nemesis. They lack mobility whilst ashore, their legs being set far back on a long, slender body, thus affording them a front-heavy and extremely ungainly form. They require a stiff breeze to be blowing over the island plateau in order to achieve take-off quickly. Failing this, they will climb – by way of a combination of outstretched wings pulling on the substrate, the hooked tip of the bill, and the sharply-hooked claws – to the top of local high points (rock outcrops) in order to achieve sufficient "airspeed" as they launch themselves into the air. They can even climb vertical rock faces as long as the surface is rough enough to afford them grip. It is not unusual to find numerous stranded birds at daybreak. They are frequently found "hiding" with their head in a dark place, unaware it seems that the remainder of their body is out in the open. The author, along with a multitude of visitors over the years, would find these birds during the course of a morning (should they have survived that long), and place them in suitable hiding places.

The annual breeding cycle of the Manx shearwater is a long one, with a pre-laying period of around 6 weeks, an incubation period of about 51 days, and a spell of up to 76 days during which the single chick is fed on a regurgitated fishy liquid. The adult birds take turns over incubation of the egg, the other usually away foraging and returning after one or two days to swap over with its mate, and similarly when the chick is small and unable to maintain its own body temperature and so requires brooding. Once the chick can thermoregulate, both parents can leave to forage, a necessity because the young shearwater needs huge amounts of calorie-rich food if it is to grow quickly enough to survive. It is as they arrive or leave when they are at a great risk of being predated by the great black-backed gull *Larus marinus*.

In late-June and early-July, numbers are swelled by the return to the island of Skokholm-born birds of 4 - 5 years of age, each seeking a potential mate and nest-site for the future. This is particularly noticeable on the darkest nights around the period of the new moon, or when the sky is cloudy and more so when it is raining. It is on nights such as these that one can really experience the magic of being in the middle of a Manx shearwater colony. Conversely, when the moon is full, very few shearwaters will be seen at all, since the adults fly in with such accuracy – obviously recognizing the terrain – that they are able to land and disappear straight down their nest-burrows without delay. Non-breeding birds, on the other hand, simply stay away to avoid being predated.

At 50 days old, young Manx shearwaters reach a peak weight (of about 600g) that exceeds that of the adult birds by one-third. They are deserted by the parents when 63 days old on average, and eventually fledge after 71 days at a weight of between 450 and 500g. When the chicks are almost ready to fledge they spend time out on the surface each night, exercising their wings, climbing rocks and leaping off in short "practise" flights. They too, are at risk of being predated, particularly when the natal burrow is finally deserted as the chicks seek to reach the sea, a journey that may take them several days as they battle through stands of dense bracken. The author frequently assisted those that became stranded on breezeless nights, placing them in burrows located on the cliff top, but not before experiencing each youngster show what was surely a sudden burst of excitement upon seeing (and smelling) the sea below, with eyes suddenly widening, and any struggle to escape ceasing, before making even stronger efforts to break free. Incidentally, all young shearwaters that the author has placed into water (presumably their first encounter with it), whether it was sea- or freshwater, immediately drank profusely.

The Manx shearwater has a particularly restricted breeding distribution, with 90 percent of the world population nesting around the coast of Britain and Ireland. The key sites are Rhum in the Inner Hebrides, Skomer and Skokholm off south-west Wales and Puffin Island off south-west Ireland (Brooke, 1990). They have specialised habitat requirements (adjacent to the sea and free of mammalian ground-predators), which few sites provide. Skokholm is thought to support the third-largest colony of this species, with an estimated 46,184 pairs (Smith

Opposite: Figure 16. A Manx Shearwater at its magnificent best – in flight low over the tops of the waves.

et al., 2001). This is thought to be at least 15 percent of the World population, and qualifies Skokholm (along with Skomer) for SPA status under Article 4.2 of the EC Birds Directive. It is a Red Data Book species and on the Amber List of the Birds of Conservation Concern (> 20 percent European population in UK, > 50 percent of the UK population in 10 or fewer sites). The birds nest in burrows across the length and breadth of the island, including in ancient earth banks that cross boggy areas and thus afford dry ground, but burrows are of greatest density on the coastal slopes and towards the western end of the island.

There have been numerous homing experiments carried out with seabirds breeding on Skokholm, and these have often been well-publicised. On 10th October 1936, *The Times* newspaper published an account of the experiments with shearwaters, puffins and petrels, carried out by the Observatory, with the Manx shearwater comprising the bulk of those tested. Easy to capture, either on the island surface or from their nesting burrows, and known to undertake long migrations, they proved to be an ideal subject. Breeding birds taken from the burrow (where they were incubating an egg) and released in Venice, Italy, returned to Skokholm at speeds that indicated that they had not searched at random, but quickly chose and followed the correct course. The main difficulty with using this species was that returning birds did so at night, so there may have been a delay caused by birds waiting offshore during daylight hours for the cover of darkness, and so leading to an underestimate in the homing time. It should be noted that not all of the birds were refound, presumed to have perished.

In subsequent years and in particular the early 1950's, many more homing experiments were carried out involving large samples. Birds released during the day from inland release points (with which they could not have been familiar) immediately orientated themselves towards Skokholm during sunny weather, but scattered in cloudy weather. Those that returned did so at speeds indicating that they possessed true navigational ability. The use of birds experienced in these homing experiments had little effect on the initial orientation, but did lead to a marked improvement in the swiftness of the return (Matthews, 1964). Most notable perhaps was a bird released in Boston, Massachusetts, U.S.A. that was found back in its burrow on Skokholm 12 ½ days later (Matthews, 1953), some 10 hours before the note confirming the bird's release in the U.S.A. was received on the island. Many of the experiments would most certainly be deemed cruel today – these were breeding birds. Interesting information was obtained as a result, including the discovery that Manx shearwater eggs that were unincubated for a period of up to 65 hours during the mid-incubation period would still hatch successfully.

Censusing a large colony of shearwaters is extremely difficult, because in addition to nesting underground, they are nocturnal. Estimates are further complicated by the presence later in the season of large numbers of non-breeders. By calculating nest densities, Lockley (1930) arrived at an estimate of 10,000 birds, subsequently amending this to 10,000 pairs (Lockley, 1942). Large scale ringing of shearwaters commenced in 1934 (Lockley, 1935), eventually enabling a mark - release - recapture figure of about 35,000 pairs and Perrins' (1967) estimate of 30,000 - 40,000 pairs supported this.

The ringing of masses of fledglings in the 1960's was quickly rewarded, when the corpse of one – estimated to have been dead for three days – was discovered on a seashore at the species' wintering area in Brazil wearing a ring that had been fixed to its leg just 16 days earlier on Skokholm. Assuming that the journey of 9,600 km had been completed in 13 days, at a rate of 740 km per day, the answer was obtained why young shearwaters fledge whilst carrying more than 100g of fat – the flight would have been undertaken non-stop. Recoveries of many Skokholm-ringed birds have shown that the majority of them spend the early part of the northern winter in the South Atlantic Ocean off the coasts of Argentina, Brazil and Uruguay. Wayward birds may undertake even longer flights, as one found off the coast of southern Australia proved in November 1961, having been ringed as a chick on Skokholm in September 1960.

The habits of these and other seabirds mean that wear on rings is great. Lockley (1942) found that standard aluminium rings (used until 1958) lasted little more than two years, thus decreasing the chance of recovery. Harris (1964a) stated that the inscription on the "double-ended" aluminium rings that replaced them for use on seabirds (inscribed twice, and placed on the bird's tarsus in such a way that the inner inscription was protected) became illegible after four, but in some instances two, seasons. These were superseded shortly afterwards by an altogether tougher variety made of monel metal, so that life tables and mortality rates could be better calculated. In total, 169,895 Manx shearwaters were ringed on Skokholm by the time ringing was forced to cease in late 1976 (Skokholm Bird Observatory Report, 1976), by decree of the land owner.

The breeding success and survival rates of Manx shearwaters on Skokholm were studied intensely in accessible burrows between 1963 and 1969 (Perrins et al., 1973). Of those eggs laid each year, about 90 percent hatch, and of the youngsters a further 90 percent survive to leave the island; i.e. 70 percent of breeding pairs will successfully produce an offspring. Data on survival of the young was obtained through the intensive ringing programme previously mentioned. It was shown that the weight of the young at fledging and the date at which they leave the island significantly affect their chances of survival. Overall, about 30 percent of young may survive to reach the breeding age of 5 - 6 years. Adult annual mortality ranged between 5 and 20 percent, but juvenile survival seemed to be sufficient to balance the losses of adults – this has been supported by recent estimates of the population size (below).

Recoveries of Manx shearwaters ringed on Skokholm prior to or during 1976 continue to be made: for example, on 30th March 1999, a bird that had been ringed as an adult on Skokholm on 30th May 1976 was recovered on the island, some 23 years later, unfortunately recently killed, but still telling part of a lengthening story. The vast majority of recoveries have come from Skokholm itself, as one would expect, and birds have been known to live to at least 30 years of age, and in fact one retrapped recently on Bardsey Island, North Wales was 55 years old. Another aspect of the lives of the Manx shearwater that ringing uncovered was that some individuals, and in particular females, settle to breed in a different colony to that from where they fledged (Brooke, 1978).

The Manx shearwater has now become well-established on the North American side of the Atlantic Ocean, and recently on Middle Lawn Island off South Newfoundland, where a bird that had been ringed on Skokholm has been found, and was perhaps one of those that established the new colony (Chambers, 1971b).

In 1997 - 98, a census of the Manx shearwater populations was made on the three islands of Skokholm, Skomer and Middleholm without the use of ringing. It was carried out by first counting all of the burrows during the winter (grid lines were laid out to facilitate the counting), and then playing a tape-recording of the call of a male bird down a sample of the burrows (to which only males respond) during the incubation period. A correction factor was then applied to allow for the proportion of males that responded; this was determined by playing the tape-recording down a sample of burrows in which eggs had been laid and where incubating birds could be examined and sexed (carried out on Skomer Island). Knowing the number of burrows sampled, the number of responses, the response rate and the total number of burrows allowed estimation of the population size (see James & Robertson, 1985). An estimated 46,184 pairs were breeding on Skokholm in 1998 (Smith et al., 2001). However, rabbit warrens and burrows with more than one entrance certainly exist, and unless these were identified successfully, there could have been an inflated estimate of colony size, although this over-estimate would probably not have been a huge one. Eight study-plots, each covering an area of 1,000 square metres, have been established on the island in order to allow some annual monitoring. Although a check of the whole breeding population at regular intervals would probably be more desirable, the time taken would be significant. It is therefore only feasible to monitor a small proportion of the birds, hence the establishment of the study-plots. These have been set up in a number of different areas in a variety of habitats, some with breeding lesser black-backed gulls within them. Significant changes in population within one or more of these areas, either an increase or decrease, could have implications for habitat or species management over the whole island.

The results of the 1998 Manx shearwater census revealed a significant increase over previous estimates in 1964 (Harris, 1966a, 1966b), and 1967 (Perrins, 1967). These involved mark-and-recapture techniques, and a measure of the number of young that had survived to fledging. The breeding success figures used to estimate total breeding population in each of these years were obtained from study burrows, and were undoubtedly accurate, and the resulting population estimates were in the region of 35,000 pairs. Thus it would seem that numbers have increased substantially over recent years. But given the differences in method, can one really be sure? There is evidence that there has indeed been an increase in the areas that were most recently farmed, i.e. ploughed (many furrows are still visible today, particularly when the island is viewed from the air; a map drawn in 1947 clearly shows those that were visible at that time). Perrins (1967) estimated 7,000 fledglings in this area, although the census was carried out less accurately here than elsewhere (Perrins, 1997). Using a breeding success of 75%, there was an estimated 9,000 pairs, whereas the 1998 census gave an estimate of about 16,000 pairs.

Estimates of adult survival on Skomer in recent years (Perrins, 1998) give figures that are lower than would be expected for a bird with such a low reproductive rate. Evidence from Rhum in the Inner Hebrides, which has probably the second largest colony in the world after Skomer, indicates that the population there may be slowly decreasing (Furness, 1997). Given that the population there and those of the Pembrokeshire islands are thought to winter in the same areas, there is cause for concern. The study-plots should shed some light on this.

A total of 84,391 burrows were counted in February 1998, as the first part of the whole-island census (see above), the average density being 861 burrows/ha (maximum 2,912/ha), though puffins use many of those on the coastal slopes and rabbits many of the others. A similar count on Skomer and Middleholm revealed that Skokholm is far more densely-burrowed than the others, as Brooke (1990) and others suggested, which is partly due to its higher edge : inland ratio and to the coastal slopes being more densely-burrowed. Many areas are extremely fragile, with burrows collapsing underfoot if people leave the footpaths.

The Manx shearwaters on Skokholm (and Skomer) suffer from a mysterious disease known as "puffinosis", first described by Dane (1948) and Dane et al. (1953). Its characteristic symptoms are blistered feet, spastic limbs and conjunctivitis, not all of which are exhibited at any one time, so there is the possibility that more than one disease may be involved. It occurs regularly in certain areas – usually wet ones – and affects mainly fledglings, of which 4 percent may be killed. Its distribution appears to have remained unchanged for many years (Brooke & Perrins, 1982). This localization is unusual amongst diseases of wild animals. Fledglings appear to contract it when they venture out of the burrow during the desertion period. Despite some detailed fieldwork, the exact cause is unknown, and circumstantial (but not experimental) evidence points to the involvement of the larvae of the trombiculid mite Neotrombicula autumnalis in transmission. However, the efficacy of a drug as a prophylactic treatment suggests there is a disease agent involved (Brooke, 1990). Perrins (1993) carried out a further study of the disease on Skomer in 1992 and 1993. In 1992 a virus was sought, and although this search failed, two new discoveries were made: 1) pathological examinations showed that birds seemed to have died of heavy bacterial infections, and the bacteria differed in different birds. It was suggested that the birds possibly become ill initially as a result of viral infection, but that death resulted because the weakened birds succumb to bacterial infections; 2) A number of birds were administered a dose of antibiotic, together with some saline solution to replace that lost from burst blisters. Most of the small sample of birds survived and were subsequently released. Then, in 1993, a small number (50) of affected birds were given one of two treatments, either the application of an antibiotic, of a saline solution, or nothing. The antibiotic seemed to bring about a good recovery, and since these control bacteria and not viruses – thought to cause the disease – it was thought that this might be further evidence that birds were actually dying of a secondary infection. The administering of the saline solution was less convincing in its effectiveness, although more survived than in the control group that received no treatment at all. Affected birds can recover from the disease. Blistered feet have been observed in other species, and this referred to as puffinosis, e.g. great black-backed gull *Larus marinus* and shag *Phalacrocorax aristotelis* on Fair Isle (Davis, P., 1966), and fulmars *Fulmarus glacialis* (Macdonald *et al.*, 1967).

It was Ronald Lockley who began the study of the Manx shearwater and eventually resulted in the publication of his book *Shearwaters* in 1942. Subsequently a monograph on the species was produced by M. de L. Brooke (1990), the Skokholm Warden employed by the Edward Grey Institute of Ornithology from 1973 - 76, following the work that involved a great many people over the years. Readers are referred to these excellent publications for further information about this wonderful bird.

The species' scientific name *Puffinus puffinus* derives from the fact that, in the Middle Ages, the plump young shearwaters – when taken for food by man – were known as "puffins", a result of their plumpness. In 1676, birds collected on the Calf of Man were named "Manx puffin". Some time later the name "shearwater" was adopted, but by which time *puffinus* had been incorporated into the scientific name.

Other factors affecting Manx Shearwaters

The island is used as a breeding site. Even during the breeding season the birds are subject to external influences outside the control of island managers. Other than safe breeding sites, greatest importance must be attached to food availability. This will affect them whether feeding in local waters during the breeding season, in winter quarters off South America, or on migration between the two. Stone *et al.* (1994) demonstrated the importance of the Irish and Celtic Seas as feeding areas for the Manx shearwater. The feeding biology is not completely understood, particularly during the winter when the birds are far from land. Monitoring of relevant fish stocks is therefore extremely difficult. Annual survival rates and breeding success, both monitored on nearby Skomer, may reflect these factors.

Manx shearwaters are capable of digging their own burrows, albeit rather slowly (personal observations). They do use the burrows of rabbits, and are capable of evicting them. Rabbits undoubtedly keep the vegetation cropped around the entrances in grassy areas, and thereby ensure that they are accessible. There is certainly competition between shearwaters and puffins, for burrows (Brooke, 1990; pers. obs.). Ashcroft (1976) found that puffins on Skomer prefer cliff-top burrows to those situated slightly further inland, where shearwaters predominate (this is exactly the case on Skokholm too). In areas where the two species bred side-by-side, egg losses were frequent. With the competitive edge so finely balanced, changes in the population dynamics of one species could affect the population of the other (Brooke, 1990).

Most Manx shearwaters remain faithful to their natal colonies. There is some interchange between colonies in the Irish Sea, permitting a degree of gene flow and thus preventing subspeciation. However, there is no proven interchange between the Welsh and Scottish colonies (Harris, 1972). A catastrophic loss of the Welsh population could therefore bring about the permanent extinction of the species in this area.

Digging by rabbits, puffins and shearwaters is likely to lead to soil losses, particularly from slopes close to cliff edges (Ninnes, 1998). This could reduce the availability of nest-sites in the future (c.f. Grassholm, in Lockley, 1969). Other natural erosion processes could also play a significant part. The loss of thrift from some areas means that the soil-building process is reduced on Skokholm, and unless stabilised by other vegetation, e.g. sea campion, the overall change will be one of loss.

Predation by great black-backed gulls (also a Feature species of the nature reserve) can be high. Counts of Manx shearwater corpses on Skokholm had been carried out since 1957, perhaps with varying degrees of diligence, up until 1997. Numbers were mirrored to a great extent by the numbers of breeding great black-backed gulls, and the correlation has been found to be statistically significant (e.g. E. Gynn, 1984). Thompson (in Betts, 1995) found shearwater remains in the close vicinity of all of the 37 great black-backed gull nests on Skokholm, whereas Poole (1992) found that 80 - 97% of nests had them on Skomer in a study over more than one year. Corkhill (1973) suggested a relatively low predation figure of 2 percent of adult shearwaters. Harris (1966a, 1966b) showed that it was mainly non-breeding shearwaters that were taken by gulls, presumably because they spend much time sitting about on the island surface at night, unlike the adults. September is the month with the highest number of casualties (measured by the number of corpses found) and it is not surprising given that this is the time when the fledglings are struggling to get to the sea, a process which can take them several days and lead to them attempting to hide during daylight hours in totally ineffective places. Diseased youngsters are even more vulnerable, commonly venturing out in the day, and often with poor eyesight due to conjunctivitis. Control methods have been employed in the past to restrict the numbers of great black-backed gulls, in particular in the late 1960's and throughout the 1970's when breeding birds were "discouraged", following a peak in number of 72 pairs in 1949. Unlike the other *Larus* gulls, their population did not increase rapidly anywhere during the 1960's (see below). They are, of course, a natural component of a "healthy" seabird colony. In the early 1980's an outbreak of botulism affected great black-backed gulls, leading to a suspension of control methods and a substantial increase in the number of breeding pairs since, to 71 nesting pairs in 2004.

Ravens are present in large numbers on neighbouring Skomer Island in late-August and September, where they predate fledgling shearwaters, but strangely this gathering does not occur on Skokholm. There are undoubtedly many other predators of shearwaters that we are not yet aware of. In 1938 the ring of a Manx Shearwater was found inside the stomach of a 40 lb angler fish *Lophius piscatorius* caught by a line from the pier at Douarnenez, France (SBOR 1938). There are many records of shearwaters with severed legs or mutilated feet, thought to be due to attacks by large predatory fish.

Opposite: Figure 17. A Manx shearwater in a typical pose, prostrate on the rabbit-grazed turf after crashing down to earth. Some seem to have an uncanny knack of landing very close to the burrow that they seek, obviously using various cues to locate it. This would prove to be easy where there are obvious landmarks, but how they find a burrow situated in a mass of bracken is a real mystery.

It is not clear whether bracken *Pteridium aquilinum* is a help or hindrance to breeding shearwaters. Since 1948, it has encroached into coastal grassland, particularly on the eastern, sheltered side of the island and into areas previously dominated by *Calluna* heath. There have been fluctuations in cover and distribution to the west and south of the island. Where there has been control in the past, many areas have been reinvaded (Ninnes, 1998). Fledglings failing to reach the sea are known to hide in it, perhaps when they are unable to find the shelter of a burrow. It does hinder them when they are moving about overland, however (Lockley, 1942, and pers. obs.). Adults too are obviously funnelled into certain areas by bracken. This is noticeable along the wider track-ways on Skokholm, particularly on nights when there is little wind, as they struggle to get away from advancing persons (pers. obs.). They frequently become tangled up with the stiff plant stems, albeit momentarily, and predatory gulls could take advantage of a shearwater in such a predicament. Bracken has been controlled in these areas in order to create "escape routes" for the birds (Skokholm Warden's Report to Dyfed Wildlife Trust, 1998) by way of swathes cut at right angles to the nearest cliff edge, but unless such work is carried out on a regular basis these areas quickly become swamped by new growth.

There remains a constant threat of flooding of burrows, particularly those situated in the central Bog and near to streams. Persistent heavy rain for consecutive days in August has occasionally caused huge mortality amongst young birds right across the island, by them being forced up onto the surface by rising water levels and then becoming easy prey for gulls (pers. obs.). So endearing are individuals of this species, the author can personally attest that one cannot simply stand by and watch such episodes – during one period when 12 centimetres of rain fell in 4 days, many thousands of burrows were flooded, and tunnels were artificially extended by placing pieces of wood, cardboard boxes, and even old washing-up bowls in the vicinity of burrow entrances, so that chicks could safely sit on the surface, but still sheltered. Once the water-level receded, many of the young birds seemed to prefer their new "burrow", and had to be encouraged back down. Although great black-backed gulls can quickly kill a shearwater, the other, smaller *Larus* gulls inflict terrible injuries, such as removing eyes, which ultimately results in the subsequent, slow death of the bird. Thankfully such events are quite rare, but with the onset of global warming they are likely to become far more frequent.

Burrows and their occupants can be easily destroyed underfoot; it is therefore a key part of management to ensure that visitors remain on the marked footpaths (sadly the "keep to paths" rule is the one most broken, with a small number of people adamant that the island should remain unrestricted so that they may satisfy their whim of, for example, sitting on a "favourite" rock outcrop despite it being situated in the middle of an extremely fragile piece of terrain or even a gull colony). Staff members only leave the paths when carrying out essential management work, even before and after the shearwater breeding season, and great care is required at all times. Counting of the nests of lesser black-backed gulls during early summer by walking through colonies is fraught with danger for both the human counters and the birds underground. An alternative method applicable to fragile islands such as Skokholm has been developed (see Walsh *et al.*, 1995), and a similar method was adopted on the island in 1996 (Thompson, 1996a) following the totally unnecessary collapse of numerous burrows (see lesser black-backed gull). Prior to the conditions in the lease from Dale Castle Estate prohibiting the trapping and handling of animals, large numbers of burrows were destroyed underfoot as Wardens and visitors carried out various studies on the Manx shearwater. Similarly, a study of rabbits carried out on Skomer Island resulted in burrows being destroyed as people attempted to capture animals at night. Such practises are completely irresponsible, and it is to be hoped that they will not be allowed to reoccur on Skokholm even though the island is now owned by the Wildlife Trust.

The self-proclaimed "sea-safari" boats, a recent intrusion into the waters around the Pembrokeshire islands, also target Manx shearwaters. The birds gather in large "rafts" on the sea in the early-evening prior to venturing ashore after dark. Boat skippers endeavour to get their vessels as close as possible to the shearwaters, and ultimately cause them to fly (pers. obs.). They are then pursued by the boats, and only nightfall brings about their relief as the "safari" is brought to an enforced halt.

Given the small number of breeding locations for the Manx shearwater, the island could be targeted by egg collectors. This has been known from Skomer, e.g. in 1993 (Skomer Warden's Report, 1993). Given that a relatively small number of persons are able to visit Skokholm during the incubation period, it is highly unlikely, and probably less likely to occur than on Skomer with its many day visitors, although an overnight stay would offer better opportunities to an egg thief.

Fire could have a serious effect on breeding shearwaters and chicks. Lockley (1947) describes the problem he encountered with fires smouldering underground on Skokholm, following the attendance of large numbers of people during the field meeting of the 8th International Ornithological Congress held on the island in 1934.

Bright lights, such as those produced by lighthouses around our coasts, can deleteriously affect Manx shearwaters as a result of attracting the birds and ultimately causing them to fly into buildings. Increasing numbers of ships are undertaking temporary mooring to the east of the island, and are very strongly illuminated at night, presumably in order to prevent collision. This has long been the case in St. Brides Bay, to the immediate north of Skomer, but no study has been carried out with regard to the effect upon nocturnal birds. The effects of the Skokholm lighthouse light are described at the end of this section.

Overleaf: Figure 18. A fledgling Manx shearwater on the cottage garden wall, with downy feathers still remaining in places. Behind, in the corner of the garden, the tops of the three Sycamore trees can be seen. These provide cover and feeding opportunities for migrant passerines, and the list of rare and scarce species seen in them is an impressive one.

<u>Storm Petrel</u> *Hydrobates pelagicus* **SPA, RDB, BCC Amber, SPEC 2**

This delightful, tiny species of the Order Procellariiformes is one that qualifies Skokholm (and Skomer) for SPA status under Article 4.1 of the EC Birds Directive. There are about 1,000 pairs currently estimated to be on Skokholm (Thompson, 2005), though a past estimate had put the population at 5,000 - 7,000 breeding pairs (Scott, 1970). It is a Red Data Book species and on the Amber List of Birds of Conservation Concern (> 50 percent of the UK population in 10 or fewer sites). There are only 41 known colonies in the UK (Lloyd *et al.*, 1991). Sadly (for us human want-to-be observers) they are, along with other small petrels, nocturnal at their breeding sites due to their immense vulnerability to predators.

Called "petrel" after Saint Peter of the Christian Holy Bible because of the way the members of the species frequently patter over the surface of the sea with legs and tiny webbed feet dangling as if walking on water, this fragile-looking bird has a hardiness that beggars belief. At just under 30 grams in weight, and elegantly built with long, slender wings and delicate tube-nosed bill, it spends the majority of its life in the open ocean, many miles from land, and visiting *terra firma* only during the breeding season. The maritime connection has also resulted in a superstition: sailors once knew it as Mother Carey's chicken, after a satanic sea-witch who evidently possessed the key to Davy Jones' locker, so mariners feared death whenever petrels gathered around a ship in rough weather. However, another belief is that Mother Carey is a corruption of *Mater Cara*, the Mother Beloved, Our Lady (Lockley, 1983), and that mariners felt they were being watched over (and looked after) by the birds. Whatever its origins, both stories do lend themselves nicely to this rather mysterious little creature.

Much census work has been carried out on Skokholm, because the island is a location that is kind to researchers, i.e. there is comfortable, if somewhat basic, accommodation, and the cliffs where the birds breed are not particularly treacherous. Studies over the years have shown that there are 3 principle habitats in which storm petrels breed on Skokholm:

1) In holes and crevices in the earth-filled, stone-lined "hedge-banks" or walls, of which there is approximately 2,070 metres length;
2) In the interstices between rocks in areas of rock-fall and boulder beach, of which there is an estimated 4,000 square metres, and where nest density can be high;
3) In "burrows" in earth situated primarily beneath overhanging rocks, of which there is an estimated area of 7,100 square metres (Vaughan & Gibbons, 1996), though nest density is particularly low in these areas.

In some cases the two last-named are difficult to distinguish between, since fallen boulders do quickly accumulate earth between them. If they don't, then it is because they are frequently washed-over by the sea during storms, and no petrel would remain there for long.

An area of rock-fall known as The Quarry, at the western end of the island, holds the greatest concentration of breeding birds. The wall habitat is thought to be "sub-optimal" (Scott, 1970) and therefore supposedly less desirable to the petrels and used only by subordinate birds. This idea is strengthened by the fact that there is a great number of sites in these walls which seem suitable for nests, and indeed which have been known to be

Overleaf: Figure 19. A Storm Petrel on Skokholm, by Andy Sands, with his kind permission.

occupied in the past but which are currently vacant, coinciding with a period of probable decline in the overall population. However, many of these "subordinate" birds must surely become experienced and successful breeders quickly – the author has seen numerous large chicks in these wall nests.

Storm petrels are rather difficult to census, due to their nocturnal habits and nests being located in inaccessible places. Lockley conducted pioneering research into storm petrels on Skokholm, and between the wars estimated the population to be at least 500 breeding pairs (Lockley, 1932b). A census in 1949 utilised the same technique as that of Lockley, where workers would crawl around the walls and cliffs where suitable-looking sites existed, sniffing for the distinctive "musky" odour of the birds. The result was "a total of storm petrel sniffs" and an estimated population of around 500 pairs. Between 1954 and 1956 island warden Peter Davis further investigated their breeding biology (P. Davis, 1957). Then, between 1966 and 1969 Derek Scott estimated – largely via the use of mist nets and the subsequent retrap data – that there were approximately 6,200 breeding pairs of storm petrels, at least 75 percent of them on boulder beaches and scree slopes. Further ringing "evidence" placed the total community size at 18,000 birds, which was taken to support the relative accuracy of the population figure (Scott, 1970), but the use of tape lures (the playing of a recording of the storm petrel song) might have complicated matters by attracting birds belonging to other colonies, e.g. Skomer, and wandering non-breeders.

Between 1989 and 1995, Skokholm warden Michael Betts made an estimate of the populations in those walls previously studied by Scott (1970). He initially began by using an image intensifier and undertook general observations. The distribution map that he drew approximately matched Scott's of 1967, but absolute numbers could not be compared because of the different methods used. In 1992, an attempt was made to locate all of the nest-sites in the island's walls by using an image intensifier and playing a tape of the petrel song to initiate a response, and it became clear that numbers had declined dramatically since 1969, with far fewer sites occupied. In 1994, Betts estimated that the The Quarry population – the area where there is a large number of nesting petrels – consisted of 1,388 calling birds. Adjustment for birds absent at sea (it was the period just prior to egg-laying) based on occupancy of marked burrows in the study-walls gave an estimate of between 1,400 and 2,800 pairs in The Quarry. The total island estimate was of 4,200 - 8,000 pairs (Betts, 1994), the large range reflecting the difficulties in carrying out such a census.

In 1995, a whole-island assessment of the distribution of nesting storm petrels was carried out. All areas found to be occupied ("sub-colonies") were measured, mapped, named and numbered (Vaughan & Gibbons, 1996). In addition, a number of study-plots of varying size were established, typically from 25 sq m to 100 sq m, depending upon bird-density within them (the greater the density, the smaller the plot). Then some of these quadrats were sampled at random, and a single visit made to each of them during daylight hours in order to carry out a more intensive study, where tape-response was used to obtain a measure of the population within each. The number of responses obtained at night far outnumber those obtained during the day, so calibration was sought by comparing the response rates obtained at night through multiple visits to some sections of wall (these being safe to visit at night) with those obtained during the day (same number of visits). The difference (the "correction factor") was then applied to the results of the single diurnal visits made to all of the other sites on the island, that is multiplying by it to obtain an estimate of total bird numbers. Although different methods were used, comparison with Scott's work established that the population was "possibly declining", with 4,400 Apparently Occupied Burrows (AOBs) estimated. Michael Betts expressed concern that the responses of the birds to the tape-recording changed as time went on, and he thought that they might be "over- exposed" to it.

In order to assist with the monitoring of population size, breeding success and survival of this species on Skokholm, it was decided that a nest-box population ought to be established. Boxes were loosely based on the model successfully used on the Shetland island of Mousa (Bolton, 1996). These were installed in two sites: 1) the walls near to the Observatory buildings; and 2) in the vicinity of The Quarry. The boxes were surrounded by stones and earth in order to mimic the natural nest-sites (Thompson, 1999). Very few boxes have since been occupied, but this is hardly surprising given that most of the natural sites that formerly housed storm petrels are empty. Until just recently permission would have been required from the landowner before any bird could be handled or ringed, so these "accessible" birds would have in any case been unable to produce any useful results. It is known that this species is very likely to desert the nest if disturbed (Scott, 1970) although recent work on Mousa has suggested that if checks are made <u>after</u> the egg has hatched, desertion is "far less likely".

A repeat of the 1995 census carried out in 2001 showed that the method used was not entirely repeatable due to a rather large difference between the ratio of diurnal : nocturnal responses, but the estimated population, and indeed the <u>actual</u> number of birds responding to the playing of the tape recording, had decreased further. Another, altogether more intensive method was designed to find an accurate response rate during daylight hours only, which involved visiting one study-plot ("RF3" in North Haven) as many times as necessary in an attempt to locate <u>all</u> nest-sites and calculate a mean response rate. Vaughan (2001) found no new sites on his ninth visit to this site, and so assumed that all nests had been located – a total of 27 AOBs. In 2002, RF3 was again visited on multiple occasions (10 times), and 32 AOBs located. In addition, a number of other plots were similarly visited, these being located in The Quarry ("rockfall") and in the Head Bay area ("rock-burrow"), to ascertain mean response rates in the different habitats. The vocalisations of the responses did seem to alter over time (becoming attenuated), and it could be that the birds were being stressed by the frequent visits.

In 2003, the study was taken to another degree, as a greater number of plots were chosen for multiple visits. Between 25th June and 13th July, 9 quadrats in "rockfall" (totalling 290 sq m in area), 7 quadrats in "rock-burrow" habitat (total 687 sq m), and four sections of wall (each with two sides of 50m length) were visited up to 10 times, where a 15-second burst of storm petrel song was played to each square metre or suitable-looking site (i.e. deemed suitable to hold an AOB), or at metre intervals along walls, in order to allow the calculation of mean response rates. This again included RF3 in North Haven, and a number of other quadrats that had previously been the subject of the single visits with tape by Vaughan (in 1995 and 2001), these being in rockfall in The Quarry, and rock-burrow sites at Head Bay. In order to increase the sample size in The Quarry, additional areas just outside these main plots were included. A number of small rockfalls were inadvertently started here by the author, despite extreme care being taken, which demonstrated the potential for more serious movements of material. Then, between 10th July and 20th August 2003, all except six of the remaining 38 coastal sites identified by Vaughan & Gibbons (1996 and 1998) were revisited and tape response used in an attempt to ascertain population size (of the six areas not visited, four were inaccessible without ropes, the other two tiny sites not relocated). Smell was also used as a factor to locate AOBs. All areas were measured and mapped. In addition, two new occupied areas of rockfall were discovered, one at Purple Point, the other in Twinlet Bay. The resulting population estimate was a little over 1,000 pairs (Thompson, 2005), and although the methodology differed somewhat from the previous study, the <u>actual</u> number of AOBs found in those areas previously surveyed had decreased. Thus this latest population figure is a definite cause for concern. During the same survey, the calls of all responding birds were recorded, in the hope that the recordings may one day be used to separate individuals by way of their (often distinctive) cries, and that in the future these can be used for various purposes, including 1) the assessment of whether birds remain faithful to a particular site and, if not, track their movements; 2) some measure of the adult lifespan of individuals. This would perhaps avoid the need to trap birds for ringing, then retrap them on a regular basis with all of the hazards that this would entail for such a sensitive species.

The breeding cycle of the storm petrel is extremely interesting. Birds are first seen back at the island in early-May. There is a pre-egg stage of about 6 weeks, when birds intermittently occupy the nest burrow. The egg-laying period is protracted, with most laid in the period from mid-June to mid-July. The average incubation period is of 41 days duration, though this can be greatly extended due to periods of absence of the adults – of up to 48 hours duration at a time – without harm to the developing embryo. Chicks require continuous brooding for the first week of life, when they are unable to regulate their body own temperature. They are fed nightly if foraging conditions remain suitable for the parent birds. Scott (1970) showed that average weight curves could not give a true indication of the growth of the chick because of the variation in a) the nestling period and b) the age at which peak weight is attained. Three types of chicks were recognised: 1) those growing at what was described as an "optimal rate" (demonstrated by half of those observed); 2) "delayed" chicks, in which the onset of feather production had been delayed due to a period of insufficient feeding; and 3) "retarded" chicks, where feeding had been insufficient throughout the nestling period. Previously well-fed young can survive for up to 96 hours without food before the growth of their plumage is affected, when they pass into a "semi-poikiliothermic state", i.e. they are unable to maintain a high body temperature, which falls to about 13°C below normal. All three types described above may attain similar weights at fledging, though the fledging period, at an average of 68 days, can be as long as 86 days. It was concluded that the species has evolved a flexible rate of growth that enables success under a wide range of food availabilities (Scott, 1970). Chicks fledge from mid- to late-September, through to early-November, and there is even a record of a chick finally fledging on 24th November 1967. The author has first-hand experience of these fledglings, still downy in places, crashing into windows on wet and stormy nights in late-October and early-November, attracted to the glow of a gaslight within (and also at the lighthouse when the light was white – see the end of this section). The lateness of the breeding season is presumably because it is timed to take advantage of late-summer shoals of sprats and other small fish (P. Davis, 1956).

Other factors that might affect Storm Petrels

During the breeding season, in the wintering quarters off South Africa, and whilst the birds are on passage between the two, food availability is of the utmost importance. Monitoring of relevant fish stocks is extremely difficult, particularly since their diet, at least outside of the breeding season, is unknown. National management of fisheries would ideally take seabirds into account (see Chapt. 4, Sect. 4 - Fishing and Fisheries).

Recoveries of most of the birds ringed on Skokholm that have been made at other nesting colonies have been up to 250 miles away from their natal colony, e.g. The Isles of Scilly, Bardsey, Copeland (N. Ireland) and Co. Kerry, though were generally far closer (Scott, 1970). Most of these birds are wandering non-breeders, which may visit several colonies during such an episode. Tape lures can be used to attract storm petrels, and as a result some ringing is currently carried out on the nearby mainland, where mist nets are set out along the cliffs (summaries of this work can be found in the annual Pembrokeshire Bird Reports). Hence there might well be a proportion of the Skokholm population that is marked. If trapping (and ringing) is reinstated on the island, this could be somewhat useful, although many, many more would have to be ringed in order to achieve a worthwhile study. A species already under pressure would then be further stressed, and for what reason? They are not in decline because they don't currently wear rings, but most certainly because of man-made factors affecting the marine environment. Given that individuals can probably be identified by their distinctive song and call, more work aught to be done to assess this, making some use of the recordings that were painstakingly made in 2003, although initiating responses is probably just as likely to disturb birds as trapping them for ringing purposes.

There is known interchange with the much smaller population of around 100 pairs on Skomer (e.g. Corkhill, 1969). Little owls *Athene noctua* are currently resident there, and known to predate storm petrels in large numbers (large relative to the size of the Skomer breeding population). This has been the situation on Skokholm in the past, something which was mentioned in the 1936 Skokholm Bird Observatory Report: "One pair succeeded in hatching a family. The nest was found to contain (July 14) two fledged young, an addled egg, and the corpses of nearly 200 storm petrels, thus repeating a similar discovery in 1934. A further larder of 25 corpses of petrels was found near the lighthouse. Subsequently five little owls, including one parent, were killed as nuisances." One of a pair of adult little owls found nesting in 1937 had a ring which had been put on its leg as a nestling (on Skokholm) on 19th July 1934, on which date it had been deported and released at Marloes, on the mainland opposite (4 miles distance). Both adults were ringed and sent off to Bath, Somerset, where they were released (Skokholm Bird Observatory Report, 1937). Other deportations were carried out in 1949 (SBOR, 1949), when a female and her three young were found. At other times, birds were shot, or attempts made to shoot them (SBOR, 1938). The continued absence of little owls on Skokholm is highly desirable.

Short-eared owls *Asio flammeus* breed on Skomer, where they are a feature species. Their pellets have been found containing remains of storm petrels on Skokholm (and Skomer), where individuals are occasionally seen during the summer months and more so in the autumn. They are thought to over-winter in small numbers, presumably feeding on the numerous house mice. Young storm petrels fledge from mid-September to the end of October, so could become prime targets for these owls – clearly it would not be desirable if they were to nest on Skokholm. The continued absence of mammalian ground-predators is of fundamental importance to the survival of the breeding population. There has been the occasional scare, when rabbit droppings have been misidentified (perhaps!) as those of a rat, and even reports of sightings of rats, but none ever confirmed.

An oil-pollution incident during the breeding season could have a disastrous impact upon the population, both breeding and non-breeding birds, since the latter are known to visit the colony in large numbers in June and July.

A key role of island management is to limit human disturbance to breeding birds. Given the nest-sites preferred by storm petrels, it is clear that any person clambering about in such areas is likely to induce a rock-fall. This could be disastrous for the birds during the breeding season, and extremely dangerous to any person. Of course, entering the breeding areas even for research purposes brings about the same degree of risk.

There has been concern that many of the island's walls have been degrading in recent years, but assessment in 2003 by way of comparisons with photographs taken in 1994 revealed very little degradation, if any (pers. obs.). However, some areas have certainly been encroached by bracken, nesting gulls and, in the east, goldenrod *Solidago virgaurea*. Given that the majority of the walls remain unchanged from 1994, these factors are thought unlikely to explain the decline witnessed in them over the past few years.

Facing page: Figure 20: The Quarry, where a large proportion of Skokholm's storm petrels breed. Note the proximity of the lighthouse. In the not-to-distant past the lighthouse keepers discarded much of their rubbish over the cliff here – rusting machinery, tools, electric cables and even paint-covered rocks can be found to this day, whilst at the top there is a very obvious fire-site with associated debris.

Larus fuscus graellsii **BCC Amber**

Britain holds about 75 percent of the race *graellsii*, with over 88,000 pairs (Lloyd *et al.* 1991), which is also found in Iceland, the Faeroes, Ireland, Holland, France, Spain and Portugal (Cramp *et al.,* 1995). The population on Skokholm has accounted for between 3 and 5 percent of the total number of this race. Following a decline from 700 pairs in 1928 to 300 in 1955, numbers increased dramatically to a peak of 4,600 pairs in 1979, followed by a general but slow decline thereafter to around 2,000 "Apparently Occupied Nests" (AONs) in 2004. In terms of importance, the population of this handsome gull – with its slate-grey back and upperwings, brilliant white head and body, yellow legs and feet, stunning red eye-ring and yellow iris – comes second only to the Manx shearwater on Skokholm, which is a surprise (and sadly, a disappointment) to most visitors to the island. A bird ringed as a nestling on Skokholm in 1960 was found dead on the island in 1988 at the age of 28 years, demonstrating the longevity of this species and faithfulness to the site.

It is truly-migratory gull, and in 1935, R.M. Lockley was able to state with confidence the arrival and departure dates for the species as 15th February and 26th September (Lockley, 1936). Ringed birds have been found in Denmark, Iceland and the Faeroe Islands, but most foreign recoveries are from the southern part of the migration route to winter quarters in France, Portugal, Spain, the Canary Islands and Morocco. However, a count of over 100 birds present on Skokholm from 27th January in 1983, and the "whole island population" there on 7th February 1998 (pers. obs.) reflect the observed change in its migratory pattern in the last 50 years or so, as birds began to migrate far-shorter distances and for shorter time-periods, and now lesser black-backed gulls that breed in Britain are found in all parts of their range at all times of year (Wernham *et al.,* 2002).

Monitoring methods: Counting the number of breeding birds can be particularly difficult on Skokholm due to the high density of nests and the flatness of the terrain with its lack of vantage points. The birds generally nest in areas where bracken grows, and this further hinders counts. In addition, there is currently a large degree of intraspecific predation of eggs and chicks, especially when they are disturbed. Counting methods have changed over the years, as follows:

- 1928 - 1971: occupied nests counted.
- 1972 - 1977: whole-island estimates made based on counts in the central "main colony" at The Bog.
- 1978 - 1991: all nests with eggs were counted, by having a line of people as counters walk in a line across each gull colony (see Figure 21).
- From 1992 to 1996, an additional count of unoccupied nests was made, to conform to national guidelines. In 1993, almost 30 percent of the total of the 4,652 nests counted were empty.
- 1996 and subsequently: A considerable number of Manx shearwater burrows were damaged by counters traversing fragile ground, and this was thought unacceptable by the author, recently-appointed as Warden at the time. There followed the adoption of a method developed on Skomer by the extremely forward-thinking and conscientious Warden Mike Alexander in the early 1980's: fragile areas are counted from vantage-points overlooking them, rather than walking across, and then a correction factor – obtained in non-fragile areas by comparing vantage-point totals with those obtained by actually walking through – is applied to give a fairly accurate estimate of the total population (details are given in Walsh *et al.,* 1995). This method undoubtedly provides a better estimate than the counts made from vantage points only, but it is not without problems: it cannot correct for non-breeding adult birds present in the colonies, and does not allow the counting of empty nests. However, these two factors might balance themselves (see below).

Over the period 1991 - 2002, the counts of empty nests varied from 11 to 44 percent (mean 22.7 percent) of the total nests actually visited, suggesting that previous population figures where empty nests were not recorded had been underestimates, but it remains unclear whether a proportion of pairs actually construct numerous nests before one bird (presumably the female) chooses one to lay the eggs in. In 1997, it was discovered that at the colony at Tarnbrook Fell Colliery in Lancashire, as many as 60 percent of pairs built more than one nest, thus leading to a probable over-estimate of the size of the population (O'Connell *et al.*, 1996). So counts of empty nests possibly resulted in an over-estimate of pairs on Skokholm but, conversely, Calladine & Harris (1996) showed that on the Isle of May in the Firth of Forth, Scotland, some gulls failed to breed every year, so any count in any one season is likely to underestimate the true size of a population. This has yet to be investigated further, but empty nests could have been those that had previously lost eggs to predation, or had yet to have eggs laid in them. Whilst Warden from 1996 - 2004, the author did, in some years, undertake counts of the total number of adult birds in each of the sub-colonies in the weeks prior to nesting, and later compare the figures with the actual number of nests counted a little later on, with the aim of trying to formulate a correction factor and one day avoid the need to walk through the areas during the nesting period, but little was done with the data obtained. As an example, in 2003, individual birds within each of the 13 main sub-colonies were counted on two or three occasions in mid-April, and totals were remarkably consistent. After nests were counted, the mean ratio of individuals to AONs (from vantage points) was 0.418, ranging from 0.32 to 0.57 (when including empty nests, where applicable, a ratio of 0.65 (individuals/nest) was achieved).

Productivity, i.e. the number of chicks raised per nesting pair, is measured in a very simple manner on Skokholm, by a count of fledged young in traditional roosts situated across the island as soon as they form in early-August. Other, more-intensive survey methods – such as mark and recapture – are commonly used on Skomer, but Craik (2000) suggests that the simpler method is just as accurate, since studies elsewhere showed that flying young of most gull species remain at the colony for a considerable period of time after their first flight. This has the advantage of greatly reducing disturbance, an important factor with intraspecific predation within the colony being rife (see below).

Causes of population change: During the war years, eggs were collected on a very large scale and the decline of the lesser black-backed gull between 1940 and 1949 was attributed to this (Harris, 1970a). The extent of egg-collecting before the war is not well-documented, although Lockley collected on a large scale, for example 3,000 eggs from 1,000 nests in 1939 (J.W.F. Davis, 1974). Subsequently, although no records were kept, egg-collecting continued with an agreement that the observatory staff collected to the east of Halfway Wall and the lighthouse staff (present until 1984) to the west (even though THLS owned just a corner of Skokholm); surplus eggs were reserved in "water glass". It has been suggested that the increase in lesser black-backed gulls from the late-1950's onwards coincided with the reduction in egg collecting (J.W.F. Davis, 1973) and the passing of protective legislation and the acquisition of the Welsh islands as nature reserves (Reed & Parr, 1997). Despite intensive ringing of gulls, there are very few records of gulls breeding anywhere than at their natal colonies (Harris, 1970a), so it is inevitable that the populations would continue to increase as long as the food supply allowed.

The dramatic increase throughout the 1970's was attributed to the availability of food, chicks being provisioned with fish such as poor cod *Trisopterus minutus*, Norway pout *T. esmarkii* and blue whiting *Micromesistius poutassou*, all species likely to be more available as discards from trawlers rather than caught naturally. Trawlers fishing for Norway lobster *Nephrops norvegicus* in the region of the "Smalls Grounds" situated some 80 km south-west of Skokholm, have been reported to be the probable source of these (Conan & Cheynier, 1980). Watson (1981) observed lesser black-backed gulls following fishing vessels which were discarding Norway pout of the sizes recorded on Skomer. There has been very little evidence of *Larus fuscus* competing for a food source with the herring gull *L. argentatus*, indeed most evidence is to the contrary (e.g. Harris, 1967a), but habits do change and new studies would shed light on this.

Peter J. Conder, Skokholm Warden from 1947 to 1954, revisited the island in 1978 and 1980 and expressed his concern at the large number of lesser black-backed gulls and their potential to deleteriously affect other species, and he even suggested that nests and eggs should be destroyed (Conder, 1980). The increase in number on Skokholm brought about an increase in bird density rather than any expansion of colony boundaries, and calculations indicated that the population could increase at the observed rate without immigration of birds from other colonies (Harris, 1970a). Conder (1980) estimated colony size and density in 1950 as 7.25 hectares and 48.3 pairs per hectare respectively, and in 1980 as 23.75ha and 183.9 pairs/ha.

Given the rate of increase of the species, it was predicted that numbers would rise from 4,600 pairs in 1980 to almost 6,000 pairs in 1984 and so – at a meeting of the Islands Management Committee in late-November 1980 – it was proposed to cull a number of adult birds in the following spring using bait laced with the narcotic alpha-chloralose. This practise was also planned for Skomer Island National Nature Reserve, following a policy of the Nature Conservancy Council at that time. However, there was not enough evidence to convince other authorities (and in particular the Royal Society for the Protection of Birds, for the land owner preferred to take the advice of that organization rather than that of the Wildlife Trust) that they were causing significant damage to other species, so the idea was rescinded as far as Skokholm was concerned. It was intended that boys from Forest Hill School, London (annual visitors to the island) should carry out the deed, much to the consternation of the RSPB. However, the cull did go ahead on Skomer in June 1991, where 1,410 gulls were killed out of a total population of about 15,000. From 1981, an annual programme of nest raking was carried out in order to restrict the colony boundaries to within "permitted areas". In 1983, the Skokholm and Skomer Management Committee decided that the increase in the number of breeding pairs that year of 17 percent was simply too much, and instigated a programme of total nest-destruction starting in 1984, with the aim to reduce the colony to within the boundaries of the gulls' distribution observed in 1952. The manpower for this extremely unpleasant "nest-raking" (destruction of eggs that often contained large embryos close to hatching), came from a group of schoolboys from Forest Hill School. In 1985, due to a shortage of manpower, only a small number of nests were destroyed. In 1986 - 87, all nests were raked with the exception of those on the cliffs of the south coast, and a steady decline in numbers followed.

From 1987, even those pairs untouched by the raking programme were often failing to raise young to fledging, e.g. particularly in 1989 and 1990 (*c.* 2,600 pairs raised 220 young between them in 1989). In 1991, following discussion of the global and European perspective for the subspecies *L. f. graellsii*, a number of "permitted areas" were again identified and consisted of The Bog (which was once the "main colony"), an area from Bread Rock to Orchid Bog on the north-eastern coast, and South Haven to Spy Rock in the south-east. Elsewhere, 570 nests were raked, comprising some 20 percent of the total population. In 1995, a further amendment was made, following poor reproductive success in the previous 8 years and the fact that the predicted increases in the number of gulls had not occurred, so just 5 percent of nests were raked. Island visitors were asked to assist with this unsavoury task, with very few of them continuing for long, given its nature (pers. obs.). Raking ceased completely in 1999, following the continuing decline in the number of breeding pairs and their extremely poor productivity (see below). Monitoring of the sub-colonies continues, and any prospect of further rapid increase or changes in distribution would undoubtedly bring about a review of policy towards them. Other areas where subcolonies exist are high are: the plateau and slopes west of North Haven/Blacksmith's Landing (continuing westward to Bread Rock and south to Orchid Bog); the area to the immediate south of Spy Rock; the western side of Crab Bay; from The Pedestal westwards to Half Way Wall/Winter Pond; East Knoll westwards to The Knoll; north and south of West Knoll.

One factor which should not be overlooked is that of the age of first breeding of the *Larus* species found on Skokholm, this being 3 - 4 years in herring and lesser black-backed gulls and 4 - 5 years in great black-backed gulls, i.e. there are a number of cohorts that are non-breeders. Therefore, complete breeding failure for 4 or 5 years will have no visible effect on the breeding population for a while, but then a rapid decline will follow (assuming there is no immigration from elsewhere). This has been dramatically shown by this bird.

The principal factor in the low breeding-success was a reduction in the availability of fish food, but why this should be so is unknown since the fishery remains active and discard levels remain high (Stone et al., 1992, and Dunn, 1993). However, fishing vessels have become larger but fewer, perhaps resulting in discards of larger quantity over shorter periods of time and at fewer locations, and hence less available to the gulls. But worse still, they now operate mostly at night. Studies on nearby Skomer by Todd (1987) confirmed earlier observations (J.W.F. Davis, 1973; Alexander, 1981) that earthworms (Lumbricidae) were an important food-item early in the year, with a change to fish during the chick-rearing period. This change in diet during the breeding season has, however, not been occurring in recent years, and birds have continued to forage on agricultural land on the nearby mainland. On Skomer in 1988 (and in many years subsequently) most chicks died within their first week of life – a result of being underweight – and regurgitate studies clearly showed that they were being fed earthworms. On Skomer in 1991, over 80 percent of chick regurgitates were of earthworms (Perrins, 1991) compared to a similar percentage that were fish in 1985 (Todd, 1986). Circumstantial evidence also exists, since the years of worst breeding failure were also affected by hot, dry summers, when earthworms are deep in the soil and hence more difficult to find. Also, on Skokholm in 2003 and 2004, pink-coloured gull pellets were widespread in the summer, and were found to consist of mineral soil, probably of mainland origin. The gulls are likely to predate the eggs and chicks of small land-birds and waders such as oystercatcher. Some also kleptoparasitize puffins and other auks, but this is insignificant (Thompson, 1996b).

Occasionally during a long-running week-long biology field course organized by the University College of Cardiff, intensive observations have been made on the flight directions taken by herring and lesser black-backed gulls, combined with checks on regurgitated gull pellets and of forced regurgitations of gull chicks to check on foods being utilised. Results in 1982 clearly showed that the majority of herring gulls flew inland, and judging by the food remains subsequently found on the island, they were heading to the docks at Milford Haven. Differences were found between the foods utilized when weekends and weekdays were compared – with noticeably more refuse being brought back during the week when refuse tips would have been open. Lesser black-backed gulls, on the other hand, were flying out to sea and chicks that were handled were regurgitating fish, but it was impossible to say for sure whether they were fishing for themselves or scavenging at fishing vessels. However, the component species and their size, identified from otolith (fish "ear bone") studies, strongly suggested that they were discards from trawlers (Ferns, 1982). The studies have been repeated at regular intervals, and in 2001 there were still large numbers of lesser black-backed gulls flying out to sea, but it may be that they have found a source of fish, albeit one that is insufficient for the needs of the breeding colony (Molloy, 2000). Some birds specialize in stealing fish from puffins that also breed on the island, termed kleptoparasitism. This is explained in more detail under the section on the puffin *Fratercula arctica*.

In addition, a high degree of intra-specific predation of eggs and small chicks has been observed, frequently during the walk-through nest counts, a phenomenon that, up until 1976, had been recorded in lesser black-backed gulls only on Skokholm. Davis & Dunn (1976) observed that there was a chain-reaction, where a bird that had lost its own clutch quickly turned predator, resulting in a rapid build-up of aggressive failed breeders. Avoidance of predation is undoubtedly the major factor that encouraged colonial nesting in this species initially, but alas is contributing to its downfall at the present time. Davis & Dunn (1976) also noted that chick survival was positively correlated with nest density and that both were related to the extent of cover afforded by vegetation. Another factor that works against the gulls is the fact that incubation of the first two eggs of each clutch of three are incubated only sporadically (so that their hatching is more synchronized), thus inviting predation at this early stage as they are left exposed (Dunn, 1973). If counts are started just before bracken has sprouted significantly, nests and/or incubating birds can be clearly seen from outside the colony (pers. obs.), so there is no need whatsoever to walk through.

Following the poor breeding success, the population has been in steady decline due to insufficient recruitment. The estimated reproductive rate of 0.07 young per pair (156 chicks from 2,143 nests with eggs in 2004), is approximately one-twelfth of that necessary to maintain the population. There is also evidence of a long term reduction in adult survival rates on Skomer (Perrins, 1994) which may have also been food-related, and this is likely to apply to Skokholm birds too. Of course, it may be that adults are leaving the colony due to the poor breeding success, although it is not commonly known for adult birds to move far from an established breeding site. A number of birds ringed on Skomer have become established breeders on Skokholm in recent years, e.g. one ringed on Skomer as a nestling in 1986 has bred in the very same spot on Skokholm from at least 1998 to 2004. One that ranged further afield was a bird ringed as a nestling on Skokholm in 1971 and found as a recently-dead adult in the mixed gull colony on Walney Island, Cumbria in 1999, aged 28 years.

Other factors affecting Lesser Black-backed Gulls

The birds use the island as a breeding site, and therefore have to forage in the vicinity. They migrate to winter quarters, increasingly to areas in the UK (and hence its status as a true migrant is starting to become unclear – see Baker, 1980) but traditionally to coastal areas of Spain, Portugal and West Africa, i.e. the western seaboard of continental Europe, but also many going to inland locations (Garcia & Guzman, 1990; Cantos, 1993). Ringing recoveries (mainly of birds that had been killed by man) have shown that immatures tend to remain at southern latitudes until they are ready to breed at four or five years of age (Wernham et al., 2002). They are therefore subject to a range of external influences both during and after the breeding season.

Interspecific fostering experiments were carried out in the 1960's, involving herring and lesser black-backed gulls, as research into migration, imprinting and interbreeding (Harris, 1970b). Many of the normally-sedentary *L. argentatus* raised by their cogeners migrated as far as France, Spain and Portugal. Subsequently, when the young reached breeding age, the males appeared equally prepared to pair with either species, though the females selected males of the "wrong" species and numerous hybrids have resulted. There were 40 "mixed" pairs on Skokholm in 1969, and even today obvious hybrids – showing characteristics mid-way between the two distinct species, such as mantle, leg and eye-ring colour – are present in small numbers, and undoubtedly there are many less-obvious examples.

Opposite: Figure 21. Counting Lesser Black-backed Gulls by walking through the colony, here at South Crags/South Pond.

In recent years, a considerable number of lesser black-backed gulls have taken to nesting on the cliffs, or cliff slopes, right around the island rather than at their usual locations on the plateau. It is possible that hybridisation had its part to play in this, although the vast majority of pairs do seem to be "true" lesser black-backed gulls. Another possibility is that the continual persecution of the species by island "managers" has brought about a change of behaviour in an attempt to escape this "predation".

From at least the period from 1974 up until the mid-1990's, hens were kept as a source of fresh eggs. Any food left after visitors' meals was given to them. However, once they were no longer kept, another method of disposing of the food was sought. It was quite easy – give it to the gulls! "Feeding time" on Home Meadow is at about 2000 hours during the summer months, and is now a great source of entertainment (see Figure 22, opposite). Sometimes hundreds of birds gather before the food is thrown, many waiting in position for a few hours beforehand. If small items such as rice grains are included, the gulls can remain on the "lawn" for a long time afterwards, until every last morsel has been removed. This must be a valuable food-source to many birds, particularly the dominant ones.

Studies of adult survival are carried out on the neighbouring island of Skomer, where around 15,000 pairs breed. The survival rates have not decreased, suggesting that food availability during the breeding season is the problem they are currently facing.

The gulls seem to prefer to situate their nests in bracken. Goodman & Gillham (1954) noted that the sparse bracken at the western end of the island was once favoured, but currently the vast majority of pairs use the tall, dense bracken to the east, a change in behaviour that has perhaps been brought about by the increase in interspecific predation of eggs and small chicks. The bracken is trampled by the birds and the ground manured, therefore its growth is restricted in the immediate vicinity of nests. Other vegetation flourishes once the gulls have left the island, e.g. the maritime cliff chickweed community, MC7 (see Subsection 3.1.2).

Some visitors regard the gulls solely as a nuisance. Where bracken has spread onto the outcrops overlooking the accommodation buildings, gulls have begun to nest, and bring with them the noise, possible aggression towards passing walkers, and mess, making matters worse. However, without the gulls Skokholm would be less like a "seabird island", since there are relatively few other seabirds, number-wise, during the daylight hours. A recent decision by the Islands Management Committee when confronted by this issue was that the thoughts of the Warden be agreed with and the birds given priority.

Large numbers of gulls produce copious amounts of guano. This is probably responsible for the eutrophication of ponds, and for the de-acidification of soils, leading to the loss of some plant species and thoughts turn to "control". However, some lichens require the enrichment, and the lichen assemblage is also a feature of the site.

A key role of island management is to limit disturbance to nesting birds. Intraspecific predation of eggs and young can be high when disturbance occurs, and pairs which have lost eggs or young then tend to become more likely to rob neighbouring nests whenever an opportunity arises (pers. obs.; Davis & Dunn, 1976). For this reason and because of destruction of Manx shearwater burrows underfoot, gull-counting methods have recently changed (see above) and the "remain on footpaths" rule was been pressed most insistently by the author.

Overleaf: Figure 22. Gulls being fed on Home Meadow. This spectacle can be clearly seen from the mainland, over two miles away.

Guillemot *Uria aalge albionis* **RDB, BCC Amber**

The guillemot is a Red Data Book species and on the Amber List of the Birds of Conservation Concern (> 20 percent of the European population in the UK, > 50 percent of the UK population in 10 or fewer sites). It is the most vocal and seemingly most argumentative of the three auks found on Skokholm. It is colonial and nests at higher densities than any other bird (Birkhead, 1977), packed tightly on narrow sea-cliff-ledges, so it is little wonder that neighbouring birds have frequent disagreements. Unlike the razorbills and puffins, the guillemots return to the island intermittently throughout the winter period, and actually occupy nesting areas, although birds are extremely wary at these times and will rapidly flee if disturbed. But it is from mid-March onwards that these visits become regular, with periods of attendance becoming cyclical, tending to be every fourth or fifth day often in association with razorbills, and becoming synchronised with periods of calmer weather (personal observations; Lloyd 1972). The function of the synchrony witnessed is undoubtedly of benefit to such a colonial species of bird, since there is safety in numbers. By early- to mid-May most of the breeding birds will have laid eggs and it is only this that brings about the permanent attendance. Eggs vary in colour from various shades of blue to cream, with spots and streaks of various colours, including black, brown and even lilac. These various colour forms are important for egg-recognition by parents. The lack of space on the nest-ledges means that it is necessary for incubating birds to do so standing virtually upright. The pyriforme (pair-shaped) single egg, laid on the bare rock, has been thought of as an adaptation to such a situation, so that when it is dislodged – a very likely scenario – its shape means that it rolls in a tight circle, which could perhaps prevent it from rolling over the edge of the nest-ledge (though, in fact, a great many of the nest-ledges aren't wide enough to permit a complete turn of an egg). This could be a coincidence; the shape also undoubtedly maximizes the amount of surface area that will be in contact with the parent's brood patch during incubation. Both parents participate in this and the eggs hatch after 32 - 36 days. The chick is semiprecocial, meaning that it has a coat of downy feathers, a good degree of mobility, but is parentally fed, and thus "intermediate" between altricial or naked "nestlings" and precocial or downy and mobile chicks – seen as a compromise between costs and benefits of each strategy. Very young guillemot chicks (also those of razorbill and puffin) are unable to maintain their body temperature by themselves, so must be brooded by the parents.

The chick leaves the ledge when just one-third grown, fluttering down to the sea on stubby secondary flight feathers only and then swims out to sea accompanied by the male parent, where the risk of predation is lessened. The female tends to remain at the nest-site for a period of up to two weeks, defending it against sub-adult birds that are at this time seeking nest-sites for future use. Suddenly, one day in early- or mid-July, all of the birds are gone and sections of the island perimeter are eerily quiet. The chick is cared for by the male, and able to fly at the age of 39 - 46 days, shortly after which time it becomes independant.

The guillemot flies strongly but, as a result of its small wing-size and relatively heavy body ("wing area to bodyweight ratio") it can only do so by way of rapid wing-beats. Birds do exhibit surprising agility when alighting on the cliffs in conditions that are frequently difficult, i.e. with strong winds and updraughts, and often with rain and sea-spray to contend with also. When on the sea in breezeless conditions, they must run along the water surface to obtain enough speed to achieve sufficient lift to take flight.

A breeding population of around 200 pairs declined in the 1940's and 1950's to 30 pairs in 1960, before increasing again to a steady 120 pairs from the late 1960's until 1980 (excluding 1969, when numbers dropped at the time of a seabird "wreck" – see below). Subsequently, further increases took place and the population reached the highest recorded level of a mean of 1,157 individuals in 2002 (1,073 in 2003), despite a drop in 1996 - 97 (of 26 percent from 1995) which was attributed to oil pollution from the *Sea Empress* (Parr *et al.* 1997).

The breeding birds are presently restricted to the north- and west-coasts, from Little Bay right around to the north-western tip of the island, where the geology has brought about the formation of suitable cliff-ledges for nesting (bands of resistant sandstones jutting out further than the softer, eroded mudstones). Some of these ledges are easily viewed on Skokholm, at an observer's eye level, from the opposite side of small bays that hold these birds (most notably at Twinlet Bay, and less so at Little Bay).

Like the majority of other marine birds, this species is long-lived and pairs have a strong bond that may last over many seasons. Their longevity tends to bring about a great deal of stability in both spatial and temporal factors within the colony, i.e. pairs do show a great degree of site fidelity, as demonstrated by Harris *et al.* (1996) in a study on the Isle of May between 1982 and 1993. It involved observations of 470 colour-ringed birds with at least one year of breeding experience prior to the study. On average, 85.7 percent of birds recorded at a site in any year were present at the same site in the following season, and of those not retaining their site, 35 percent had moved to another site, 25 percent were non-breeders in that year, and 40 percent were not seen. The same ringed population shed light on the typical survival rates of guillemots, and the fact that they did not necessarily breed every year, though it seems that site loss is the cause of non-breeding (Harris & Wanless, 1996). It was not possible to be certain whether a non-breeder had moved of its own volition, been evicted by its mate or displaced by a superior competitor for that mate.

Virtually all female guillemots continue to visit the colony after their mate has taken the chick to sea. In a study by Harris & Wanless (2003), there were significant differences between years, but the average time between a chick fledging and a female last being seen at the colony was 13 days (range 0 to 36). In over 99 percent of instances, the female was at her breeding site. On 5 percent of days she was joined by another male, and in a few cases (8 percent of those days) copulation was observed. None of these matings persisted into the next season, even when the original male did not return; thus, there was no support for the hypothesis that females might be looking for replacement mates in case they were widowed. The most successful females (in terms of breeding output over several years) tended to have the longest periods of post-fledging visiting, apparently because such birds fledged their chicks early in the season, but there was no difference in daily frequency of attendance. It was concluded that successful males and females were maximizing time spent occupying the best breeding sites, even to the extent that only one adult took the chick to sea to complete its development.

Prolonged attendance at nest-sites after successful breeding appears to be rare (though doubtless under-recorded) among seabirds where many species either have post-fledging care (presumably by both sexes) or desert the colony before the chick fledges (references in Schreiber & Burger, 2002). Where such attendance has been documented (e.g. gannet *Morus bassanus*, Atlantic puffin *Fratercula arctica*, and some other auks; see Nelson, 2001; Harris, 1984), site ownership appears to be the primary purpose. The same is probably true for species such as the herring gull *Larus argentatus*, and northern fulmar *Fulmarus glacialis* that attend colonies outside the breeding season (Salomonsen, 1955; Coulson and Butterfield, 1986; Fugler *et al.*, 1987; pers. obs.).

Figure 23, overleaf: The cliffs of Mad Bay, from Twinlet Bay in the foreground, to Mad Bay Point in the distance. There are many suitable cliff-ledges for nesting Guillemots, where the layers of sandstone have resisted erosion whilst the softer mudstones have been worn back.

In Brünnich's guillemot *Uria lomvia*, males also join successful females at the end of the season and may take over the site the next season if the original male is absent, though it appears unclear whether the end of the season pairings continue (Gaston and Hipfner, 2000). Although female common guillemots *U. aalge* do form temporary pairs at the end of the season with the occasional copulation occurring, these are very infrequent and none of the pairs observed by Harris & Wanless (2003) continued into the following year. There was therefore no support for the hypothesis that a female was assessing the potential of future mates and they concluded that she was present in order to retain ownership of a high-quality breeding site.

Counting methods. Individual birds situated only on the nesting cliffs are counted during the first three weeks of June. These counts are prone to many inaccuracies, since i) the birds are tightly packed onto ledges, ii) some of the colonies on Skokholm are countable only from a boat, and iii) the number of individuals ashore at any one moment fluctuates from day to day.

Prior to 1997, attempts were made to count the number of pairs, or rather the incubating birds. This was perhaps relatively easy when there were very few breeding, but trying to decide how many individuals have an egg beneath them on densely-packed ledges is an altogether different matter. However, national guidelines only require a count of individual birds (Walsh *et al.*, 1995). From 1990, the number of individuals was counted in addition to "apparently-incubating birds". From 1996, only individuals were counted, i.e. no estimate made of incubating birds. Today, whole-island counts are somewhat difficult, particularly of those birds which have to be counted from the sea. In the period 1938 - 46, and in 1951 - 58, 1962, 1964 - 66, and 1980, no count was made.

Since 1981, a series of counts – usually 10 in number – has been carried out at four study-plots during spells of suitable weather (wind not more than force 4, good visibility) on 10 different days during the period 1st - 21st June. These are of individual birds and are repeated at exactly the same time on each of the days. The results are sent to The Seabird Group. The numbers in these plots have shown a steady increase, reflecting the increase in the whole-island counts and so would appear to be a genuine reflection of the general condition. However, in 2003, there was a lower rate of increase of birds in the study-plots compared to whole-island counts, thought to be due to a lack of availability of new nest-sites within them. To counteract this, two new plots were established, one by extension of an existing one, the other completely detached and in an area where a new sub-colony had been established just two years previously and which was showing signs of rapid expansion. One of the old plots was deemed unsafe to visit due to erosion at the cliff-top, and it was decided that a safety-line would be required for future visits. The fully-occupied plots are still of value, particularly in the case of a decline in the population and also if whole-island counts could not be carried out for any reason.

Knowledge of the size of the breeding population gives vital information, but whole island counts are prone to errors. In most years until recently, rather than the preferred 5 counts (for the purpose of statistical analysis, with mean values and standard deviation reported), just single counts have been made. The small size of the colony on Skokholm is insignificant in national terms anyway. There are other difficulties: numbers of loafing birds are known to fluctuate from day-to-day and from hour-to-hour; since 1996, some birds have nested in two small "caves" amongst boulders on The Bluff, and these are impossible to count directly without flushing and consequent loss of eggs, so estimates have been made for these by way of counting birds loafing nearby, but the numbers involved are small.

Breeding success is estimated by close observation of a number of ledges in study-plots, where nest-sites are plotted on a photograph of the colony and daily checks made on progress from when the first egg is laid through to the fledging of the last chick. This is a very time-consuming operation, and insignificant compared to a similar but much larger study being carried out annually on Skomer.

There are no means of assessing adult survival of the birds breeding on Skokholm (very few wear rings), although studies are carried out on neighbouring Skomer, for which a long and unrivalled data set exists. This could be useful in helping to assess population changes of any significance. Chick-feeding rates are also assessed on Skomer.

Factors affecting the Guillemot

Food availability throughout the year is of utmost importance to the population. Breeding, moulting and wintering areas must be taken into account when planning conservation measures for this species. The feeding ranges of guillemots are not well-known. They are absent from the colonies for 3 to 5 days at a time at the beginning of the breeding cycle before egg-laying, presumably because food is scarce at that time, but this seems to become more available once the chick has hatched. Birkhead (1976) counted guillemots along a 10 km transect leading away from Skomer Island, and the results showed that they were travelling at least that distance to find food. Bradstreet & Brown (1985) calculated that the possible feeding-range of guillemots was between 56 and 146 km, though emphasized that these figures would be exaggerated due to time spent locating and capturing prey. Stone et al. (1992) also found this, with birds found as far as 45km away from Skokholm and Skomer (the distance their transects extended to). However, very few birds were seen carrying fish. Ideally, national management of fisheries would take seabirds into account, for there are many factors other than food availability and competition with man for food, such as entanglement with nets (see Chapter 4). Starving birds are more likely to be vulnerable to oiling, pollution, predators and disease, so the factors can be compounded.

Guillemots are very vulnerable to being killed as a result of oil-pollution incidents, because the oil floats on water and swimming birds are likely to come into contact with it. Liquid oil soaks into the plumage, destroying its insulation and buoyancy properties, with obvious consequences. Preening the oil out of the feathers leads to its ingestion. Poisoning may also occur as birds inhale fumes. Such pollution remains a very real threat around the Pembrokeshire islands.

Other pollutants in our seas undoubtedly have the potential to kill seabirds. The "seabird wreck" of 1969 included many thousands of guillemots, the deaths of which may have been caused by the release and utilization of toxic chemicals (polychlorinated biphenyls or PCBs) from fat reserves during a prolonged period of rough seas that would have prevented effective foraging (Holdgate, 1971 in Lloyd et al., 1991).

Limiting disturbance by visitors is of key importance, for guillemots are prone to leave their ledges at the first hint of a person getting closer than is usual. The insistence that visitors remain on the footpath system ensures that this is, or at least should be, rare. Disturbance from the sea is more frequent, as dive-craft and lobster-potting boats come close. Occasionally, adults have been caused to flee when military aircraft have flown low

Opposite: Figure 24: A Guillemot prospecting for nest-sites on Skokholm. The species has been establishing new subcolonies recently.

over them, but the granting of a year-round air exclusion zone by the Ministry of Defence has hopefully now negated this factor. In the pre-laying period in March and April, and during periods when one of a pair is "off duty", guillemots spend much of their time on the sea beneath the nesting-cliff indulging in social activities, pair bonding and so on. The recent arrival of the "wildlife tour" boats, consisting of rigid-hulled inflatable boats or RHIBs (with a shallow draught that enables them to venture close into the shore) are a growing threat to these activities. The effects of such disturbance are not yet understood, but are sure to be detrimental.

The continued absence of mammalian ground-predators is important, though less so for this species because of the natural inaccessibility of the majority of nest-sites. There is, however, some cause for concern about the rapid increase in the numbers of fulmars *Fulmarus glacialis*. There have been occasions when guillemots have been forced to abandon their eggs by fulmars aggressively seeking new nest-sites (pers. obs.).

Chicks are occasionally predated on the nest-ledges by the *Larus* gulls and particularly when they leave the cliffs in their attempt to reach the sea. The gulls are regarded as a natural component of the seabird assemblage on Skokholm, and *Larus fuscus* is also a feature in its own right. The other *Larus* gulls are an integral part of the seabird assemblage, also an island feature.

Personal observations of breeding success at two of the study-plots showed that the birds have frequently achieved a rate above the national average. It has been proposed that the nest-sites are such that there is relatively little intraspecific competition between neighbouring birds, that egg-losses are unlikely due to displacement, and that they are high-quality (i.e. experienced) individuals. Harris *et al.* (1997) made similar observations on the Isle of May. This might warrant further investigation on Skokholm, for example by careful analysis of nest-ledges.

Razorbill *Alca torda islandica* SPA, RDB, BCC Amber

This is undoubtedly the most attractive of the British auks, and its poise and gentle mannerisms mean that it simply exudes an air of superiority over the others. From their first return to the waters around the island in late-February the birds are in pairs, where they are constantly "billing" as part of the rebuilding of the pair bond. This is most unlike the guillemots and puffins, which form untidy aggregates. The species is far more mild-mannered than its relatives too, and prefers to nest in places that afford it more seclusion.

Britain holds about 20 percent of the world population of 500,000 - 700,000 individuals (Lloyd *et al.*, 1991). This species jointly qualifies Skokholm and Skomer for SPA status under Article 4.2 of the EC Birds Directive. It is a Red Data Book species and on the Amber List of Birds of Conservation Concern (> 50 percent of the UK population in 10 or fewer sites). From a peak of 1,000 pairs estimated on Skokholm in 1937, there was a gradual decline (coupled with an abrupt one following the "seabird wreck" of 1969 – see "guillemot" previously) to about 400 pairs in the 1970's and 1980's. Subsequently there has been a steady increase, with an estimated mean of 1,285 individuals in 2002. There were no counts made in years 1923 - 36, 1938 - 46, 1951 - 58, 1960 - 62, 1964 - 65 and 1980. Productivity in study-plots with exposed nest-sites that allow easy viewing has been above the national average in 1996 - 98 and in 2000 (it was not studied in 1999).

As with the other two auk species breeding on Skokholm, razorbills exhibit alternating periods of attendance and absence at the colony (Plumb, 1965) that cannot be solely explained in terms of weather, food availability or social stimulation individually, and may be the result of a direct interaction of all three factors (Corkhill, 1970). Razorbills are relatively long-lived, with Skokholm-ringed birds still present as breeders some 18 to 20 years following ringing (Lloyd, 1974).

The majority of birds on Skokholm nest in rock-crevices and beneath boulders right around the island perimeter, though many are also found on cliff-ledges near to or even amongst guillemots. They are a great favourite with the island's human visitors, for at dusk in June and July, the part-grown youngsters are seen leaping from the nest-ledges and then heading out to sea with the male parent, away from the dangers of life at a boisterous seabird colony, but into a world with many other uncertainties – truly a heart-wrenching phenomenon to see. Observations of fledging have been described by various authors, e.g. Lawman (1975) and Thompson (1995), with cliff-ledge sites being easiest to observe. The swing in mood of a fledgling is obvious, with bouts of excitement alternating with periods of what would seem to be sheer terror. Parent birds will be encouraging their youngster to take the plunge (a leap of up to 25 metres), the chick will be flapping its stubby wings (secondary feathers only) as fast as possible by way of preparation for the launch, only to suddenly lose its nerve, rush to the back of the ledge, and cower beneath a comforting adult. At this stage, no further attempt will be made that evening. However, the majority of pairs on Skokholm nest beneath boulders (the usual situation for this species), where chicks can be left unattended with some degree of safety, but the fledging process can be fraught with danger for youngsters emerging from such sites – the interstices form many traps from which they cannot escape, and soon perish (pers. obs.).

Overleaf: Figure 25. The south-coast cliffs are generally unsuitable for nesting seabirds, since there are very few flat ledges. However, the occasional patch of boulders resulting from rockfalls provides nest-sites for both razorbill and storm petrel. The gathering of razorbills in the foreground consists mainly of immature birds, on a "loafing rock", where they interact socially and probably initiate pair-bonds.

A three-year study of the breeding biology of this species was carried out on Skokholm between 1971 and 1973 (Lloyd, 1976). Birds that had been previously ringed allowed the gathering of information on the effects of age on breeding success. It was shown that about 30 percent of eggs were predated by herring gulls, but 93 percent of chicks that did hatch subsequently "fledged" (left the island) successfully. Generally, the most successful breeders were the most experienced. They also laid the largest eggs, a factor known to increase the chances of survival of the chick during the critical first 7 to 10 days of life. The pairs that laid their egg earliest were also the most successful, and only these had time to replace a lost egg. Frequent checking of nest-sites probably leads to desertion of eggs (Brun, 1958).

The effect of wear on the aluminium rings used in the pre-war period was great, meaning that they generally lasted just two years or less, and hence there were few ringing-recoveries then. Monel rings were introduced in the early 1960's, but these were hardly better. Subsequently (by 1966) rings were shaped to fit the flattened tarsi of the razorbill and the inscription positioned on one side where it was clearly visible and readable from a distance using a telescope – and less prone to wear (Lloyd & Perrins, 1977).

Razorbills possess two brood patches, but only lay one egg. The ability of parent birds to raise an additional chick to fledging was studied on Skokholm, first by Plumb (1965) – who ascertained that it was possible, but did not study comparative growth rates, or post-fledging survival – and then further by Lloyd (1977). In this study, following the discovery that razorbills were unable to recognize their own eggs or chicks (Lloyd, 1976), a second youngster was introduced to 14 nest-sites the day after each site's "true" chick had hatched. Each site was a boulder one, where both parents usually leave a youngster alone whilst they go off to forage (unlike exposed cliff-ledge sites), so minimizing the risk of predation and allowing higher rates of feeding to those twinned birds. In 9 of the 14 experimental sites, one of the chicks remained lighter in weight than the other, and appeared to receive fewer feeds, ultimately culminating in its sad demise. In the other 5 sites, both young grew normally, but the complicating factor arrived when one fledged accompanied by one adult (usually the male – see previously), the remaining chick received less food and, although initially at a weight suitable for fledging, ultimately lost weight and all were presumed to have perished. It seems that one of the adults of a pair does not have the ability to lead a chick to sea, as one would have strongly suspected in the first place.

About 9,000 razorbills were ringed on the island up to 1976, many with coloured bands to enable easy identification of age classes, and although Lloyd (1974) showed that just 3 percent of marked birds were ever recovered (often those that were hunted by man or killed by oil spills), the Bird Ringing Scheme proved its worth and enabled the movements and survival of British birds to be documented. It showed that British razorbills are truly migratory in their first two years of life, with many recoveries made from the Bay of Biscay (by hunters), and normally return to their natal colony to breed from three or four years of age onward, and then retain the same nest-site year after year. Adults subsequently disperse randomly from the breeding colonies, i.e. third- and fourth-year birds are recovered mainly from the English Channel, the Irish Sea and north of the Bay of Biscay. Estimates by Lloyd & Perrins (1977), mainly based on findings on Skokholm from 1963 - 1973 showed that only 13 young per 100 pairs per year were surviving to breeding age (4 - 5 years) to balance the 16 - 20 adults per 100 pairs annual mortality, suggesting that the population is extremely vulnerable to any changes in adult survival.

Counting methods. The census method has changed over the years. Between 1928 and 1969, counting methods varied from an assessment of the number of nests to one of individual birds. From 1970 onward, eggs were sought by searching amongst boulders and scree to give a count of breeding pairs. From 1991 to 1996, in addition to seeking incubating birds or eggs, the total number of individuals was counted, by noting the number of birds loafing in the vicinity of suitable nest-sites and then by flushing hidden birds from crevices (this is method that is currently accepted). From 1997, due to the discovery that a number of guillemots were nesting amongst the razorbills (in at least two locations) and the loss of guillemot eggs in these areas as a result of a counter entering them and causing the birds to panic, the practise was altered again. A method recommended by authorities on seabird-counting was adopted: visible birds at just a <u>proportion</u> of accessible sub-colonies are counted from a vantage point, then the counter enters these areas and counts <u>all</u> birds, including those flushed from beneath the boulders. Then the ratio of birds visible from the vantage point to the total number of birds in each sub-colony is calculated, and the average figure is used to estimate the total number of adults in the undisturbed areas (see Walsh *et al.*, 1995). Inaccessible sites are counted from the sea – these are generally not boulder colonies, but exposed cliff-ledge sites. Up to five counts are made over a period of two weeks, and the mean value and standard deviation reported.

<u>Factors affecting Razorbills</u>

Threats to razorbills are similar to those affecting the guillemot (previously), but in addition some herring and lesser black-backed gulls have been reported (Conder, 1952) robbing razorbills of their catch of fish (see page 145 – factors affecting puffins – for more details on this "kleptoparasitism").

Puffin *Fratercula arctica grabae* SPA, BCC Amber, SPEC 2

The puffin is probably the most sought-after bird on Skokholm. They nest around virtually all of the perimeter of the island, in varying density, with highest numbers seen in the vicinity of Crab Bay, South Haven, Peter's Bay and North Haven. Two bird-watching hides are situated in two of the subcolonies (Crab Bay and South Haven), allowing views of some birds from less than a metre away. Unfortunately, like most of the nesting species on the island, they are only present for the breeding season that has its peak of activity from early-May through to mid-July. Even if people have never actually seen a live puffin, they are aware of what one looks like, through television producers having them as a popular choice for natural history programmes and cartoons, and they also frequently feature in paintings and comic books. Its large, brightly-coloured and triangularly-shaped bill, orange webbed-feet and waddling gait make it a most amusing bird to observe.

From Lockley's figure of 20,000 pairs in 1928 (Skokholm Bird Observatory Report, 1937), numbers fell to between 5,000 and 10,000 pairs in 1953 (Conder, 1953) and to 2,500 pairs by 1970 (SBOR, 1970). The most recent estimate of between 2,000 and 2,500 breeding pairs was made in 1990 (Betts, 1990). Counts of individual birds are made each spring (see below); there were 4,308 individuals on 27th March 2004. Puffins, like other burrow-nesting seabirds, are difficult to census (see below), but counting errors are unlikely to account for the recorded decline on Skokholm.

Towards the end of March the first few birds return to the waters around the island, steadily increasing in number over a few days until there are thousands, presumably the whole Skokholm population, but they are extremely wary and do not venture ashore. After reaching a peak, they suddenly vanish. Then in the last few days of the month, or in early-April, they return in strength and the first landings are made, rights to burrows are re-established, and spring-cleaning begins. The island perimeter suddenly reverberates with their call, a sound that is often likened to a rumbling stomach! In late-April or in early-May the single egg is laid, and 40 days later the sight of some adults coming ashore with a beakful of fish means that the first of the youngsters have hatched. By late-June and into July, suddenly there are many more "adult" birds loafing about on the cliff-top slopes. These are actually immature birds, of between one (rarely) and four years of age, investigating what life in the breeding colony is all about. At the same time, the chicks are preparing to fledge and are frequently seen standing at their burrow entrance, looking about, exercising their wings, and then being chased back underground by their anxious parents. The air in the vicinity of the colony reeks of fishy guano. The young eventually leave the island under the cover of darkness, and are thus rarely seen doing so by human observers. Then one day all of the birds will suddenly have gone, to spend the winter months far from land – in the middle of the Irish Sea in the case of the adults, and further south for the youngsters. There is an eerie silence on the island once they have gone.

To take a rather more scientific look at the above, one shall quote the figures obtained by Ashcroft (1979) on Skomer Island between 1972 and 1977, by way of observing colour-ringed adults. She found that the adult annual survival rate was 95 percent (i.e. 5 percent die every year); that each year 20 to 27 percent of adults were without nesting-burrows (i.e. there is competition for them), and that 2 percent were absent from the colony; that 64 percent of pairs with a burrow managed to raise a chick to fledging, with 5 to 16 percent of pairs did not lay an egg, 22 to 25 percent of eggs did not hatch, and 5 percent of chicks died. Juvenile puffins first returned to the colony at two, or more usually three, years of age, whilst 4 years was the earliest age for first breeding. Between 10 and 16 percent of fledglings survived to breeding age, but it was unclear whether this was enough to counteract adult mortality. In her study, Ashcroft had to create inspection hatches in order to observe the contents of nests, but reportedly did allow for the well-known tendency of puffins to desert the egg if disturbed during laying and incubation (e.g. Lockley, 1934). However, even then, in the first year of study the productivity in the research burrows was "much less" than in undisturbed ones, and subsequently the regularity of checking the nests was reduced in order to lessen the impact (Ashcroft, 1976).

R.M. Lockley was the first to study puffins on Skokholm, doing so from 1928 onwards. His work eventually resulted in the publication of the book *Puffins* (1953), by which time he drew on information from numerous other sources in addition to using his own observations. However, one factor in the life cycle of the species that he (nor numerous others subsequently) did not fathom accurately was whether the chick was deserted by its parents as it is in the Manx shearwater. Lockley (1934) and Myrberget (1962) both stated that they were abandoned before they fledged. However, Hudson (1979) discovered otherwise in a study carried out on Skomer. It was already known that food-provisioning rates increases steadily with the growth of the chick until it reaches about 26 days old, and then gradually decreases towards fledging at about 40 days, though the amount of fish brought remains approximately the same (Ashcroft, 1976; Ashcroft, 1979). Hudson sought to answer two questions:

1. Do changes in the chick's behaviour bring about the reduction in the amount of food provisioned?

2. Would it be advantageous to the chick to receive more food than the adults bring prior to fledging?

As is the norm with so many of these investigations, Hudson interfered with the natural way of things: 15 youngsters were removed from the nest and reared in artificial burrows. They were split into three groups of five, and each group exposed to a different feeding regime – the chicks in one group were given the maximum amount that parents could supply (varying with the age of the chick – see below); another given as much as each bird could eat; and the birds in the third group were given the amount that they would normally receive on average each day from their parents throughout their growth period (varying with their age – see above). Question 1 above was answered thus: the chicks ate all that was given to them. Therefore it must be a "decision" on the part of the adults that brings about the reduction in the amount of food supplied. Question 2 was answered thus: no matter what the amount of food supplied, all three groups reached the fledgling stage at approximately the same weight. It was not known how the extra energy was dissipated in those birds fed more food than "usual", but thought to be in greater body maintenance, or a decrease in digestive efficiency.

Hudson asked another question: how do adults determine how much to feed their chick? This was answered using another manipulation, that of exchanging chicks of similar or different ages, and observing if the feeding behaviour of the adults altered to suit the age of the replacement chick (Ashcroft had previously discovered that provisioning rates reach a peak at 26 days – see above). The results were as follows: when chicks of the same age were exchanged, the foster parents accepted and fed them the same quantity of fish; when old chicks replaced young chicks, they were fed less than the standard amount for their age, i.e. the foster parents brought the same quantity of food that their own, younger chick would have been allocated; when young chicks replaced older ones, they were fed more food than necessary, i.e. the foster parents brought the same quantity of food that their own, larger chick would have been allocated. Thus, all foster parents continued along their previous feeding schedule, irrespective of the age of their "new" chick. All of the young fledged at approximately the same weight, and thus it were proven that the chicks are not deserted and that it is the chick that determines when feeding stops, i.e. by fledging.

Since the catching of any animal was prohibited on Skokholm between 1977 and until just recently, studies like the aforementioned could not take place. This is not a great loss as far as puffins are concerned, given that there are no restrictions on the neighbouring island of Skomer, with its far larger population there.

Counting methods. In accordance with national guidelines, at least one count is made of individuals on days of "peak attendance" in the first three weeks of April, prior to egg-laying. This has typically been carried out at 1900 BST, but in year 2001 the author noticed that there might have been a change in the behaviour of puffins, since at 1900 birds were simply no longer present or were rapidly leaving the area. So counts were carried out throughout the days that followed, and it was clear that birds were present in their peak numbers far earlier in the afternoon. In addition to the time of day, the advent of early nesting (i.e. egg-laying) would obviously have a huge effect on the counts, since incubating birds are not standing about on the surface or resting on the sea. Observations of the number of puffins bringing fish ashore in June and July to feed young in a study area in Crab Bay, Skokholm, have suggested that the timing of breeding varies quite significantly from year to year (see below), and therefore so also would periods of attendance and thus the number of birds above ground. Hence it is extremely important to take careful note of the patterns of attendance and to undertake counts as numbers peak. The author's personal experience of numerous censuses has shown that it is far easier to count puffins that are on the sea, and that, early on in April, <u>all</u> of the birds can be on the water at one time, rather than some be ashore, some in the air, and others at sea, and so counting is made easier and is less prone to huge errors. Recommendations along these lines made by the author to the Islands Management Committee were accepted in the spring of 2002.

Counts have also been made in the first week of July, also on days of peak attendance and which at this time of year includes a large proportion of immature birds. This may be useful in assessing the long-term health of the population, should one ask the question: "Are there sufficient immature birds to balance losses of adults through age-related mortality?" Such counts are extremely difficult to make, and prone to a large degree of error, because of the activity of the many birds – a variable proportion in flight, others in and out of burrows, and still more sat on the sea, often obscured by waves. It really requires a number of counters, and then great care must be taken to accurately demarcate the boundaries of adjacent count areas. Birds within the "rafts" move about constantly, bringing about shape changes and often leading to adjacent groups merging together within a matter of moments, so counters of adjacent groups should commence side-by-side before moving off in opposite directions to continue counting each section. Some sections of coastline have very fragile terrain underfoot and also breeding gulls situated in them. It is foolhardy to walk these lengths, for three very obvious reasons: it is impossible to count birds whilst having to watch one's step; frantic gulls make for inaccurate counting of puffins; and puffin and shearwater burrows are collapsed underfoot. The author commenced the use of a number of fixed points from which counts could be made of the areas of sea beneath such areas, and it is hoped that their use will be continued. In addition to the aforementioned difficulties, the assessment of whether "peak attendance" is being achieved (and that counting should proceed) at any one moment is very subjective, and so ideally counts would be carried out daily for a number of days.

<u>Factors affecting Puffins</u>

Kleptoparasitism, the stealing of food from a different species, is widespread in the bird world. The interaction between gulls and puffins has been has been well documented (e.g. Harris, 1984). Observations of this phenomenon have been carried out on various occasions on Skokholm, first by Lockley (1953) and then Roberts *et al.* (1963), during which time there was a noticeable increase in the number of "rogue" gulls practicing kleptoparasitism. Since 1981 this has been watched more systematically by lecturers and students from the University College of Cardiff, and more recently by island staff and volunteers, on the first Thursday of the month of July. Lockley reported two or three "rogue" herring gulls in 1947, whilst on 23rd July 1963 up to 12 herring gulls and one great black-backed gull were recorded carrying out kleptoparasitism. In all years recently and certainly since 1981 (Howgate, 1986), lesser black-backed gulls have replaced herring gulls as kleptoparasites in Crab Bay, and since 2000 one or two great black-backed gulls have also been active in this respect. Each gull will have a territory that it defends from other gulls, though there are of course no limits for the great black-backed gulls, which tend to roam about at will. The number of gulls within any given area changes over time, and quite clearly there are more when puffin activity is at its greatest (see below).

The puffins adopt a number of strategies to overcome the gull attacks, the most well-known being the "wheeling" habit, which involves large numbers of birds simultaneously flying in a huge circle over the nest-slopes, a practise that is thought to confuse predators, and of course confer some degree of safety to each individual through the large number of birds being present. Others will land well away from the burrow that they intend to visit, and wait until the nearby gull becomes distracted or turns away, at which moment the puffin will dash across the slope and dart into the entrance. Some seem to try to lure the gull away from its position, presumably because the puffin's burrow is situated where the gull is stood (Thompson, 1996b).

Watches are made from dawn until dusk for puffins returning with fish with which to feed their young. The resulting graphs of time versus the number of puffin "fish-landings" show a particular pattern, with a large peak in the number of landings an hour or two after daybreak, and with a smaller peak in the early evening, with smaller but nevertheless steady numbers returning throughout the day. The number of gull attacks is recorded, as are successful attacks, and statistical analysis of data from numerous years has showed that approximately 25 percent of all puffins landing with fish are attacked, and of these attacks about 20 to 25 percent are successful, that is, about 6.5 percent of puffin fish-landings are robbed. Statistical analysis of the data obtained over the years has demonstrated that there are no significant changes from year to year, in all aspects of the study: there is a significant association between the number of fish-landings and gull attacks, and also with successful gull attacks. This demonstrates that the habit of "wheeling" (see above) observed does not confuse the gulls into missing the birds that land with fish, but this is undoubtedly due to the fact that each gull tends to remain stationary in any one area, and once a puffin lands within that spot – an inevitable happening – the gull stands a good chance of catching it. Only those puffins that are carrying food are targeted, the shiny fish clearly obvious from some distance away. However, there are frequent occasions when a gull will chase loafing puffins from the cliff-slopes, as if showing frustration at them not being busy foraging.

A change in the timing of the Cardiff University biology field course to a period three weeks earlier (mid-June), has led to observations being made that have suggested that the puffin breeding season has been commencing earlier on occasion, since numbers of puffins bringing fish ashore in July have decreased somewhat, whereas those in June have increased. The discovery of puffins incubating earth- and vegetation-stained eggs (i.e. not newly laid) in mid- to late-April has strengthened this theory (pers. obs.), but it requires further investigation. There are still significant differences though between the two months, with July still having more fish landings than the month of June, with the exception of year 2000, and only longer-term studies would truly shed light on this.

Opposite: Figure 26. Crab Bay seen from Theatre Cove. The campion-covered slopes of Crab Bay are home to hundreds of pairs of Puffins.

In Britain as a whole, puffins are thought to have declined between 1947 and 1960, and to have remained fairly stable at the resulting lower level during the 1970's and 1980's (Lloyd *et al.*, 1991), a similar situation to that observed on Skokholm. Local factors such as rats, oil pollution at sea and interference by man are thought to have been responsible for some of the declines. But changes in food availability at sea, associated with warming of the North Atlantic up until 1950, was probably the cause of the more widespread declines (Harris, 1984).

The population uses the island as a breeding site, and is therefore subject to many external influences outside, but even during, this period. Food availability throughout the year is of utmost importance to the population. Studies carried out locally revealed that puffins often forage very close to the colonies, mostly within 3 to 5 km of Skomer, and none were seen returning with fish for the chicks at a distance of over 13 km (Corkhill, 1973). Stone *et al.* (1992) made similar observations. Seasonal changes in the composition of chick diets are apparently due more to changes in the availability of different prey species than to changes in the parents' foraging behaviour (Ashcroft, 1976). At British colonies, sandlance *Ammodytes* spp. are brought to chicks at first, followed by calorie-rich sprats *Sprattus sprattus* which move inshore just as the sandlance move away. The result is the provisioning of the chicks with a more-energy-rich food supply during their period of maximum growth (Nettleship & Birkhead, 1985).

As with the other auks, puffins are particularly vulnerable to oil-pollution incidents. Lockley (1953) attributed the dramatic decline in numbers on Skokholm to increased incidences of oil-spillage. Starving birds are more likely to be vulnerable to pollution, predators and disease, so the factors can be compounded e.g. the seabird wreck of 1969. Ideally, national management of fisheries would take seabirds into account. Low input assessment of feeding rates is carried out on Skomer.

The continued absence of mammalian ground-predators on the island is of fundamental importance to this species. Avian predators of puffins on Skokholm include peregrine *Falco peregrinus* (of which there is currently one breeding pair) and great black-backed gull *Larus marinus* (71 pairs in 2004), both of which are frequently seen catching puffins. In addition, puffin remains have been found at the buzzard *Buteo buteo* nest in Wreck Cove in recent years (pers. obs.), but these could have been collected as carrion rather than hunted.

Although puffins are known to be able to dig their own burrows, competition with rabbits and particularly Manx shearwaters for sites does occur. Ashcroft (1976) found that puffins on Skomer prefer cliff-top burrows to those slightly further inland, where shearwaters predominate. In areas where the two species bred side-by-side, egg-losses were frequent. With the competitive edge so finely balanced, changes in the population dynamics of one species could affect the population of the other (Brooke, 1990), and the low post-fledging survival of puffins may render them less able to afford any resulting loss of productivity. However, the average annual survival rate of adult puffins is among the highest recorded for birds (Harris, 1984), and is higher than in adult Manx shearwaters (Brooke, 1990).

Digging by rabbits, puffins and Manx shearwaters is likely to lead to soil losses, particularly from slopes close to cliff-edges (Ninnes, 1998). This could reduce the availability of nest-sites in the future and result in relocation of the birds, should alternative sites exist. The once-large puffin colony on nearby Grassholm was thought to have met its demise as the mat of red fescue grass that the birds had burrowed into became eroded away underfoot, leading to burrow-roof collapse. This was after its zenith in 1890, and Lockley suggests that the colony on Skokholm grew as a result of birds moving from Grassholm (in Lockley, 1938 and 1969). Cliff-top slopes where puffins nest generally have very little vegetation above ground level at the end of the nesting season. The fragility of the terrain in puffin colonies means that it is of fundamental importance to ensure that these areas are not walked over. On Skokholm there is no unauthorised access off footpaths, but even authorised departure can be disastrous – Dickinson (1958) reported that he caused the collapse of numerous burrows during his study of the very same thing, and suggested that such work should not be repeated.

Burrow collapse can be brought about by prolongued drought (through the by-then chiefly mineral-based soils being eroded and then blown away) or heavy rain (by washing the soil away). These cases are rare but loss can be great when they occur. The loss of thrift from some areas means that soil formation is reduced on Skokholm, and unless stabilised by other vegetation, e.g. sea campion, any existing soil is likely to be washed or blown away.

Jackdaws *Corvus monedula* are known to predate puffin eggs, and were in fact the prime thief on Skomer at one time (Ashcroft, 1976). They have been seen entering burrows on Skokholm, presumably in search of them (pers. obs.), but could have simply been seeking soil-dwelling invertebrates. There have been approximately 10 to 30 pairs nesting on Skokholm in recent years (see page 169).

Bracken has been encroaching onto cliff-top slopes used by puffins for nesting, and this may deter puffins from occupying burrows that were used prior to bracken invasion. The herbicide *Asulam* has been sprayed onto the bracken in some of these areas, resulting in the successful check of its growth, and puffins have again been observed investigating the newly-exposed burrows in this area (personal observations).

Burrow-nesting birds such as puffins are particularly vulnerable to fire. Sea campion becomes tinder-dry in hot summers, and could be susceptible to ignition, so all human visitors are advised of this upon arrival.

Disturbance by boats is a recent happening, as with the other auks, but it is this species that is most closely targeted by the "sea safari", and as a result disruption of their daily activities has been greatest. Rafts of birds are closely approached and frequently entered by the boats, causing them to scatter and leave the area (pers. obs.). The long-term effect of this is unknown, but it is feasible to think that breeding success will be deleteriously affected, and non-breeding birds could even be dissuaded from returning to their natal colony.

OTHER COMPONENTS OF THE SEABIRD ASSEMBLAGE.

These are fulmar *Fulmarus glacialis*, herring gull *Larus argentatus* and great black-backed gull *Larus marinus*. Shag *Phalacrocorax aristotelis* has bred occasionally, in 1932 - 35, 1936 - 37 (2 pairs) and in 1987.

Fulmar *Fulmarus glacialis*

The fulmar is another member of the Order Procellariiformes, or "tubenoses". Its name originated from Old Norse *full*, meaning fowl, and *mar*, meaning gull, and derived from its ability to spit foul-smelling fishy stomach oil as a means of defense against predators. It is somewhat similar in appearance to, and can be confused with, a *Larus* gull, in terms of its plumage, but its bulbous head and long, narrow and generally-straight wings make it quite unmistakable in flight, which consists of agile glides interspersed with shallow wing-flapping.

In 1931, this species was "occasionally seen cruising near the island in May and June each year" (Lockley, 1936). The 1937 Skokholm Bird Observatory Report mentions a great increase in sightings and asks, "Is this an omen of future colonization?" At this time, the fulmar was beginning to undertake a rapid expansion of range around the British Isles, from its first known site on the St. Kilda group of islands situated to the west of the Outer Hebrides. A pair first bred on Skokholm in 1967, and numbers have increased dramatically, virtually annually, since then. The population increases that were experienced during the 1970's and 1980's of this species (and of a number of other seabirds) have been attributed to increased food supply from discards and offal from fishing boats.

In 2003, there were 146 Apparently Occupied Sites (AOS) recorded on Skokholm, with the majority situated on narrow ledges of the sheer, rugged cliffs of the northwest coast. Nest location is of particular importance to fulmars, since the birds have poor mobility on land, and need to be able to fly directly to and from the nest. Counting simply involves locating the occupied nest-ledges in May, but this must be done on at least three occasions since not all pairs breed each year and ledges may be temporarily occupied by non-breeders on some days. The result is a number of Apparently Occupied Sites. Three counts have not always been carried out, and because it is often difficult to decide whether a bird is actually incubating, prospecting or simply loafing, perceived annual increases might not have actually occurred, though over the longer term this has certainly been quite marked. Fulmar nest-sites are also counted in the various Seabird Group study-plots – see page 135.

This species' ability to spit oil is particularly useful to the chick since, being left alone in the nest for relatively long periods of time whilst the parent birds are foraging at sea, it could be vulnerable to predation. This confers great benefits to it from other means – both parents are able to forage throughout the day. The advantages must outweigh the energetic losses encountered as a result of a chick spitting an amount of the calorie-rich oil rather than metabolizing it. Reproductive success is easily calculated – large youngsters (balls of silvery down, "balding" in places as the downy feathers are moulted) are counted in the first-half of August, and the total reported per AOS. Most sites can be seen from the land, but some require a trip in a boat. In recent years the reproductive rate has been about 0.5 young / AOS, or one chick raised from every two nests.

Opposite: Figure 27. A Fulmar at its nest at The Dents on Skokholm.

There have been numerous recent observations of fulmars causing other cliff-nesting birds to desert their eggs during "ledge takeovers", through spitting oil at the occupants until they are driven away. But this species remains a favourite amongst the island's human inhabitants, thanks to its habit of soaring spectacularly on the updrafts (often just a few metres away from, and obviously showing an interest in, an observer), and the frequent visiting of neighbouring nest-sites that initiates bouts of throaty cackling and head-jerking from the occupants. It is the last of the diurnal seabirds to complete its annual breeding cycle on Skokholm each year, with the young fledging in mid- to late-August. The adults return periodically to their nest-ledges from late-November onwards, generally on calm days.

Herring Gull *Larus argentatus* **BCC Amber**

This, the archetypal "seagull", welcomes visitors to Skokholm since a number of pairs nest in the vicinity of the landing place at South Haven. In contrast to the lesser black-backed gulls, the herring gulls on the island have only ever formed a small component of the British population – certainly less than one percent – and it is a species that has declined by over 40 percent in the last half century.

Birds are generally sedentary, with most ring-recoveries of British and Irish birds made within a few tens of kilometers from their sites of ringing (Wernham *et al.*, 2002). Skokholm birds are present intermittently for much of the time outside the breeding season, except for a period between late-August and early-November, when they are known to move only locally, many to the various local ship docks. It is indeed a pleasure to hear them in the early hours of mid-November mornings, their calls ringing out and announcing their return to an island that is otherwise extremely quiet bird-wise. Most pairs re-occupy their nest-sites at this time and territorial disputes are commonplace.

Population size. Numbers increased steadily from around 300 pairs in 1937, to a level of about 1,400 pairs during the 1970's, a rate of increase of about 4 percent per annum. The population then suffered a rapid decline, culminating in numbers stabilizing at about 250 pairs in 1989 - 90. Most of the largest herring gull colonies in Britain also declined in the 1970's, by almost half between the national seabird censuses of 1969 - 70 and 1985 - 87 (Lloyd *et al.*, 1991). Then, from 1996 and unlike on neighbouring Skomer, the population once again began slowly increasing, by 70 pairs in two years to 1998, but has fluctuated somewhat wildly from year to year since.

Monitoring methods. Counting herring gulls is far more straightforward than with the lesser black-backed gull, since most nests are located on the cliffs and can be easily viewed from above. A few pairs nest on rock outcrops or walls in the centre of the island, and this seems to be increasing. All are mapped each year.

Annual breeding success is monitored on Skokholm by way of revisiting all of the nests within a sample area that incorporates the coastline of an area known as "The Neck" at the eastern tip of the island. This is an ideal sample area because the cliffs are low, a path runs around much of its length, there are few other birds (of other species) to disturb during the counts, and it consists of approximately one-sixth of the island's coastline. Over a ten year period 1994 - 2003, the proportion of the whole-island population found nesting on The Neck increased from approximately one-quarter to just under one-half. The reason for this is unknown. During the same period, the average number of young raised per pair within the sample area each season was 0.75. This figure was lower than it might have been due to rough seas causing nests and eggs or young chicks to be washed away in 1997 and 2002, and also because of predation by newly-established pairs of great black-backed gulls in 2003 and 2004 on that section of coast.

Causes of population change. The dramatic early increase was probably at least partly the result of protection following the establishment of the nature reserve. Until the decline of the fish-docks at nearby Milford Haven in the 1980's, perhaps 40 percent of Skokholm's herring gulls (wearing colour rings that enabled accurate identification) took advantage of the food source there or of other waste foods nearby (unlike lesser black-backed gulls), and it was reported that such birds had a higher breeding success – raising three times the number of young – than those not taking waste (J.W.F. Davis, 1973). The decline in numbers from the late 1970's was thought to be attributable to these same gulls suffering botulism *Clostridium botulinum* poisoning, due to intense feeding by adult birds at rubbish tips during the delivery of refuse and before it could be covered. It was mainly adult birds that died from the disease, with very few immatures affected, undoubtedly due to their exclusion from the feeding mêlée by the more aggressive adults. Improvements in tip management have caused the gulls to revert to feeding on mainland fields, or on the rocky shore where they are determined hunters of limpets (pers. obs.), although apparently unable to remove the larger specimens from the rocks that are perhaps more the forte of the oystercatcher (Harris, 1967b). However, some herring gulls do rob oystercatchers of their prize (pers. obs.). Regurgitations by herring gulls ("pellets") often consist solely of small limpet shells (pers. obs.) and this has allowed closer observation of the choices that they make when collecting. Different species of limpet are taken to varying degrees, perhaps depending upon their position in the zonation exhibited some are exposed only infrequently – those inhabiting the lower shore – compared with others, or live in rock-pools. Conder (1952) discovered that *Patella aspersa* was most-commonly eaten, and that they had originated from rock-pools because they had the alga *Lithothamnion* growing on them. These limpets would not have been as firmly attached as those exposed out of water, hence they would have been relatively easy to remove.

There has always been very little observed competition with lesser black-backed gulls for food, with the exception perhaps of those birds attending boats that have rod-fishermen on board, when both species are frequently seen side-by-side. This is a recent happening, with a rapid increase in the number of pleasure craft being present around the island. For these reasons, it is unclear why the number of herring gulls on Skokholm is so very much lower than in the past.

There is a small number of hybrid gulls on Skokholm, resulting from cross-fostering experiments between herring and lesser black-backed gulls (Harris, 1970b). These were part of the research into migration, imprinting and interbreeding of these two species. Following some preliminary work in 1962 on Skomer, numerous eggs were interchanged between the species on Skokholm in 1963 and 1966, resulting in 500 chicks of the non-migratory *Larus argentatus* and 400 of the migratory *L. fuscus* spp. *graellsii* being raised by adults of the other species. Many of the normally sedentary *L. argentatus* (Harris, 1964b) that were raised by their cogeners migrated as far as France, Spain and Portugal. Subsequently, when the young reached breeding age, the males appeared equally prepared to pair with either species, though the females selected males of the "wrong" species and numerous hybrids have resulted. A number of obvious hybrids are present today, each being noted and mapped during annual counts of the two parent species, although undoubtedly many of the less-obvious hybrids go unnoticed.

At one nest belonging to herring gulls, in 2004 the author observed a site "take-over" by a fulmar that actually "incubated" the clutch of gulls' eggs for many hours, until eventually leaving so that the rightful owners – extremely stressed throughout their ordeal – were able to return. The fulmar is also a part of "the seabird assemblage", and thus a feature of the island.

Great Black-backed Gull *Larus marinus*

This is the largest of the British gulls, with a wingspan of around 1.6 metres, and is an awesome sight. Its deep, gruff "contact calls" are reminiscent of the bark of a large dog, whilst the "long call" sounds rather like a particularly taunting, evil burst of human laughter. But on the whole they are far less aggressive towards man than might be expected, rarely flying closer than a metre above the head of anyone venturing too close to a nest or young and – in this respect – most unlike its smaller cogener, the lesser black-backed gull.

As with the herring gull, the great black-backed gulls breeding on Skokholm do not represent a significant proportion of the British and Irish populations, but is approximately between 10 and 20 percent of the Welsh total.

This species is Skokholm's top predator, its size giving it a huge advantage over the smaller species. It obtains a large proportion of its food on the island, mainly by predation of Manx shearwaters (Brooke, 1990), rabbits, gull chicks and eggs (Harris, 1965), puffins (Dickinson, 1958) and storm petrels (Scott, 1970). Recent studies have shown the diet to consist almost entirely of Manx shearwater and rabbit, with a small percentage of other bird species, fish and waste (e.g. Poole, 1992; Betts, 1992; Thompson in Betts, 1995; Mallindine, 2001), but pairs nesting in puffin colonies, for example, may take a higher proportion of these. Cannibalism is also occasionally seen, with chicks of neighbouring pairs being seized when the opportunity arises, most usually brought about by human disturbance (pers. obs.). It has been regarded as a threat to the Manx shearwater population on the island – see below.

Recoveries of ringed great black-backed gulls have shown (Harris, 1962) that they undertake relatively short movements, a position reiterated recently (Wernham *et al.*, 2002), with adults to a median distance of 54 km, and immature birds to 115 km, all to mainland sites. Fledglings attain a median distance of 13 km shortly after fledging, but to 256 km in December, and by the following May are back to within 98 km of the colony.

Prior to the 1960's, little work had been done on the measurements of biometrics of British marine gulls. The control programme instigated on Skokholm and Skomer at this time (see below) provided material to allow this (Harris, 1964c). Males of great black-backed gulls were found to be significantly larger than females in all respects, and that about 96 percent of all birds could be sexed by way of bill-measurements.

Population size and causes of change: The species is easily monitored by a count of occupied nests from late-April through to mid-May, and which are found singly on rock outcrops, walls, or on the few rocky stacks, or in a loose colony situated in the central Bog. The population rose dramatically from 31 breeding pairs in 1928 to 72 pairs in 1949. Concern about the impact of these gulls on Manx shearwaters lead the instigation of control measures from 1949 by way of the destruction of nests and adults, e.g. 50 out of a total of 60 breeding birds were shot in 1959. In 1961, at least 12 pairs attempted to breed, but all nests were destroyed and 25 adults shot. Despite such drastic measures, large numbers of birds thought to be visiting from Skomer and Grassholm islands were present in the late-summer, and took a heavy toll on shearwaters; even in 1961, following the severe control of the breeding birds, 1,153 shearwater carcasses were found (when 60 gulls were present in the autumn). Destruction of adult birds ended in the late 1970's as control was considered to be unnecessary, since even in colonies not subject to control the gull numbers did not increase, suggesting that density-dependant factors were controlling colony size. However, "egg-pricking" (making a small hole in the shell that results in the death of the embryo) was carried out on Skokholm as recently as 1984 (Warden's Report, 1984), this control probably more depending on the opinions of the Warden in post at the time rather than policy. These control measures largely explained the decline on Skokholm from a peak of 72 pairs in 1949 to a level of 10 pairs by 1960. Between five and 16 pairs then bred (an outbreak of botulism during the 1980's caused them more problems) until 1990, and since then there has been a marked increase. In 2003, there were 65 Apparently Occupied Nests, and in 2004 there were 71, with a roost of over 200 birds present in September. They then become scarcer in October, with small numbers present in the months of November and December. Breeding success is monitored annually by watching each nest closely in late-May and searching for young that are able to fly. Between 1989 and 2004, an average of 1.09 chicks was raised per breeding pair.

The great black-backed gull as a threat to Manx shearwaters

In 1957, in an attempt to assess predation of Manx shearwaters, a daily count of shearwater corpses was started and this continued until 1997 (they ceased because it was considered that carrion-feeding invertebrates would be threatened by corpse removal – see page 180). A direct correlation between the number of corpses and size of great black-backed gull population was shown, proving that this gull was the major factor in shearwater predation (Gynn, 1984; Betts, 1992). For example, in 1967, when the Manx shearwater breeding population was estimated at 35,000 - 37,000 pairs (Perrins, 1967) and 10 pairs of great black-backed gulls were present, 816 shearwater corpses were collected (representing less than one percent of the population when juveniles and immatures are taken in to account). In 1991, with twenty breeding pairs of the gull (and with 20 young fledging), 2,703 shearwater corpses were collected between 1st April and 31st October, 24 percent of them fledglings (Betts 1992a). In 1996, 37 pairs bred, 52 young fledged and 2537 corpses were collected, 35 percent of which were thought to be fledglings. The sudden "removal" of a number of gulls shows equally their effect – in 1957 there were 2536 shearwater corpses found, then 2048 in 1958, but just 988 corpses in 1959 following the "elimination" (by shooting) of 50 gulls (Barham, 1959). Such losses are not, at present, thought to threaten the long-term population of Manx shearwaters. It has been suggested that an increase in the number of shearwaters (and rabbits) being killed by these gulls in 1991 - 92 was brought about by closure of rubbish tips on the nearby mainland, for the species is also a scavenger.

Shag *Phalacrocorax aristotelis*

Single pairs have bred in 1932 - 35, two pairs 1936 - 37, and one pair in 1987. Numerous pairs nest annually on the nearby islands of Grassholm and Skomer. Birds are seen virtually daily throughout the year, usually foraging close inshore, or resting on supralittoral rocks. In periods of rough seas, up to 8 have been seen roosting on The Anticline in the company of oystercatchers, and up to 12 on The Stack.

OTHER BREEDING BIRDS

Canada Goose *Branta canadensis*

First recorded at Skokholm in 1952, then there were about a dozen records between 1972 and 1996, in all months, following the establishment of a sizable flock in Pembrokeshire from introduced stock. In 1997 and 1998, parties frequently undertook trips from the mainland. This culminated in a single pair making a (failed) breeding attempt in 1999, increasing steadily to seven pairs in 2004, with a non-breeding flock of up to 20 birds visiting from the mainland each day. Nests were controlled (eggs replaced with wooden "dummies" or hard-boiled eggs) between 2002 and 2004 in an effort to curb the increase on the island, under a licence issued by the Wildlife Section of the National Assembly for Wales. This came about when the Islands Management Committee decided that they did not want to shoulder the blame if mainland farmers started to complain that they were losing their crops as a result of the activities of the geese; that is, the islands might be seen as the breeding grounds for geese; another was that their droppings were bringing about eutrophication of the various ponds. There was a sudden change of heart on this, with CCW realizing that there were no grounds for such control (many other species defaecate in the ponds, but these weren't grounds upon which to control them; and Canada geese breed in far larger numbers elsewhere in Pembrokeshire) and thus the issuing of licences ceased.

Mallard *Anas platyrhynchos*

Previously an intermittent breeding species, with 5 records between 1936 and 1981, there have been up to three nesting pairs each year since 1985. In most years, very few young survive, most being predated by lesser black-backed gulls, but in 1988 about 25 young fledged successfully. Following the breeding season, sightings are infrequent until the autumn rains inject life back into the ponds. Then parties of varying size make visits under cover of darkness, and are occasionally present in daylight hours (highest count of 72 on the early morning of 20th October 2004), but are easily disturbed and caused to take flight.

Shoveler *Anas clypeata*

A sporadic visitor prior to 1964, but frequent since, during the months August to June. Pairs became a regular feature from the mid-1960's, during the month of April, but there have been just a handful of breeding records, with the first in 1988. There were three pairs in the period 1993 – 1996 and one in 1999, all having little success, the ducklings usually being predated by lesser black-backed gulls and the adults then departing by early-June. Breeding was suspected in 2003. Flights of duck frequently arrive after dusk in the period October to December, and although shoveler are heard their numbers cannot be ascertained, and they have departed by dawn. In some autumns there have been no records at all. Occasional winter visits have revealed up to 40 birds, but they are very shy and quickly fly away if disturbed.

Buzzard *Buteo buteo*

Between 1927 and 1951 a pair bred virtually annually, but apparently unsuccessfully, with a second pair present in 1948. A nest was also built in 1954. Then this species was absent as a breeding bird, despite *Myxomatosis* bringing about the virtual extinction of rabbits on the mainland (as well as breeding buzzards), at a time when Skokholm and its large disease-free rabbit population would surely have been a sanctuary for them. Skomer remained so, despite a *Myxomatosis* outbreak, as the buzzards found an alternative food-supply in the form of the island's seabirds. In 1980, after an absence of 26 years as a breeding species, a pair built a nest on a sheltered cliff within metres of the favoured sites (in North Haven) of 1927 - 1951. Then a single pair bred between 1982 and 1989, on a cliff-ledge in North Haven every year except the last when peregrine falcons took over the site and the buzzards relocated to Hog Bay. A pair returned to breed in 1997, at a completely new site on a sheltered ledge deep in Wreck Cove. No young were produced that first year, but there has been a good success rate thereafter, with up to three young fledging 1998 - 2001, 2003 and 2004, but none in 2002. The 2004 nest was in a different position, on a rock outcrop on the south side of the same bay, easily reached on foot (pers. obs.). No reports of breeding buzzards were received in 2005 but, amazingly, they are easily overlooked.

A study into the diet of buzzards on Skomer was carried out in the early 1960's (Davis & Saunders, 1965), which found that the main prey item was rabbit, though puffin featured highest during the nesting season. In the autumn and winter the diet was more varied, with bank voles *Clethrionomys glareolus*, wood mouse *Apodemus sylvaticus*, shrews *Sorex* sp., frogs, lizards, beetles, earthworms, various beetles and small birds included. Although there are no shrews, wood mice or voles on Skokholm, the house mouse *Mus musculus* is very abundant, as are frogs, newts, insects and of course birds. In 1980, on Skokholm the nest and surrounding cliff-ledges were checked for prey remains following the fledging of two young. The proportions of the number of corpses of various prey species found were as follows: puffin, 59 percent; Manx shearwater, 23 percent; and rabbit 18 percent (Warman & Warman, 1985). This was perhaps a surprisingly low number of rabbits given that there were an estimated 5,000 - 6,000 present on the island at that time. What is not certain is whether any of them were obtained as carrion or actively hunted. Interestingly, there were no remains of black rabbits, despite assertions by Berry (1977) that they would be more vulnerable to predation because of their colouration. Manx shearwater corpses too are always plentiful on the island, whereas puffin corpses are rarely found, so this would suggest that the buzzards were actively hunting the latter (the number of puffin corpses found each year by human observers right across the island over the previous 10 years was, on average, just 13). Lockley (1947) reported that the buzzards hunt shearwaters before dawn. Inexperienced shearwaters undoubtedly fail to hide away sufficiently on occasion, and it could be that these birds are spotted by the keen eyes of the buzzards.

The *Larus* gulls that nest in large numbers on the island are always greatly distressed by the sight of a buzzard flying over them, and the reason for this is not particularly clear (this also occurs when sparrowhawks *Accipiter nisus* fly low through gull colonies, and they are most definitely <u>not</u> hunting gulls.). However, in May 2001, a buzzard was seen perched on a herring gull's nest situated on a small cliff-ledge and was tearing two small chicks apart (pers. obs.) – perhaps it was not an isolated incident.

Peregrine *Falco peregrinus* **RDB, Schedule 1 species (afforded additional protection whilst nesting), BCC Amber, SPEC 3**

This mythical falcon is a delight to behold, particularly in a setting such as Skokholm. A pair is resident throughout the year, finding sufficient food in the form of breeding seabirds, migrant waders and passerines, and over-wintering thrushes, starlings and ducks. Puffins are frequent prey items during the summer, and occasionally lesser black-backed gulls have been taken (pers. obs.), though a check of the eyrie at the end of the breeding season in 1998 revealed the remains of collared dove, greenfinch, and linnet and nothing else.

Peregrines have bred intermittently on Skokholm. There was one pair recorded by Lockley in 1930 and 1932, and sightings of birds were infrequent at other times. There was no breeding subsequently until 1987, as peregrines passed through a period of very low population levels brought about chiefly by pesticides used in seed-dressings entering the food chain (Ratcliffe, 1970). Six different sites have been used in the years since the resumption of breeding in 1988, including bare cliff-ledges and the disused nests of ravens and buzzards. Of these recent breeding attempts, they were successful from 1988 - 94, but then failed every year until 2000, when one chick fledged. In 2001, the single egg failed to hatch and in 2002 the untimely arrival of a particularly-aggressive immature female caused the territory-holding pair to desert. Breeding was not proven in 2003 or 2004.

In 1993, two of the three eggs failed to hatch. Two orphaned chicks from a mainland eyrie (at least one of their parents and two siblings had been shot) had been in care on the mainland, and up for adoption. They were introduced into the nest alongside the single resident youngster, and despite the initial hostility of the Skokholm-born bird, all 3 were successfully raised by the resident pair of adults, despite a large age difference. The introduced birds had been ringed prior to delivery to the island, and upon fledging one towed the remains of a Manx shearwater behind it, one foot of the dead bird trapped between the falcon's leg and ring, for days. They were the first ringed birds of any species to fledge on Skokholm since the cessation of ringing in 1976.

The Warden obtains a license each year from CCW, allowing inspection of the nest in order to monitor breeding success, but the siting of the eyrie usually precludes any detailed observations being made.

Factors affecting the Peregrine

During the Second World War, the Destruction of Peregrines Order 1940 made it lawful for any person to take or destroy peregrines or their eggs in certain coastal areas, including Pembrokeshire. Illegal persecution certainly occurred elsewhere. This was in order to protect carrier pigeons, particularly those released by airmen who had crash-landed when on sea patrol around the western and north-eastern coasts of Britain. The order was revoked in February 1946, and it is thought that there were no long-term effects on the population of peregrines in Wales (Ratcliffe, 1980).

In 1960, the pigeon fanciers of south Wales petitioned the Home Office in an attempt to get the legal protection for peregrines removed. A study into status of the falcon was initiated, and shortly afterwards it became clear that numbers were dropping at an alarming rate. The crash in the British population due to pesticides has been well documented elsewhere, e.g. Ratcliffe (1980).

Peregrines are considered to be a natural component of the island fauna. But, given the importance of the seabird assemblage on Skokholm, there could be cause for concern if, for example, razorbills *Alca torda* began to feature highly in the peregrine's diet.

Footpaths are closed in the vicinity of the nest, wherever it may be located, so disturbance from the island plateau is limited. However, the low cliffs mean that sea-borne craft and unauthorised landings may be likely to cause disturbance. The author was fortunate to obtain the assistance of the Marine Unit of Dyfed-Powys Police in trying to prevent sea-borne disturbance – boats entering the bay where the falcons were nesting were asked to leave by the police.

Moorhen *Gallinula chloropus*

A pair bred annually until 1936, probably in 1938 (only discovered at night, with the aid of a hand-lamp), and then again in 1954, from 1967 - 73 and in 1975, and then between one and three pairs nested annually from 1996, at North Pond, Orchid Bog and The Well (formerly called Heligoland Marsh). Despite the paucity of vegetation cover, they are usually extremely difficult to locate in the spring, but for their ear-shattering calls that draw attention to them from time to time. However, they seem to gain confidence as the pond vegetation grows to its maximum height in June, and are often seen out in the middle of a pond full of gulls even when accompanying tiny chicks (this ultimately brings about the demise of most young). Usually having two broods per year, the juveniles of the first brood have been frequently observed feeding their younger siblings of the later brood. Once the vegetation dies off in the autumn, most birds seem to vacate the island, although a small, concrete-lined pond to the north of the Wheelhouse was home to one or two birds throughout the winters of 2000 - 2001 through to 2003 - 2004. In British moorhens, the pair bond is typically monogamous, but often lasts for a single season only unless a territory is held throughout the year. In southern Britain, some pairs are known to have remained in territories all year round where climate and food supply permit, but other than the aforementioned birds – which therefore did seem to be a pair – none have been seen elsewhere on the island outside of the breeding season. However, their secretive nature means that they may simply be overlooked.

Oystercatcher *Haematopus ostralegus* **BCC Amber**

This handsome, lively bird is currently the only wader to breed on the island. In late-winter and early-spring, oystercatchers are present in high-tide roosts on the rocky-shore of up to 120 birds, though they are rarely seen on the island plateau at this time of year, many preferring to forage on the more-productive estuaries of the Milford Haven waterway. On moonlit nights in March they are heard on the island, uttering their piping call loudly whilst presumably indulging in territorial disputes. Visits become more frequent and then suddenly in late-April or early-May they are all in pairs in their traditional breeding territories. Birds are long-lived, as typified by an individual that was ringed as an adult on Skokholm in May 1974, and was recovered dead on the island in February 1998, the corpse being a fresh one.

The Skokholm population has been the subject of numerous pioneering studies over the years. The first was of the incubation period of this species, when 51 nests were visited each morning, and more frequently during periods of laying and hatching (Keighley & Buxton, 1948). No nests were deserted, the authors suggesting that the population was quite used to such disturbance, and the resulting incubation-period stated at 26 - 27 days. Harris (1967b) studied the biology of the oystercatcher between 1963 and 1965. All of the adults were all trapped and ringed, and sexed by way of bill measurements. It was found that, with few exceptions, pairs remained faithful and occupied the same territory from one year to the next. It seemed that the male was responsible for maintaining the territory. Some bred at three years old, but most did so when four or five. Young birds were generally prevented from holding territories by population pressure. The average adult survival rate was 89 percent per annum.

Numbers are remarkably stable at about 40 - 50 breeding pairs, nesting all across the island plateau in various habitats and also on rock outcrops, with a few even on gently-sloping cliffs. Many of the nest-sites – the actual nest scrapes – are used year after year, those on rock outcrops being lined with tiny pieces of mudstone, whilst those pairs nesting on the grassland areas seem to have a preference for small twigs of wood sage *Teucrium scorodonia*. Many nests are situated within lesser black-backed gull colonies, and these are inevitably heavily predated. The recent rapid spread of goldenrod *Solidago virgaurea* across Home Meadow has suddenly transformed a particularly poor territory into a more successful one (pers. obs.). Usually three eggs are laid (but clutches of two and 4 eggs are common – Nedderman, 1953), and early-hatched young are more successful than later ones. Counts of territory-holding pairs are made by way of a British Trust for Ornithology "Common Bird Census", where birds exhibiting "nesting" behaviour are mapped on 10 different days between April and June.

Subsequently, individual species maps are drawn up, and the resulting picture demonstrates where territorial boundaries are situated. A search for nests is more accurate, but causes a great deal of disturbance and egg-losses (see below).

The presence of large numbers of apparently sexually-mature non-breeding adults led Harris (1970c) to believe that the availability of suitable territory was limiting the size of the breeding population. He removed a number of breeding birds temporarily, mainly one bird of a number of pairs, but also a number of complete pairs. Replacement mates of the former quickly appeared, mainly by birds that had previously been present in the non-breeding roost. Of those territories that had both members of a pair removed, none were taken over by new pairs, but some parts of the territory were taken over by neighbouring pairs as an alteration to the boundary, but not extension of, their own territories. Captured birds were eventually released, three having lost a considerable amount of weight and hence placed on suitable feeding grounds 5 miles away on the mainland. One subsequently returned to the island, found a mate, but didn't breed. The other releases caused numerous fights, with two of the males regaining their territories but not breeding, presumably because of the lateness in the season.

Numerous studies on the selection of prey items by oystercatchers have been carried out, most notably by Safriel (1967), who found that most of the 40 - 50 pairs that nest on Skokholm feed their young primarily on invertebrate prey that is found on the island plateau. In this way, adults could guard their young at the same time, although those breeding later than most turned to predating limpets on the rocky shore, whilst yet others specialized in doing so. Concentrations of empty, and therefore presumably preyed-upon, limpet shells are found in many locations on Skokholm, coinciding with oystercatcher breeding territories. Samples of these shells can be compared with live limpets from on the rocky shores around the island, and if the variances of shell lengths, widths and heights are compared, they are found to be significantly greater in the shore samples. This illustrates that the birds are preying selectively on certain limpets based upon size, and is an example of "optimal foraging" where the most profitable prey is taken whenever it is encountered (e.g. Botham, 1999). Interestingly, it has previously been shown that gulls *Larus* sp. on Skokholm mostly eat smaller limpets than oystercatchers, so interspecific competition between the two is limited in this respect (Harris, 1965).

Factors affecting the Oystercatcher

With such a high density of territories, it is inevitable that a degree of disturbance to some of the nesting birds occurs when visiting persons are walking around the island, even though they are (or at least should be) on the marked footpaths. Those pairs that leave their nests during such disturbances are very likely to have eggs predated by gulls or ravens. The annual count of lesser black-backed gulls (that involves persons walking through the gull colonies) invariably results in predation of those nests located amongst the gulls (pers. obs.).

Most of the Skokholm oystercatchers are not present on the island throughout the whole year, leaving at the end of the breeding season and returning in the early spring. Adult birds ringed on Skokholm have mainly been recovered from south Wales, and two in Devon (Harris & Brooke, 1974). In the winter of 1973 - 74 there was a huge cull of oystercatchers in the Burry Estuary where they were thought to be threatening the cockle *Cardium edule* industry. In total 7,020 birds were shot, some 30 percent of the Burry flock, but just one was reported to have been a Skokholm bird. This cull does not appear to have affected long-term numbers of oystercatchers, and subsequent scientific research showed that factors other than oystercatchers play a dominant role in determining the cockle crop (Horwood & Goss-Custard, 1977).

Harris (1967b) studied the breeding biology of oystercatchers on Skokholm from 1963 - 65 and found that breeding success was 0.9 young per pair, and annual adult mortality 11 percent, giving a surplus of 76 percent of young for recruitment into the population to maintain it. Predation by both lesser and great black-backed gulls is the main cause of egg- and chick-loss, and breeding success of oystercatchers has dropped dramatically with the recent increase in these species to between 0.1 – 0.5 young per pair. It is suspected that reproduction is just exceeding mortality at present, and assuming that there is no immigration from other areas, the population is precariously balanced. Some herring gulls have been seen robbing oystercatchers of their limpet prey just as they go to pass them on to their chicks (pers. obs.).

Recoveries of ringed Skokholm-born oystercatchers in the first four years of their life have mainly been made from along the length of the northern and western coasts of France and of north-western Spain (countries where shooting of any passing bird is considered to be sport, albeit often illegal), so they are clearly away from the protective influence of island managers.

Harris (1967b) also reported on gut parasite investigations carried out on two oystercatchers found dead on Skokholm. The helminth worm fauna of the two birds was completely different and, knowing the habitats and/or host species of the various helminths, it was clear that one of the birds had foraged on fields and rocky shores, the other on sandy shores (see page 181).

Lapwing *Vanellus vanellus*

This beautiful and rather charismatic wading bird is threatened globally due to the loss of its habitat, and even on mainland Pembrokeshire – an area that many might consider to be a haven for wildlife – there have been very few breeding birds in recent years, coinciding with land-drainage and the growing of early wheat. On Skokholm at least one pair has bred virtually annually since recording began, usually in a colony of varying density in the damp, grassy central area of the island known as The Bog. The population peaked in the 1950's and 1960's (except for a sudden, short-lived crash following the harsh winter of 1962 - 63), with a post-breeding flock numbering about 150 birds being a regular sight in the months of September and October up until 1977. Numbers subsequently declined, although 250 were present on 9th January 1982 (during a hard winter). From 2001 there have been no breeding birds, and even very few sightings of any on passage.

After the raven, the lapwing was the earliest bird to lay eggs on Skokholm, but they have always been the target of corvids and gulls, and in most years very few chicks fledged. In a typical year when numbers were at their peak, Vernon (1952) made observations of 16 nests. Egg-laying commenced on 24th March, and of the 65 eggs laid, 48 percent failed to hatch (40 percent lost to predators and the other 8 percent deserted). There was no record made of fledging success.

The largest movement of lapwings over Skokholm was recorded by R.M. Lockley in December 1927, when thousands of birds flew westwards in an attempt to escape the harshness of a severe winter in Britain. Hundreds actually crossed the Atlantic and reached Canada. Many stopped off on the island, but were soon dead or dying as a result of starvation.

Woodpigeon *Columba palumbus*

This species was very rarely recorded on Skokholm until the 1960's, when it became an occasional visitor in all months, though most in March and April. Breeding was first suspected in 1989, and confirmed in 1993. There were three pairs in 1994, nests being found on or just above the ground in bracken. From 1996 to 2002, a pair bred virtually annually on the stony beach of a small sea-cave, the nest being constructed of the fresh flowers and stalks of thrift *Armeria maritima* on at least one occasion (pers. obs.). Another nest was found amongst large boulders on the beach of Peter's Bay one September, containing two eggs, but was subsequently washed away by stormy seas in a period of spring tides. Always under threat from the resident peregrines, they generally keep low over the ground when flying, but in 2002 three pairs were quickly reduced to a solitary bird, presumably by the actions of a particularly aggressive immature female falcon. There was only a solitary woodpigeon present throughout 2003, and occasionally a pair in 2004. Apart from the breeding birds, very few others are seen (occasional autumn flocks make brief visits, e.g. 6 on 11th November 1999, and 9 on 9th November 2001, when both parties lost one of their number to a peregrine), suggesting that recolonization following the loss of such a tiny breeding population is likely to take a considerable time.

Skylark *Alauda arvensis* **BCC Red**

The breeding population increased from just a handful of pairs in the pre- and immediately post-war period to the highest recorded level of 48 pairs in 1965, before there was a gradual but steady decline to the 2002 figure of just three territory-holding males. There was just a small increase in the few years since. It is always a pleasure to hear this delightful songster rise up into the sky on cloudless spring and summer days, but one wonders for how much longer the privilege will continue, given its failing fortune on the UK mainland.

There are records of large movements in the autumn, of up to an estimated 1,200 birds in one day, but there are rarely more than a few groups of up to 50 recorded today, a reflection of this species' trend nationally.

Swallow *Hirundo rustica* **BCC Amber, SPEC 3**

Previously an intermittent breeder, with one pair in just eleven years between 1928 and 1990, usually nesting in a small hut built in a gap in a rock outcrop near to the lighthouse. Then there were two or three pairs annually, one always in the lighthouse hut and on a cliff in South Haven to 1994, but since 1995 the cliff has been shunned in favour of the garage that houses the island dumper truck (constructed in the late-1980's). A third pair nested in 2001 and 2002 under a small eave of the Warden's office, afforded some cover by the foliage of small sycamore trees that grow in the adjacent garden.

This is the most frequently-encountered migrant bird, with up to 3,000 being recorded daily in late-April and early-May, and up to 5,000 daily in the period September to mid-October.

Meadow Pipit *Anthus pratensis*

Always abundant, the breeding population reached its peak of 60 pairs in 1950, but then declined slowly, to less than 20 pairs in the 1980's and early 1990's, followed by a recent increase to 40 territory-holding males in 2003. Numbers undoubtedly depend to some degree upon movements of birds in the spring, since most disappear in

162

the autumn, although R.M. Lockley's ringing programme in the 1930's did show that at least some birds returned in successive years (Lockley, 1947). Up to 350 have been recorded on passage in March and up to 1,000 in late-September. Small numbers are present during the winter. The song-flight of this delightful bird is virtually incessant from mid-March to the end of June, and then heard intermittently in the autumn.

Rock Pipit *Anthus petrosus*

This resilient pipit is resident on Skokholm, inhabiting the cliffs during the summer months when pairs each defend a territory, but forming loose flocks that also wander over the plateau during the autumn and winter. The average number of breeding pairs in recent years is about 35, ascertained mainly by carrying out 10 Common Bird Census "visits" (British Trust for Ornithology scheme) on a circuit of the island that completely misses a great many of the suitable cliff sites and so most certainly brings about an underestimate. Although the author did not specifically search for nests, he came across only a handful of them during 10 successive summers spent on the island, demonstrating how well they are hidden. The highest population count ever obtained was of 67 pairs in 1957. Frequently song-flights are carried out in October and November, indicating that at least some territories are held at this time.

Over 2,000 rock pipits were ringed on Skokholm up to 1963, but because there hadn't been a single long-distant recovery, this was considered to be a great waste of money (Harris, 1963). Unfortunately the opportunity to study the banded breeding birds for the purpose of gaining information on the age structure of the population, weight variation through the year, and so on, was not taken despite individuals being retrapped on the island frequently (P.R. Evans, 1966).

Pied Wagtail *Motacilla alba*

Until recently, single pairs bred roughly once every two years on average, and annually 1962 - 66 and 1985 – 92. There were 3 pairs in 1993 and 1994, and between two and five pairs 1995 - 2004. Favoured nesting-sites are in the walls around the Observatory buildings, under the eaves of the store hut near South Haven, in the store hut at the lighthouse, and occasionally in rocky inlets such as North Haven, Twinlet Bay, Peter's Bay and Purple Cove (pers. obs.). A relatively-large flock, presumably consisting of the breeding birds and their offspring, builds up in late-summer, the birds roosting in the planted trees and bushes growing in the shelter at the eastern side of the buildings, but virtually all disappear by early-October. Personal observations, and the feeding (virtually by hand) of a pair in the yard of the observatory buildings, has shown that birds do return to the same spot in successive years.

There is a small passage of pied wagtails in the spring (March to May), and it is perhaps from these that the small breeding population has built-up in recent years. Hundreds have been recorded on migration in the autumn, but they are often mixed with white wagtails *Motacilla alba alba* (see Appendix VIII) and it is thus difficult to ascertain true numbers.

Wren *Troglodytes troglodytes*

It seems incredible that such a tiny bird could possibly survive for long on Skokholm, but it has been a breeding species every year since 1988. Its song is now an integral part of the island "soundscape", much to the surprise of first-time visitors. Probably more incredible is the fact that it was previously only recorded as a winter visitor to the island and, given that birds were known to return in successive winters (SBOR, 1957), an extremely hardy one at that. Of course, the mildness of the maritime climate undoubtedly makes Skokholm a more habitable site than further inland. Over 45 were recorded in the winter of 1967 - 68 and 1974 - 75, but peak numbers have been counted in October (200 in 1974), when a considerable passage can occur, and birds are frequently seen foraging down rabbit burrows.

The species reached its peak as a breeding bird in 1994, with 19 pairs. Cold and wet winters obviously take their toll on numbers, that of 2001 - 02 resulting in just 8 territory-holding males being found the following summer. It is well-known that small populations on islands are prone to extinction, and there are several examples of intermittent breeding in some species as a result of periods of extinction and recolonization (e.g. Lack, 1942). Having two broods is commonplace, so a sizeable population can build up by late-summer, although birds are surprisingly difficult to locate since they generally inhabit the dense bracken.

Dunnock *Prunella modularis* **BCC Amber**

Up to 7 pairs bred annually between 1928 and 1939, and up to 12 pairs between 1964 and 1981; then two pairs in 1987, 1994 and 1995, and one in 1988, 1989 and 1991 - 93. Breeding was suspected but not confirmed in 1996, 1997 and 1998, as two "pairs" were present throughout the spring, with singing heard daily, and then one singing bird in April of 2002. More recently, small numbers have been seen in late-winter (presumed to have spent the winter months on the island), and again in the autumn (1999, 2002 and 2003). Birds in juvenile plumage have been the first to arrive in early-October (pers. obs.), and thus probably originate from the nearby mainland.

Wheatear *Oenanthe oenanthe*

This delightful little bird has been the subject of a great deal of study on Skokholm over many years, culminating in the production of the monograph *The Wheatear* in 1990 by Peter Conder, island Warden from 1947 - 54. The arrival of the first males in early-March is often the very first sign of the imminent coming of spring. They quickly occupy territories and as soon as the females arrive they commence their energetic song flights. They are restricted to areas of short, rabbit-grazed turf, where they can forage for ground-living invertebrates, and nest either in burrows or, more rarely, in the stone-dressed earth-walls.

A breeding population of about a dozen pairs increased post-war to a peak of 38 pairs in 1951 and 1952. A sharp decline followed in the early 1970's, back to pre-war figures, followed by a gradual increase to 22 pairs in 1990, then further to 29 pairs in 1995. Since then, numbers have fluctuated between a high of 17 Apparently Occupied Territories (1997) and a low of 5 AOTs (in 1999).

Birds of the larger and sometimes more-colourful Greenland race *O.o. leucorhoa* pass through in late-April to early-May (confused with Skokholm's own breeding birds and hence never very obvious unless they are present in fairly large numbers) and again in September and October.

Blackbird *Turdus merula* **BCC Amber**

Like the wren, the Skokholm population of blackbirds is always "living on the edge", and has undergone regular periods of extinction and recolonization. One or two pairs bred 1928 - 35, then none until 1970. More successful attempts at colonization followed, with between 3 and 6 pairs in the period 1975 - 1981, but none in 1982, then one in 1983 increasing to 9 pairs in 1990. Four or five pairs have bred each year since, two or three in the yards around the buildings – where they have become accustomed to visiting the kitchen window in search of a sympathetic cook with a handful of scraps – and a few others generally in bramble or elder-bushes nearby. The behaviour described above clearly confirms that there is indeed a "resident" island population (although see below), even in the absence of ringing. In early-August the majority of the then-swelled (with offspring) population suddenly disappear from view, into the cover of dense bracken elsewhere on the island (presumably in order to moult), and suddenly reappear in late-August in fresh plumage just as the elderberries ripen on the bushes around the Observatory buildings, and "begging" recommences at the kitchen window.

The breeding birds seem to have their own dialect, a phenomenon reported from other isolated populations, for example Bardsey Island (Loxton & Silcocks, 1997). The song is much simpler than that heard on the mainland, and some human visitors have described it as "monotonous", but it is a very special part of being on Skokholm and fits in perfectly with the idea of escape from the norm that many of the island's visitors seek. The song seems to be entirely learnt. Members of the Wildlife Sound Recording Society (WSRS) have made recordings of the songs, and confirmed that there are indeed differences from mainland populations. In 2003, Margaret Rebbeck of WSRS very kindly analysed 8 recordings of the song of a Skokholm bird (made by Gareth Jones) and compared the sonograms so produced with two similarly-sized samples of recordings made of two mainland birds. Margaret's comments were as follows: "All three birds have much the same structure to their songs, i.e. a clear loud phrase without harmonics though some have trills or vibrato, followed usually by a phrase of complex notes including harmonics and formants (rather harsh sounds to the human ear). There is a clear difference between the Skokholm blackbird and the other two in the number of repetitions and in the low proportion of trills and vibrato (poor vocabulary and perhaps poor virtuosity). Part of the song is however reminiscent of golden oriole *Oriolus oriolus*, with clear, pure notes without ornamentation."

Many of the breeding birds seem to over-winter, and were certainly still present until the island was vacated by the author in late-November or early-December (easily identified by their behaviour with respect to approaching the author for scraps of food), so it is difficult to separate these individuals from passage birds if any movement is of a small magnitude. However, large movements have been recorded in October in the past, with up to 1,000 birds being estimated. Ringing of blackbirds on Bardsey has shown that those born there may leave the island in the autumn, but do return to breed (if they survive the winter). This is well known in blackbirds (Werth, 1947), and explains why there have been periods of absence for this species on Bardsey and Skokholm.

Gulls and even jackdaws have been seen predating blackbird fledglings, and on one occasion the author saw a lesser black-backed gull take advantage of two fighting adult female blackbirds and capture one whilst it was preoccupied.

Overleaf: Figure 28. A male Skokholm Blackbird sings from its perch – a shearwater wind vane – situated at the top of the Wheelhouse roof.

Sedge Warbler *Acrocephalus schoenobaenus*

A common passage-migrant, it is hardly surprising that there have been numerous breeding records, but these have mainly been made in recent years, with 4 or 5 pairs currently finding suitable cover in the vegetation of the marshes around the springs in the east, and around the buildings. Their presence in the vicinity of the buildings can easily be explained because much planting of trees and shrubs was carried out in the early 1990's, and many of these have now reached a good size (previously there was little in the way of cover here), and they seem to favour *Fuchsia* bushes. Rabbit-exclosures erected around the marshes have encouraged a luxuriant growth of vegetation there. The breeding records are as follows: single pairs 1928 - 30, 1983, 1986, 1988 and 1990 - 92, two in 1989 and 1993, three pairs in 1994 and 5 in the period 1995 - 2004. The incessant warbling of males seeking to attract mates in the spring and early-summer is strangely out of place on a seabird island, but a welcome sound nevertheless.

Migration peaks are seen in early- to mid-May and again, albeit to a lesser degree, in August and September. The spring figures have declined markedly from those of the 1940's and 1950's when up to 100 were estimated on occasion, with 250 in May 1953; counts in the 1960's and 1970's were of the order of 40 - 50 birds, declining to 20 or less in the 1980's and 1990's. Trapping undoubtedly resulted in more birds being counted than can be estimated without such a practise.

Chough *Pyrrhocorax pyrrhocorax* **Red Data Book, Schedule 1 species (afforded additional protection whilst nesting), BCC Amber, SPEC 3**

The population on Skomer and Skokholm accounts for about one percent of the UK population. The Welsh population represents over half of the UK total.

A pair bred successfully in 1928 (R.M. Lockley doesn't say where in any of his published books), and although birds in obvious pairs very occasionally lingered into May and were even seen mating (at Purple Cove in April 1965), there was no further definite breeding attempt recorded until 1992, when three young fledged "from the Purple Cove area" (the nest-site was not found). Further attempts in 1993 and 1994 were not successful. In May 1995, the nest-site was discovered by the author in a cave in Steep Bay (by way of simple but patient observations of the movements of the adults), and one chick fledged a few weeks later. Another chick was found dead beneath the nest during a visit to investigate the exact siting of the nest. Close inspection of the site revealed that the roof of the cave was collapsing, for pieces of rock were found in the nest cup, and plans were made to install a nest-box, but this was not carried out. In 1996, no young were seen to fledge. In 1997, one fledged and in 1998 three. In the late-summer of 1998 the nest-site was revisited, and it was discovered that the nest-ledge was almost completely lost beneath material falling from the roof of the cave. A nest box was fitted, shoring up the roof of the cave, and in 1999 three young fledged from it, one in 2002, two in 2004 and three in 2005, but in 2000, 2001 and 2003 no young were seen. A second pair built a nest in the roof of the entrance to Peter's Cave in 2000, but failed in the breeding attempt. During rough seas in a south-easterly gale in October, this nest was washed away, demonstrating the unsuitability of the site.

Wool is preferred by choughs to line the nest-cup and provide insulation, and in the mid- to late-1990's the resident pair made use of a sheep's fleece imported and pegged out for this purpose. When this has not been available, rabbit fur has been used instead, collected with much gusto from carcasses.

Numbers of choughs occasionally increase in the autumn, with a highest count of 32 made in September 1965. At least 13 were present in October 1999, and 18 on 14th October 2003, but usually just two birds – presumably the breeding pair – are present, and wonderfully inseparable.

The Warden obtains a license each year from CCW, to allow inspection of the nest, but the inaccessibility of the cave and the presence of other nesting species normally preclude this unless very special efforts are made. The Pembrokeshire Chough Conservation Strategy (Hodges, 1994) contains many policies, including the following which are pertinent to Skokholm: the continuation of monitoring programmes; mapping of feeding areas; appropriate land management, and the provision of artificial nest-sites where required.

Factors affecting the Chough

Choughs are closely linked with the the typical short-sward and invertebrate species associated with livestock grazing (e.g. Donovan, 1972). On Skokholm, the rabbit-grazed and salt-spray-affected vegetation, with areas of bare earth, is ideal (Meyer *et al.*, 1994). Of particular importance is the coastal grassland (especially the *Festuca rubra - Armeria maritima* maritime grassland) and the short vegetation around inland rock outcrops. Why choughs failed to breed regularly during the years when Lockley had held livestock on the island, or subsequently when Soay sheep and goats were present is unclear, since the Pembrokeshire population is considered to have been fairly stable during the present century (in Donovan & Rees, 1994). This habitat could be lost if rabbit numbers were to decrease dramatically. At present, the spread of sea campion *Silene uniflora* is threatening to engulf areas of thrift *Armeria maritima,* the favoured foraging places of the birds. Ants, of which there are plenty on Skokholm, have been shown to be a major food-item in the diet of chicks, but otherwise beetle- and fly-larvae (craneflies in particular) are favoured (Meyer *et al.*, 1994). The rabbit population currently suffers both Viral Haemorrhagic Disease and *Myxomatosis*, but to date there is no direct evidence of an effect on the birds.

Given that the Skokholm population has fluctuated over the long term, with a long period of absence, it is likely that a cold spell of weather resulting in high mortality of birds could easily result in the extinction of this species as a breeding species. There are many places in the vicinity of extant populations that appear suitable for choughs, but are never colonised, suggesting that birds are in short supply (Bignal *et al.*, 1997). This could apply to the Pembrokeshire population, and loss of Skokholm's birds could mean a long time before recolonization.

At present, neither of Skokholm's breeding choughs is ringed. This makes it impossible to identify individuals and ascertain whether the pair is a long-established one. Newly-established pairings might explain the poor reproductive success seen on Skokholm, since it seems that pair quality is the overriding factor in breeding success, not necessarily site quality (Bignal *et al.*, 1997), although the condition of the nest-cave (see above) may be the main factor on Skokholm. Until just recently, the lease from Dale Castle Estate had precluded any ringing programme that might be necessary, but since birds are ringed on the nearby mainland there is the possibility of such individuals taking up residence on Skokholm. A flock of 18 choughs present on Skokholm on 14th October 2003 included 4 colour-ringed birds, of which one combination was successfully noted. Enquiries revealed that it had been ringed locally (at Castlemartin in Pembrokeshire) as a chick earlier in the same year.

Since the site is an island, it is less likely to be affected by disturbance or harmful agricultural practises, factors that are very likely to affect mainland sites. The food supply on Skokholm is likely to remain plentiful, as long as natural processes maintain the vegetation – the rabbit population is very important in this respect.

The area in the vicinity of the bay containing one of the nest-caves is out-of-bounds to visitors (they are asked to remain on the footpaths). The other has a path along a cliff-top overlooking the cave, but not directly above it. However, access to the heart of both bays is possible by boat, and "sea safari" craft have frequently been seen venturing into the areas. This could have a deleterious affect on breeding; the author was instrumental in obtaining assistance from the Marine Unit of the Dyfed-Powys Police in making patrols of the sensitive area (similarly with the nest-site of peregrine falcons) and asking boat-owners to move away.

Peregrine falcons, also a feature of the SSSI, can be a threat to choughs. The remains of a chough wearing colour rings was discovered during the storm petrel survey in the summer of 2003. Enquiries revealed that it had been ringed within the Castlemartin Coast SPA, at a nest-site known as Deep Throat on 19th May 2002. It was apparently the last survivor of a brood of 4 – one didn't fledge and the other two were both caught soon after fledging by a peregrine that was nesting nearby.

Jackdaw *Corvus monedula*

Jackdaws were once only regular spring visitors to Skokholm, in association with rooks *Corvus frugilegus*. In the 1950's autumn visits were also recorded, and birds remained for the summer of 1963. Concurrently, a breeding population had become established on Skomer, with 200 pairs at its peak, and it was perhaps overspill from this that ultimately gave rise to the first breeding record on Skokholm – of three pairs – in 1965. Numbers quickly increased to a peak of 60 pairs in 1975 and 1978 (Lawman, 1974), but subsequent decline brought the figure down to 10 pairs in 1995. It has approximately remained at this figure ever since, although there was a sudden but temporary increase to 30 pairs in 2003, back down to 13 in 2004.

It is a delight to watch the birds industriously collect nest-material, making flights to a collecting area usually directly "inland" of the nest-site, and this is mainly carried out during the early-morning and late-afternoon. Stems of bracken are favoured for the bulk of the nest, and rabbit fur for the lining. However, some nests contain in their structure whole shearwater wings and various bird and mammal bones (pers. obs.). The bulk of the day seems to be spent foraging, in flocks.

Lawman (2000) recalls scrambling to reach the nests situated in cliff-top burrows in order to monitor breeding success, and discovered that this was very poor, possibly due to competition for the burrows by puffins, shearwaters and rabbits, and intraspecific competition from other jackdaws. Richform & Lawman (1978) asked many questions about how and why the Skokholm population survived, given the poor breeding success and knowledge of the survival of adults and juveniles across Britain, but did not find answers. Large numbers of jackdaws had been killed by island managers on Skomer in the 1960's and early 1970's, but despite this, the number of breeding pairs was still approximately the same in 1972 as it was in 1964. It is therefore assumed that immigration keeps the two populations from disappearing altogether, and in which case begs the question, why do they come to the island in the first place? Perhaps it is because of the abundance of nest-sites, or the relatively predator-free environment (except of course when it is fashionable to label the species as a "pest" and shoot them).

Jackdaws can be particularly efficient predators, and observations have been made of three or four birds cooperating to rob oystercatcher nests (pers. obs.), and in the early 1970's they were thought to be responsible for a significant proportion of egg-losses by razorbills (Lawman, 2000). However, most of the food fed to nestlings on Skokholm in 1975 - 76 consisted of grain – which indicates that visits were made to the mainland – and invertebrate food, including a high proportion of relatively "low-grade" insects such as tiny sawfly larvae (Richform & Lawman, 1978). This would presumably explain the poor reproductive rate.

In the autumn they are periodically absent, particularly during periods of rough weather, which seems to indicate that they roost overnight on the mainland and are then unable to return to the island on such days. Up to 500 birds have been recorded together in the autumn, and it is quite a sight to see them gather in the air at once when a peregrine or other raptor enters the scene.

Carrion Crow *Corvus corone*

Prior to the early 1960's up to 12 pairs bred, declining to just two pairs by 1982, and with no breeding at all in the periods 1984 - 85 and 1991 - 95. Subsequently 4 or 5 pairs have bred annually, with mixed success, this rather unusual given the intelligence of this bird and its recent spread in much of the UK. Nests are usually situated on cliff-ledges, often particularly conspicuous, though occasionally some are impossible to locate at all. One pair nested in two consecutive years on the top of a rock pinnacle in East Bay that was, during spells of rough seas, just out of reach of the waves at neap tides, and in one of the two years the young were forced to leave the nest as a result of spring tides coupled with onshore winds. They were at fledging age, and all four managed to fly on very wet wings and survived their ordeal. The adults fed the young on a large number of eggs, mainly those of razorbills – the nearby colonies were quickly robbed of the first and then replacement eggs – but also gulls and Manx shearwaters. How they obtained the eggs from the burrow-nesting birds is unknown. Thankfully such determined egg predation seems to be rare on Skokholm. A species that previously bred, the lapwing *Vanellus vanellus*, did lose eggs to crows (Vernon, 1952), but ravens and gulls also took their toll (pers. obs.).

There are frequent aerial battles with ravens *Corvus corax*, with the latter invariably chasing the crows off, but it is unclear which of the two species initiates the disputes – it is probably both.

Raven *Corvus corax*

One pair has bred each year since recording began, with two pairs in 1966. There are a few "traditional" nest-sites (possible locations are obviously limited on such a small island), namely Raven Gully, Steep Bay, Wildgoose Bay, Calf Bay, Rat Bay and Twinlet Bay. Up to 6 young have fledged.

In 1936, two chicks were taken from the nest and hand-reared "for the purpose of studying raven psychology" (Skokholm Bird Observatory Report for 1936). They "proved amusing friends until they at last flew off, able to fend for themselves". In 2001, the single youngster became entangled in fishing line that had been used to construct the nest, and it was rescued by officers of the Royal Society for the Prevention of Cruelty to Animals (RSPCA) on 10th May, who then thought it necessary to carry out euthanasia because its feet had become deformed due to its ordeal (see Figure 27). It was, however (at the author's request), spared such a fate and soon released on the cliff-top near to the nest-site. It was quickly re-adopted by its noticeably-excited parents, and despite being unable to uncurl its toes and having to hop about on deformed feet, was ultimately successful, fledging "officially" about a week later. It subsequently spent much time in the vicinity of the island's human population, obviously fascinated by people, and became ever more curious as time went on – it would land just a metre away from the author (and others), and was even keen to play as it picked at and dropped plant material next to an observer. It finally disappeared in the autumn, as is always the case with young ravens at that time of year as they vacate their parents' territory.

Pellets and food-remains were collected from the area around the nest-site at Steep Bay by Bogucki & Chambers (1970), and prey items found mainly to be of Manx shearwater, puffin and rabbit; some pellets also contained limpet shells. Were the birds hunting Manx shearwaters before dawn, or even on moonlit nights, or did they steal carcasses from great black-backed gulls during daylight hours, as has been commonly seen (pers. obs.) when the ravens have chicks to feed?

Large flocks of ravens are occasionally seen over the island in the autumn (highest count of 60 on 15th September 2002), when their "cronking" calls draw attention to their superb acrobatic displays. On nearby Skomer, flocks descend annually in September to predate fledgling Manx shearwaters, but for some reason this does not occur on Skokholm.

Along with the single resident pair of buzzards and peregrines, the ravens are regarded by the author as the rightful owners and guardians of the island, all three being species that are typical of those rare places that still remain wild and thus unspoilt – a reflection of the current situation on Skokholm. Long may it remain so.

In one year recently the ravens were forced from their nest (under-construction at the time) by a pair of fulmars, this for a period of a few days, but did somehow reclaim it (pers. obs.). As fulmar numbers continue to rise (see page 150), there is the possibility that ravens could one day be excluded as a breeding species.

Overleaf: Figure 29. RSPCA officers Rowan Barker and Simon Aggett valiantly came to the rescue of the single raven chick of 2001. Notice the mass of fine fishing line (from various sources) wrapped around its leg.

<u>Starling</u> *Sternus vulgaris* **BCC Amber**

This is another of those breeding species that may be a surprise to some. Initially only a visitor on passage in autumn when, to quote Lockley (1936), "large armies move towards Ireland and also SW to the open sea" and also present for some time during the winter months. The first breeding record came in 1946, when 2 pairs bred in the roof of the Trinity House Lighthouse Service store hut situated above South Haven. The population increased markedly from the mid-1960's, with birds mainly nesting on the cliffs, reaching a peak of 53 pairs by the end of that decade. Decline followed (reflecting a national trend) to 8 pairs in 1990, 6 by 1995 and subsequently there have been between 2 and 6 pairs to 2004, all nesting in cliff-crevices. The few males are often seen singing, but not often heard because, with starlings only nesting at Twinlet Bay and Little Bay, the lively chatter is usually masked by the noise of the sea crashing against the rocks beneath.

Large numbers of juvenile birds (and some adults) arrive on the island throughout July, and remain as they gradually moult into their first adult plumage. The feeding flocks are mesmerizing to watch, as birds advance across the fields in waves – those at the rear fly over the others to the front of the advancing flock, only to be very quickly overtaken by the next wave – in their incessant search for invertebrate food in the grasslands. The ground becomes perforated with innumerable small holes as a result. The constant chattering (and bickering) is also intriguing. Numbers generally fluctuate around the 200 mark in July and August. On one morning in August 1997, 257 birds were counted by the author as they steadily left a roost site on the cliff in North Haven in small parties. A few usually attempt to roost under the eaves of The Wheelhouse, but they are usually scared away by the comings and goings of people. There are fewer in September, but then numbers increase again in October and November, again to around 200, but with just over 300 on 15th November 1998. They have all dispersed by the following April. An estimated 10,000 starlings flew south on 6th November 1970.

A ring recovered from the remains of a starling in a peregrine pellet in November 1987 had been put on the bird in Lithuania.

Other nationally-important bird species

Another breeding species included in the 1996 *Birds of Conservation Concern* Red List (greater than 50 percent decline in the UK breeding population over the previous 25 years) is linnet *Carduelis cannabina* (one pair bred 1997 - 99). Other Red List species which frequently occur on Skokholm on passage are hen harrier *Circus cyaneus* (also SPEC 3), merlin *Falco columbarius*, turtle dove *Streptopelia turtur* (also SPEC 3), song thrush *Turdus philomelos*, and spotted flycatcher *Muscicapa striata*.

Other Amber List species which regularly occur on Skokholm are wigeon *Anas penelope*, teal *Anas crecca*, shoveler *Anas clypeata*, water rail *Rallus aquaticus*, turnstone *Arenaria interpres*, purple sandpiper *Calidris maritima*, golden plover *Pluvialis apricaria*, snipe *Gallinago gallinago*, whimbrel *Numenius phaeopus*, redstart *Phoenicurus phoenicurus*, ring ouzel *Turdus torquatus*, fieldfare *Turdus pilaris*, redwing *Turdus iliacus*, and goldfinch *Carduelis carduelis*. Stock dove *Columba oenas* previously bred on Skokholm in large numbers (62 pairs in 1975), but now occurs extremely rarely as a brief visitor, similar to the days before its colonization.

Further details on these can be found in Appendix VIII.

The Skokholm lighthouse and bird attractions

The phenomenon of night-flying birds being attracted to lighthouses has long been recognized (e.g. Clarke, 1912). There are three main factors which lead to attractions: the time of year (spring and autumn migration periods); the time of night and phase of the moon (the degree of darkness); and cloud, rain and fog (reduced visibility, when sky and horizon are obscured). The attraction mechanism is not clear, although it is obvious that nocturnal migrants become disorientated when the stars – their navigation aids – are obscured by clouds, and they are then attracted to a point of light such as that emitted by a lighthouse.

Those lighthouses with white lights are far more "attractive" than those with red ones, but with other sources of illumination nearby, i.e. street lamps, houses, and so on they become less of a problem. The intensity, pattern and duration of the flashes of light may also attract birds to different degrees; Bardsey lighthouse, a notorious bird-killer (Richards, 1960), has an Effective Intensity of 677,000 Candelas, a range of 27 kilometres and a flash duration of 0.06 seconds. The flashes are produced in groups of 5, every 15 seconds. One of the more dreadful events recorded was in the autumn of 1995, when more than 600 redwings *Turdus iliacus* were killed as they struck the lighthouse (Jones, 1995). It has been discovered at Bardsey that on those nights when a weather front is over or within 50 kilometres of the lighthouse, birds are more likely to be attracted (P.H. Jones, pers. comm.).

The Skokholm lighthouse is situated at the south-western tip of the island, in the same area as that found most suitable by many of the island's seabirds – including half of the island's storm petrels and a huge density of Manx shearwaters – but having a relatively-dim red light with a range of 17 nautical miles (nM) since its establishment in 1915, it has rarely caused problems for birds. Following a review of navigational requirements, Trinity House Lighthouse Service (THLS) decided that a 15 nM range was needed, with an emergency light of 10 nM. The latter caused the first problem for THLS, for their "service standard emergency light" was unable to produce the required range as a red light (i.e. with a red filter), but could as a white one. Concurrently, THLS was planning to install a "lamp-changer" into single lamp installations such as Skokholm, in order to safeguard the integrity of the main light. This modernization was planned for 1999 - 2000, but given the problem with the emergency light, it was decided to proceed with the complete change immediately.

On 8th April 1996, THLS fitted the lamp-changer to the Skokholm lighthouse (so allowing the immediate and automatic replacement of a bulb should it fail), entailing the replacement of a single 1,000W bulb with two smaller 70W halogen lamps that would fit into the existing optic. These bulbs possess less power and are therefore unable to produce the required range through the red filters. The filters were therefore removed and the light was "changed" from red to white, producing 140,000 Candelas, with a range of 21 nM, and a flash duration of 0.38 seconds every 10 seconds. Thus Skokholm's lighthouse has much less power, but a longer flash duration when compared with the Bardsey light. Throughout the first few months following the conversion, numerous Manx shearwaters were found on the three flat roofs and at the base of the building, particularly following nights of fog and drizzle and when there was little or no moonlight, and they had undoubtedly flown into the tower. Those birds surviving the collision (for how long?) were unable to escape from the roofs due to the surrounding parapet wall (30 centimetres high), and were being predated by gulls and ravens at dawn (pers. obs.). Refuges in the form of makeshift wooden tunnels were placed on the roofs, so that those trapped there would be afforded some shelter, and could be counted. Eventually, ramps were positioned on the roofs to allow the birds to escape themselves, but many were found attempting to hide beneath them, rather than climb to freedom, so new ones were required which spanned the whole of each corner of the roof and did not give birds the option of crawling beneath them. Spotlamps were very kindly fitted to the tower by THLS in 1997, in an attempt to illuminate the whole building, but rather than allow the birds to see the hazard and avoid it, many more shearwaters were "attracted", rather like moths to a flame (Thompson & Purcell, 1998).

It was clear that there were four main factors involved:

1) The rotating beams of white light affected Manx shearwaters in flight.

Birds could be clearly seen as they flew through the white beams, and on occasion they were seen flying down the length of a beam, ultimately striking the glass of the tower. Prior to the colour change, there were very few reports of birds found on the roofs (personal communication with THLS staff). However, in 1996, following the colour change, 48 shearwaters were discovered, half of them dead. Mortalities were attributed to both predation of trapped birds by gulls and to collision with the building.

2) The rotating white light-beams affected birds on the ground.

To the stationary object, the lighthouse will produce a flash every 10 seconds, produced by a fourth order catadiotropic rotating lens system comprising six equal and symmetrical lens panels. Thus there are 6 beams of light rotating at any one time. The duration of each flash is 0.38 seconds, i.e. a stationary object on the same plane as the light beam will be illuminated for a total of 2.28 seconds each minute. This seemed to be ample time for a predatory gull to achieve a "fix" on a target shearwater (pers. obs.). Areas of ground up to a kilometre away were brightly illuminated by the white light, e.g. Northern Plain, where numerous shearwaters breed. In addition, there was a terrific glare emitted by the light source, outside of the actual beams, which illuminates the ground some 70 to 80 metres around the lighthouse. Early in the spring immediately following the colour change there were numerous shearwater corpses found within this area, but noticeably fewer elsewhere (pers. obs.). Unfortunately no systematic sampling was carried out to check this.

3) The spotlamps affected flying birds.

Numbers of Manx shearwaters "attracted" to the lighthouse increased with the introduction of the spotlamps. Fledging birds attempting to leave the island for the first time were seen to fly straight towards and into the illuminated building. In the Quarry, where a large proportion of the island's storm petrels breed, the glare from the lamps caused much of the area to be brightly lit up. It was not ascertained whether the illumination resulted in greater predation of the petrels.

4) The spotlamps affected birds on the ground.

Great black-backed gulls were observed hunting young Manx shearwaters – exercising on the surface prior to fledging – in an area in the immediate vicinity of the building illuminated by the glare from the spotlamps.

Observations were carried out by the author nightly during the two week period around the new moon – including checks of the roof of the lighthouse – virtually every month subsequently. However, on 15th May 1998, THLS Estates and Planning Officer wrote to the Wildlife Trust, advising of "concerns about safety issues in accessing the lighthouse unaccompanied by T.H. staff", and that Trust staff or any other person were "not to access T.H. property until further notice." So ended the official checks of the roof, except on the few occasions when THLS staff members were present.

The establishment of a red sector was requested by the author after simple observations of the Admiralty Chart, which showed an area to the north of the island where the light was "partially obscured to mariners" (046 - 078 degrees, True). THLS kindly obliged following measurements of light intensity, by erecting a number of red perspex panels in the tower, and also replaced the 70W bulb with one of 35W. The range of the light in the red sector was reduced to 10nM and to 19nM in the white. Ground illumination from the main optic in the red sector was immediately reduced to 5 percent of the previous figure, and even less than that produced by the original red light (Tutt, 1999). In the spring of 1999 the diesel engines were replaced by a bank of solar panels; consequently the power supplied to the light was reduced and the light intensity decreased dramatically. It was a huge relief, but also a disappointment that the change in optics couldn't have waited until the solarization programme was carried out, particularly since THLS keepers have long been aware of the problems that lighthouses cause to birds, since The Smalls lighthouse, situated just a few kilometres to the west of Skokholm, has long caused deaths (Smith, 1960). Thankfully there was not a major attraction of migrant birds during the period when the light was at its brightest. Skokholm is therefore very different in this respect from Bardsey, but it could be that the migration paths of affected bird species have so far taken them beyond the reach of the light.

Figure 30: Refuges placed in the corners of the flat roof of the lighthouse. On some nights there weren't enough to go around and the birds ended up sitting on top – note that there are already 2 or more shearwaters in the box beneath the exposed bird. They would inflict injuries on each other in their quest for the best hiding place. The gloss-painted parapet behind is clearly not surmountable.

Subsection 3.2.3. Reptiles and amphibians

Just one reptile is resident on the island: the slow worm *Anguis fragilis* is most frequently found beneath pieces of corrugated metal-sheeting situated near to the observatory buildings. It seems likely that the species is quite widespread and common, but no systematic work has been carried out and its burrowing abilities mean it is easily overlooked. There are occasional sightings of them being preyed upon by gulls and corvids.

Turtles have occasionally been seen offshore, as follows:

Loggerhead *Caretta caretta*: a small turtle thought to be this species was in the water off Crab Bay on 4th June 1992.

Leatherback *Dermochelys coriacea*: a very large specimen estimated to be at least 3 metres long was seen off the Head on 29th June 1992, and another on 3rd July 2001.

Two unidentified turtles were seen in the summer of 2001.

Lockley (1947) reports that he did introduce common lizards *Lacerta vivipara* to Skokholm. There are occasional unconfirmed sightings, though these are more likely to be of newts (see below).

Common frogs *Rana temporaria* are recorded regularly in small numbers, especially on wet nights. They spawn sometimes as early as January (A. Davis, 1956a and Lockley, 1947) which makes them possibly the earliest breeding population in the British Isles (cf. Smith, M., 1951) but cold weather may greatly reduce the number of tadpoles which survive. All water-bodies are used for breeding, but especially South Pond and the many ditches draining The Bog, but most of these ponds dry out before the tadpoles are able to survive out of water. In February 1998, the whole island was traversed whilst counting burrows as part of a Manx shearwater census. In the process, frogspawn was also counted, and totalled over 300 clumps, so the island population is likely to be considerable.

Two specimens of the common toad *Bufo bufo* were introduced to Skokholm by R.M. Lockley in 1939. The island card-index contains one record of a toad in 1947 which was probably brought across either from Skomer or the mainland, and one for 1990 which had certainly come from Skomer in a helicopter net (it was returned there the same day). There are still occasional unconfirmed reports, but no toad spawn has ever been found.

Palmate newts *Triturus helveticus* are commonly encountered on Skokholm, particularly around the buildings in the autumn when they are searching for hibernacula. Vernon (SBOR 1973) found North Pond to be the main breeding area, as would be expected given that this is the only large permanent waterbody present, and since it is visited by large numbers of gulls, nutrient enrichment and concurrent increase in primary and secondary production result in lots of food for newts. Sample dipping using a net suggested that thousands of immatures were present in the pond in late June 1993 (Warden's Report for 1993). Newts have been found in all water bodies except the pool at The Dip.

Subsection 3.2.4. Fish

The only freshwater fish recorded on Skokholm is the migratory common eel *Anguilla anguilla* which has been recorded in various ponds during digging operations. Lockley (1947) reported elvers wriggling up the cliffs at freshwater out-falls. They are thought to climb streams flowing to the sea from Crab Bay, North Haven and South Haven. In the waters around the island there are frequent sightings of ballan wrasse *Labrus bergylta* and sandeels *Ammodytes* spp., and searches of the many rock-pools reveal various blennies *Blennius* spp. and gobies *Gobius* spp. In late-summer, shoals of mackerel *Scomber scombrus* are widespread, and a popular source of sport for rod-and-line fishermen on boats dotted on the sea around the island.

Subsection 3.2.5. Invertebrates

Introduction

Much work was carried out on surveying Skokholm's invertebrate fauna in the late 1940's and 1950's, when there was probably more published information (in the scientific literature) available about the natural history of the island than of any other site in Britain, but there is a decided lack of knowledge about the current status of the vast majority of these species found on Skokholm today. Most of these are listed on the island's collection of record cards.

The relatively-high number of invertebrate species recorded on Skokholm (and Skomer and Bardsey) probably reflects the stimulus given to recorders by nature reserve and/or bird observatory status, the fact that it is an island, and the interest shown by resident wardens. However, analysis of invertebrate records by Loxton (1995) revealed that the level of recording varied between taxa, as did the degree of expertise involved. The majority of records on Skokholm were made in the 1950's or earlier, e.g. the majority of spider records were made during one month in 1934 (Bristowe, 1935). The sporadic sampling since then has made it extremely difficult to detect evidence of colonization or extinction.

Rees (1983) listed the habitats of interest found on Skokholm as "highly modified maritime grasslands... and much bracken". Thrift and sea campion are known to be of particular importance. Crevices on cliffs and their associated flora are also important for some invertebrates, e.g. the amphipod *Orchestia gammarella* (A. Davis, 1955). Thankfully, monitoring and management currently focuses on these habitats – which are also features of the reserve – in the hope of maintaining them in good condition, so the invertebrate fauna should also remain okay. Other obvious invertebrate habitats include ponds (both seasonal and permanent), lichen communities, ruderal plant communities, rabbit dung, and the nests of birds, including burrows. Given the distance from the mainland, it is likely that immobile species would be unable to re-colonize the island following extinction. Parasites on the various birds and animals may also be of interest, particularly those found on, and specific to, the seabirds. Insects, too, have their own parasites such as mites.

A summary of the invertebrates recorded on Skokholm can be found in Rees (1983). These were regarded as important at the time of the survey, "especially Coleoptera and Lepidoptera", but recording has expanded to cover the length and breadth of the British Isles, so the overall status of many of the species found has changed. Thus the invertebrate assemblage is no longer deemed to be of sufficient importance to warrant mention in the

SSSI notification and management statement drawn up by the Countryside Council for Wales (the latter has been based on the management plan that was written by the author with advice from CCW).

A special mention aught to be made of G.B. Thompson who, in 1936, stressed to parasitologists the virtues of obtaining parasites for study from live birds caught for ringing purposes, rather than killing birds specifically to obtain them. This also highlighted another important aspect of the work of Bird Observatories at that time.

There are no known reference collections, except for butterflies and moths (made in 1976), and of spiders (made in 2000 - 01).

Nomenclature changes in recent years have meant that the record card system currently requires overhauling, and many species recorded on Skokholm in more recent years have not been entered onto these cards. The author has, for the production of this book, checked all invertebrate names and made any necessary alterations in the species lists found in Appendix IX.

Each key invertebrate habitat is considered in turn:

Maritime cliff and associated crevice habitat: The larvae of two moths with local status, namely the thrift clearwing *Bembecia muscaeformis* and black-banded *Polymixtis xanthomista*, feed on cliff vegetation. The larvae of the marbled green moth *Cryphia muralis* eat saxicolous lichens. Natural erosion of sea-cliffs is likely to destroy habitats, as well as create them. Piles of fallen rocks form suitable habitats for various invertebrates, e.g. the spider *Drassodes cupreus*.

Coastal grassland: This contains a range of plant communities, and these are undoubtedly of varying importance to invertebrates. All are influenced by numerous biotic factors. Bare or thinly-vegetated ground is of great importance to numerous species, particularly those areas that receive lots of sunshine. Several small patches exist on shallow soils, for example the south-facing banks of South Haven, adjacent to the lime kiln, and around the numerous rock outcrops – these are favoured by many mining bees and wasps, for example. Bare soil where rabbits are constantly re-digging warrens is probably of less importance.

Bracken: This is interspersed with other habitats, particularly acid grassland, with sorrels, wood sage, goldenrod and various grasses forming an understorey. The varied structure provides a whole range of invertebrate habitats, whilst flowering plants, particularly ragwort *Senecio vulgaris*, provide copious amounts of nectar and pollen for insects. Gull and rabbit activity, such as manuring, trampling and digging or scratching, result in patches of bare earth. Orb-web spiders are commonly found in bracken in the autumn, and many moths have larvae that eat this plant.

Saxicolous lichens: Components of this assemblage are maintained by manuring by seabirds.

Nests, burrows, carrion and dung: Nests provide suitable habitats for a large variety of invertebrates. They are particularly warm and dry when being used by their builders, but form a degree of shelter even when unused, and frequently contain droppings. Burrows are similarly-used as birds' nests, with or without a lining of grass (the presence or absence of which is dependant upon the species involved). They also provide access to plant roots for some invertebrates. Bird- and rabbit-droppings, food-remains, and moulted feathers in burrows all provide suitable habitats. The corpses of birds and rabbits are littered across the island, with associated flesh, sinew and bone. Those of Manx shearwaters were previously cleared away (as a way of counting them) and disposed of in the sea, but it is currently policy to leave dead birds where they lie, for the benefit of the many invertebrates that feed on them. Rabbit dung is extremely plentiful, most noticeably on the short-grazed turf of the coastal grassland.

Seasonal and permanent ponds: The island ponds are subject to wide variations in water level. Seasonal pools provide suitable habitats for invertebrates which are specialized to survive dry periods and which rely upon an absence of larger predatory species such as newts or large water beetles e.g. *Dytiscus* sp. (unable to survive in the pools because of their relatively-long maturation periods). Any changes to the existing hydrology could alter the degree of seasonality and potentially affect the fauna. Gulls may have caused a degree of eutrophication of the water bodies and, if so, might have altered their invertebrate interest, particularly by altering the pH or encouraging the growth of a dense mat of vegetation. Deoxygenation of the water is also likely. Open water is maintained by active management in some areas. The bare, moist margins of seasonal pools provide a habitat which is used by those invertebrates whose larvae inhabit damp mud.

Ruderal plant communities: i.e. those found in "waste places" near human habitation. These form one of the lushest and most invertebrate-rich habitats on Skokholm, with a high density of flowers during the summer months and consisting of rank vegetation in the form of coarse grasses, various thistles *Cirsium* spp., hogweed *Heracleum sphondylium* and stinging nettles *Urtica dioica* and *U. urens*.

Notes on some groups and species of particular interest follow:

The Protozoa

Not surprisingly, Skokholm's protozoan fauna has not been thoroughly investigated, although Davis (1956a) lists 5 freshwater species. In addition, two marine species and one from the gut of an insect are recorded in the island's card index.

The marine dinoflagellate *Noctiluca scintillans* has been described as one of the "marvels of the ocean". It is commonly known as the "sea-sparkle" and is widespread in coastal regions across the world. Floating in their millions, these organisms frequently "bioluminesce" when disturbed, hence the name. Fledgling puffins, reaching the sea for the first time on calm evenings in July, bring about flashes of luminescence as they hit the surface of the sea (pers. obs.), most likely caused by this protozoan. Unfortunately, this bloom-forming species is also associated with fish and marine invertebrate mortality events – in vast numbers they can form "red tides" – and although this species does not produce a toxin in the true sense of the word, it has been found to accumulate toxic levels of ammonia, which is then excreted into the surrounding waters and possibly acts as the killing-agent in such blooms. There are areas where it has even been implicated in the decline of fisheries.

Phylum: Coelenterata. Class: Hydrozoa. Family: Velellidae

Although little to do with the ecology of Skokholm, the few "stranding" occurrences of the wonderful By-the-wind Sailor *Velella velella* are spectacular (and gulls eat them), their skeleton mast supporting a thin sail that brings about their dispersal. Hundreds of thousands washed up on the local shores brings about an extremely unpleasant smell as they rot. There were two strandings in recent years, in May 2002, and again in 2004.

Phylum Platyhelminthes. Class: Trematoda. Order: Digenea (parasitic flatworms)

Harris (1967b) reported on gut parasites in two oystercatchers *Haematopus ostralegus*. The flatworm *Parvatrema homoeotecnum* was found to number thousands in one bird, and since the intermediate host for this species is *Littorina* spp. or *Patella* spp., it had evidently been foraging on a rocky shore. The other oystercatcher contained hundreds of immature *Gymnophalloides oedemiae*, and since this species inhabits cockle *Cardium edule*, that bird had been foraging on sandy shores.

Phylum Mollusca. Class: Gastropoda (slugs and snails)

A study of the distribution of dominant animals in relation to exposure on Skokholm shores was carried out by Cremer *et al.* (1965). Transects were set up in 10 locations around the island and the degree of exposure estimated using previously-developed scales such as that of Ballantine (1961). A number of indicator species were recorded and a simple abundance scale was formed, ranging from "abundant" to "occasional". The distribution and abundance of most animals followed the patterns previously described elsewhere, though the number of species found on the most exposed shores was higher. Interesting features of the littoral fauna included: 1) the small size of *Littorina obtusata*; 2) the association of *Laesaea rubra* with the mussel *Mytilus edulis*, with *Laesaea* only found on the byssus thread or around the hinge line of the mussel; 3) large aggregations of *Nucella lapillus*; 4) a distinctive form of the limpet *Patella vulgata* fund among the population on the sheltered shores; 5) a large extension of the upper limit of species, particularly *Littorina saxatilis* and *L. neritoides*, on the most exposed shores.

In 1990 and 1991, Slieker *et al.* (1994) studied the marine molluscs of Skokholm between the lowest low-water mark and the supralittoral zone and found 114 species. Of these, 49 were new records for the island, and 4 new to the Bristol Channel. As is to be expected from an island with a rocky coastline, bivalves were poorly represented. As a result of their findings, the authors recommended that the sublittoral zone around Skokholm should be afforded Marine Nature Reserve status.

Angela Davis (1956a) listed 7 species of gastropods during a study of the freshwater fauna. The snail *Hydrobia jenkinsi* was commonly found in all seepages on the cliff-slopes of the island, frequently found seeking shelter in the rock-crevices during dry weather. Marsh snails *Succinea* sp. were discovered in Orchid Bog Stream in 1955, yet had not been found during a survey there in 1950. This suggested that the snail had been a recent introduction, and its colonization of other nearby wet areas might confirm this, but it has not been sought subsequently.

The smooth jet slug *Milax gagates* is a pest in gardens and on agricultural land across Britain, but is found on Skokholm in its more natural habitat of grassland by the sea. The most commonly-encountered slug species is the great black slug *Arion ater*, which grows to 20 cm in length, and is very variable in colour, in shades of black, red, orange or grey or black with a red fringe. These are found across the length and breadth of the island, but mainly in areas with bracken cover, and are most commonly seen on damp nights when they venture out into the open. Frequent nightly excursions by human visitors along the main trackway to the lighthouse in search of Manx shearwaters lead to tens being crushed underfoot each night, thus giving some idea of the size of the population.

The banded snail *Cepaea nemoralis*, frequently with a yellow or pink ground-colour to the shell, forms colonies in a few moist, sheltered "waste places" – particularly amongst dense herbage such as nettle-beds, bracken and hogweed – in the vicinity of the observatory buildings, at The Well, the lime-kiln and at Garden Rocks (Lees *et al.* 1986). They are active in the daytime in mild, damp weather but rest in sheltered positions attached to plants at other times. They are a favourite food of the song thrush *Turdus philomelos*, a winter visitor to the island, and the shells are often found at favoured anvils alongside those of the more common garden snail *Helix aspersa*.

A study of topographic memory in limpets *Patella* spp. was carried out on Skokholm (J.W.F. Davis 1970). It was well known that individual limpets occupied a regular position on the rock – their "scar" – to which they returned following grazing expeditions. The scar matches the shape of the limpet, thereby bringing about close adhesion to the surface and great resistance to any attempts by predators to remove it. Davis concluded that homing of each limpet to its scar was achieved by a large degree of topographic memory, with chemical clues utilized in the final stages.

What started as a simple "mark and recapture" population study on the part of a group of school children on a biology field course developed into a long-term experiment on the age-structure of a population of the toothed topshell *Monodonta lineata*, which ultimately gathered data over a period of 16 years (Stanbury, 1974). A species of the middle shore, and hence easily reached at all phases of the tidal cycle (neaps as well as springs), individuals within the confines of South Haven were measured, marked and released. Repeat studies each year revealed that a) individuals can live for up to 15 years; b) mortality was caused by the apex of the shell wearing away; and c) cold winters caused high mortality.

Phylum Annelida. Class: Oligochaeta. Suborder: Lumbricina (earthworms)

A brief survey in 2002 and 2003 by the author (square clods of earth with sides of 30cm and a depth of 20cm were dug out in various locations, and carefully broken up to reveal the worms) revealed two species new to the island list, this now totalling 9 species in all. These new ones were: *Aporrectodea longa* from wet grassland at East Bog; and *Octolasium tyrtaeum tyrtaeum* from an area of damp *Holcus lanatus*-dominated grassland on Northern Plain. Those recorded again after initial surveys in 1950 were: *Aporrectodea chlorotica* (from wet grassland at Orchid and East Bogs), and *Lumbricus castaneus* and *L. rubellus* (from wet grassland on the northern slopes of Northern Plain).

Phylum Arthropoda. Subphylum: Chelicerata. Class Arachnida

Order: Araneae (spiders)

The fauna is fairly well-known, since the arachnologist W.S. Bristowe spent three weeks in August of 1934 collecting spiders on Skokholm (Bristowe, 1935). He had previously surveyed Skomer, Ramsey and Grassholm islands, and also the Bishops and Clerks islets. Throughout the period 1998 - 2000, efforts were made to update the spider records, and some species new to the island were found (Thompson, 2000). The list totals 66 species at present, of which 21 were recorded in both 1934 and 2000, 25 only in 1934, and 20 only in 2000. This would suggest that there are undoubtedly far more to discover. The identification of "difficult" species was kindly made or verified for the author by Peter Harvey of the British Arachnological Society.

The term "twitching" has been coined to describe the activity of bird-watchers that rush around to see rarities that have been reported on a network. Seeking spiders can be similar, for twitch one must in order to encounter the great variety that exists, even on a small offshore island, for the wonderful thing is that different species appear, or at least become mature, at different times of year, so there is always something of interest about. And contrary to how it might often seem, they don't all live in human habitation.

Bristowe found the spider *Clubiona genevensis* on Skokholm, this being one of only two sites in Wales, and which is a Red Data Book species, category 3 (rare). It is adult between March and June and occurs beneath stones and amongst herbage on coastal heaths and grasslands. No detailed searches have been made for this spider since Bristowe's visit, and it has not been found since, although a recent repeat of his survey on the nearby island of Ramsey was successful (Dawson, 2000).

The coastal grasslands in early spring are literally "alive" with spiders on sunny days, and in particular south-facing coastal slopes, where a few species of wolf-spider (Lycosidae) can be seen scampering over the top of the vegetation. Never forming webs, they are active hunters, chasing down their prey with the aid of a large pair of forward-facing eyes. Williamson (1949) made observations on the ecology of the lycosids on Skokholm, to test Gause's (1934) theory that no two species occupying the same habitat have the same ecology. He found seven species in his search for lycosids, exactly the same ones that were recorded in 1934 by Bristowe. The largest, *Trochosa terricola*, generally hides during the day. The other six are diurnal hunters, and their distribution differs to varying degrees. Open-water or grass with standing-water is occupied by *Pirata piratica*. At the other extreme the short, dry grassland habitat is occupied by *Pardosa monticola*, whilst the distribution of the other 4 species – *Pardosa nigriceps, P. proxima, P. pullata* and *Alopecosa pulverulenta* – overlaps in short wet grass with marsh pennywort *Hydrocotyle vulgaris* and silverweed *Potentilla anserina*, and areas with relatively tall Yorkshire fog grass *Holcus lanatus*. Thus *P. piraticus* and *P. monticola* will never compete directly with each other, and probably rarely with the other species. The fact that the others do coexist would suggest that are ecological differences between them, so Williamson searched and ultimately found differences in their methods of hunting that would suggest the capture of different prey species (or at least proportions of them). Another has recently been discovered on the island, this being *Pardosa agrestis*, a nationally scarce (Notable B) species, i.e. found in 30 to 100 of Britain's 10km squares (Thompson, 2000).

Other ground-dwelling spiders are frequently encountered. To find the curious crab-spider *Xysticus cristatus* one must look a little more carefully, since unlike the wolf-spiders, it moves only slowly. But what a mover! It lives up to its name by lunging in all sorts of directions, including sideways, and its abdomen is even shaped like the carapace of a crab. Another species of crab-spider, *Oxyptila sanctuaria* – local and generally rare in Britain – has also been recorded (just once, in 2000), on the short turf of the dry coastal grassland, whilst sun-drenched rocks and walls are the places to find the widespread zebra spider *Salticus scenicus*.

One species of theriid spider found on Skokholm, *Enoplognatha ovata*, has been the subject of a colour-morph study, and the frequency of different varieties in the Welsh populations studied is significantly greater than that for mainland Europe (Fowles, 1994). This species was not listed by Bristowe (1935), and was first recorded by the author in 1996, and again in 1999, very distinctive in its splendid pink and white attire.

The purse-web spider *Atypus affinis* was, until recently, listed on the island record cards just once, in 1950, which is hardly surprising given its secretive habits. This is the only "mygalomorph" spider found in Britain, easily identified courtesy of its large, forward-pointing chelicerae. The author chanced upon a male as it wandered across a cliff-top slope at the top of Cave Bay in 1998. This species is renowned for being very sedentary, with the males spending at least 4 years sitting in their rather sock-like but completely-sealed silken tube, part-buried in the soil and thus very difficult to locate. But they are not totally inactive. There is an aerial portion of the tube which is extremely well-camouflaged with earth particles, giving it a root-like appearance. Early arachnologists were intrigued by this. How could a spider which was supposedly sealed within a tube manage to feed? Did it eat earthworms? Some tried for years to solve the mystery, and eventually it was found that the above-ground portion of the silk tube did have a function, and it did involve food. The spider waits until an insect touches the exposed part and then, like a flash, rushes to the top and strikes through the tube from within. The shocked insect is then dragged down and killed. The spider then hurries back to the top of the tube to repair the damage, before sitting down to its meal.

The fact that the 1998 discovery was of a male did make perfect sense, for the females never leave their tube. The males, once mature after a period of 4 years, leave the relative safety of their hole (never to return), in order to find a mate. So where there is a male, there must be a colony of females. All that one then had to do was turn over all of the vegetation in sight to find them. Thankfully the spreading habit of sea campion means that it is easy to gently lift back many shoots at once, and by doing so a colony of a dozen tubes was found – the first record of the species for almost 50 years.

But what of our male spider, his mate, and their offspring? Well, he finds the tube of a female and announces his presence. The female doesn't rush to the top and impale him with her splendid fangs. No, she does nothing but allow him to enter as he tears a hole in the silk. But then she seals the hole behind him and he is doomed, for after mating she eats him, furnishing herself with the nutrients required to produce a batch of eggs. The following summer these eggs are laid and in the autumn the spiderlings hatch. The female is a doting mother and looks after the youngsters until the following spring. She then bites a hole in the tube and sets them free, to face a restful life of at least 4 years – if all goes well – on a sun-drenched slope on their very own dream island.

A further search for *Atypus affinis* was initiated in 1999 by the author and this proved particularly fruitful, with two locations found. An area of rockfall known as The Quarry was found to have a particularly large population (245 occupied webs of various sizes were found in November 2001), with each purse-web being located beneath rocks or stones, an unusual habitat for this species (each stone was labelled with red paint depicting the number of webs found beneath). People wandering aimlessly or carelessly through The Quarry will threaten this spider. It is local in its distribution within Britain and is the subject of a Species Action Plan in Pembrokeshire.

Cave spiders *Meta menardi* and *M. merianae* also have "local" status in Britain, and both are frequently encountered on Skokholm. They differ greatly in their habitat preferences, with the larger *M. menardi* preferring the damp, dark depths of the largest caves (including the aptly named Spider Cave and in particular one in Steep Bay), where the large egg-sacs are to be found hanging from the rock-face and under close guard by the female. *Meta merianae* is frequently found within bird-watching hides and buildings, and all over the cliffs as well as in the illuminated regions of the sea-caves.

The theriid spider *Steatoda grossa* is a species that would surely be much-favoured by the island's human visitors, if they were to discover it was present, since the spiders are mainly found in visitor bedrooms beneath bedside cabinets where they capture passing ground beetles and woodlice. Another common inhabitant of human dwellings is the cribellate spider *Amaurobius similis*, a species that produces the most wonderful blue-tinged web (when new) on windows or beneath items on shelves, that quickly becomes littered with the remains of moths. More often beneath wood-piles, the woodlouse-eating spider *Dysdera crocata* has the most enormous inward-pointing fangs that are ideal for piercing the armoured carapace of its favoured prey.

The familiar orb webs are particularly common in late-summer and autumn. The common garden or cross spider *Araneus diadematus* is widespread, in bracken, on cliffs and on buildings and is by far the most obvious species on Skokholm at this time of year. Far less common is *Larinioides cornutus*, occasionally seen guarding egg-tents amongst the flower-heads of jointed rush *Juncus articulatus*. Spells of fog or mist leave the webs adorned with water droplets far more beautiful than any pearl necklace. Less adventurous by far is *Zygiella x-notata*, which is generally found only inside the buildings, with females being particularly conspicuous in late winter and early spring as they guard their egg-sacs in the corners of window frames, behind the glass in sunny situations.

Sheets of gossamer cover swathes of vegetation in the vicinity of North Pond on still, warm days in October and November. Closer inspection reveals many thousands of Linyphiids (money spiders) of various species, including *Erigone atra*, *E. dentipalpis* and *Porrhomma pygmaeum*, and immature specimens of the various wolf spiders (see previously). Curiously, this concentration only occurs in this one area of the island.

Overleaf: Figure 31. Female cave spider *Meta menardi* on its egg-sac in Steep Bay cave.

Order: Opiliones (Harvest-spiders)

Skokholm is of particular interest for its harvest spiders. Bristowe (1935) discovered an Opilione new to Britain, *Nelima gothica* (formerly called *N. sylvatica*), which was subsequently found to be the dominant species on the island (Brown & Sankey, 1949). The species has a tendency to congregate under suitable cover during the daytime, usually rocks fringed with vegetation and generally avoiding long grass (as in other species of harvest spider,) and individuals are mainly active at dusk and after dark. It has since been found elsewhere in the British Isles, in a few widely-scattered localities, but mainly on islands. Observations on the food, enemies and parasites of *N. gothica* were made across the British Isles by Sankey (1949), including Skokholm. M.H. Jones made a study of the distribution of all species on Skokholm (1949).

Order: Acarina (mites)

The island's human population is greatly affected by a species of mite that is never knowingly seen – the "bracken bug" or harvest mite *Neotrombicula autumnalis.* The larvae are parasitic on warm-blooded animals, attaching themselves to a part of the body where the skin is thin (groin and armpits commonly), and forming a feeding tube from where they imbibe lymph. They cause itchy red blotches on the victim's skin. The adults are free-living in the soil. Circumstantial (but not experimental) evidence points to the involvement of the larvae of this mite in the transmission of "puffinosis", the disease affecting Manx shearwaters on Skokholm.

Order: Pseudoscorpiones

The false scorpion *Neobisium maritimum* inhabits the intertidal band on the rocky-shore, from the splash zone down. It survives the twice-daily period of inundation by retreating into crevices where pockets of air are trapped. Most British records are from the west coast of England and Wales.

Subphylum: Crustacea

Class: Malacostraca

Order: Isopoda (woodlice)

Five species of woodlouse have been recorded on the island. A variety of animals inhabit the rock crevices above the tide line, but the most obvious on Skokholm is the sea slater *Ligia oceanica.* This is Britain's largest woodlouse, and is a sight to behold at up to 3 centimetres in length. Its nocturnal habits mean that one has to search in order to find it. However, on Skokholm it also inhabits the area around the harbour at South Haven, and simply moving items stored there usually reveals some. A mark-and-recapture experiment was carried out in South Haven in 1955, with 1,000 individuals marked with cellulose paint, and subsequent recapture led to an estimate of 8,000 animals there.

Other species include *Oniscus asellus*, one of the commonest and most ubiquitous of British woodlice. It occurs in moist shady places in the vicinity of the buildings, most often beneath wood-piles, but perhaps more surprisingly it is particularly common beneath the festoons of sea campion foliage on cliff-slopes. Virtually half the size, but twice as fast, is the striped woodlouse *Philoscia muscorum*, found across the island in a wide range of habitats, most commonly beneath stones. Often seen during the day is the common pill woodlouse *Armadillidium vulgare*, a species with a predominantly coastal distribution in western Britain but common elsewhere. The water slater *Asellus meridianus* has been found in the ponds.

Bellamy (1975) and Roscoe (1975) have investigated polymorphisms in *Porcellio* and *Armadillidium* and their data on the frequencies of different morphs may possibly be useful as an index of stability in the island's ecosystems.

Order: Amphipoda

A. Davies (1955) studied the habitats of two very different amphipods on Skokholm. One was *Orchestia gammarella,* a terrestrial species that is found in damp situations all across the island. Able to turn itself upright (as opposed to struggling along on its side as in other Amphipods) it also has the ability to hop by way of rapid extension of the flexed abdomen. On Skokholm it reaches an exceptional height above sea-level. The other species studied was *Gammarus duebeni,* which is found in brackish and sometimes fresh-water, common in the cliff-pools of the south and west coasts of the island. Only unpolluted pools are inhabited, those affected by gulls or containing animal corpses being devoid of this species, hence those just above the splash zone being most populated. Shallow water in sunny locations – and so subject to large daily variations in temperature – was also devoid of this amphipod. A. Davis (1960) also studied the breeding cycles of *G. duebeni* on the island, and identified that unfavourable conditions such as overcrowding and a reduction in the flow of fresh water brought about a temporary cessation in breeding until conditions improved.

In general the large size of the boulders at the top of the few beaches that exist on Skokholm and the firm bedding of those at the lowest levels makes the distribution of the larger species that dwell beneath stones rather irregular. Seven species in addition to those mentioned above were found by Davis, all are listed in Appendix IX.

Subphylum: Uniramia

Class: Insecta

Subclass: Apterygota

Order: Collembola (springtails)

Gough (1971) listed and provided an identification key for 36 species found during a preliminary survey on Skokholm late in the summer of 1969. The habitats surveyed were under stones, in soil and leaf litter, in moss, on vegetation, the littoral zone, and on the surface of fresh water. Habitats not surveyed include birds' nests, corpses, fungi and the observatory buildings. Three species discovered were the first British records, namely *Xenylla acauda* from moss, *Folsomia bisetosa* from the mud of an almost-dry pond, and *Onychiurus meridiatus* from dry, sandy soil. Of particular note was the variation in the number of "anal spines" on *Friesea truncata*, with about 50 percent – a huge proportion – of the population having four or five spines, as opposed to the normal three. The species *Cyphoderus albinus* is myrmecophilous (ant-loving), and is found under stones where ants are frequent on the island.

Subclass: Pterygota

Order: Odonata (dragonflies and damselflies)

Sixteen species have been recorded, of which 4 are known to have bred: the blue-tailed damselfly *Ischnura elegans*, recorded every year and occasionally in large numbers, with larvae found in North Pond and the man-made Cottage Garden pond; the common blue damselfly *Enallagma cyathigerum*, rarely encountered on Skokholm but with numerous present and nymphs found in North Pond in 1994; the common darter *Sympetrum striolatum*, larvae being found in Orchid Bog and Heligoland Marsh (The Well Pool) in 1956, and a female was observed ovipositing at East Bog in July 1997 – it is probably the most-frequently sighted dragonfly second only to *Ischnura elegans*; the broad-bodied chaser *Libellula depressa*, seen ovipositing in North Pond on 16th June 1994, just the second year for this species on the island following a number of sightings in mid-summer 1992.

Other species that have been encountered only rarely are: beautiful demoiselle *Calopteryx virgo* (2 records), hairy dragonfly *Brachytron pratense* (1), four-spot chaser *Libellula quadrimaculata* (1) and large red damselfly *Pyrrhosoma nymphula* (2), these all in the spring and early-summer; emerald damselfly *Lestes sponsa* (1), golden-ringed dragonfly *Cordulegaster boltonii* (1), common hawker *Aeshna cyanea* and emperor *Anax imperator* (numerous records, one or two annually from 1988 onward) in mid-summer; white-legged damselfly *Platycnemis pennipes* (1), azure damselfly *Coenagrion puella* (6 records, including a mating pair in August 1982), ruddy darter (2), and southern hawker *Aeshna juncea* (1) in late-summer and early-autumn; and finally migrant hawker *Aeshna mixta* (also in late-summer and early-autumn), with numerous records since the first in 1996 and perhaps reflecting the spread of this species in southern Britain (although it is known that there are often massive influxes from the continent in late-summer).

An immature male yellow-winged darter *Sympetrum flaveolum*, a vagrant from continental Europe, was captured on 29th August 1955 and now resides in the British Museum; an influx into Britain in August 1995 brought one male to Skokholm on the very same date as in 1955, whilst many were in the locality (on mainland Pembrokeshire and on neighbouring Skomer, discovered in some number at the latter by the author), part of a rare movement into Wales.

Order: Orthoptera (grasshoppers)

There are two species recorded annually, the common green grasshopper *Omocestus viridulus* and common field grasshopper *Chorthippus brunneus*. The latter seems to be restricted to open, sunny areas, whereas *O. viridulus* is widespread through areas of bracken with an understorey of ground ivy *Glechoma hederacea*, goldenrod *Solidago virgaurea* and sorrels *Rumex* spp. A third species, the striped grasshopper *Stenobothrus lineatus* was apparently recorded on 30th August 1990, a single male, but not again since. There are no known locations for this species in Wales, so the record is perhaps an error. Samples of *Chorthippus brunneus* on Skokholm have been shown to be significantly smaller than their mainland counterparts (Duncan, 1960).

Order: Mallophaga (bird lice)

Fourteen species have been recorded, including *Trabeculus aviator*, specific to Manx shearwaters, and the first British record of *Halipeurus diversus* (found on a Manx shearwater).

Order: Hemiptera (bugs)

Only aquatic "heteroptera" and the aphids and leafhoppers of the "homoptera" have received detailed attention. Note that the name heteroptera is used in two very different ways in modern classifications – it commonly appears as a suborder within Hemiptera (but has been of the rank Order), but also as a rankless (i.e. non-Linnaean) grouping of infraorders within the suborder **Prosorrhyncha** of the order Hemiptera. It is a breaking of naming convention to use the ending "-ptera" for any rank above genus other than an order - although since it is a "convention" rather than a "rule of nomenclature", taxonomists are free to violate it. However, its use does bring about an internal conflict, i.e. the order Hemiptera has a suborder named Heteroptera. The infraorders Gerromorpha and Nepomorpha contain most of the aquatic and semi-aquatic members of the suborder. The **Auchenorrhyncha** is the suborder of the Hemiptera that contains most of the members of what was traditionally known as the Homoptera – in which leafhoppers and spittlebugs are included. Another suborder, the **Sternorrhyncha**, contains the aphids (and scale insects).

Aquatic species from A. Davis (1956b) numbered fifteen species. Lesser water boatmen *Corixa punctata* and *C. distincta* were the commonest species in 1955 and have been recorded frequently in other years. In dry summers, all water may disappear from the few ponds, so recolonization must take place through immigration from the mainland.

One of the most obvious of all Skokholm insects is the European tarnished plant bug *Lygus rugulipennis*, with numerous specimens present on the flower heads of various thistles in mid-summer, typical of its association with ruderal plant communities.

Pearson (1951) used Cody-type kites with insect nets attached to them in an attempt to quantify the extent of aerial activity of insects over Skokholm, and at a height where catches would not be contaminated by the island fauna (the island fauna was sampled by using a sticky trap at a height of just over a metre). Generally conditions were too windy, although on calmer days, when the breeze was more likely to be coming from the mainland to the east and hence carry more insects, they were too light to fly the kite. However, some interesting results were obtained with aphids, where of the five species caught in the kite nets, only one was found on the island itself during a ground-survey. Pearson (1952) subsequently listed 8 species of aphid. In general, as might be expected, the degree of insect aerial activity at lower altitudes is extremely dependant upon the weather conditions prevailing at the time, and given the exposed nature of Skokholm it is perhaps a wonder that the large number of species found inhabit the site at all.

Of the leaf-hoppers and others, the Skokholm fauna is considered to be impoverished when compared to similar habitats elsewhere, with just 16 species recorded (Bowen, 1975). Studies on the distribution of various colour-morphs of a dominant species of leafhopper *Philaenus spumarius* have been carried out on the island. Stewart & Lees (1996) studied the colour/pattern polymorphism of *Philaenus spumarius* in England and Wales and refer to the island populations in terms of the stability of morph frequencies shown over a period of 10 years, but the results have yet to be published for much of the Skokholm data.

Other commonly-encountered homopterans are the leaf-hoppers *Cicadella viridis* and *Evacanthus interruptus*, both brightly coloured and immediately recognisable.

Order: Coleoptera (beetles)

Water beetles were collected by G.A. Walton (1933) in late-August. Then an intensive survey of Skokholm's coleopterous fauna was carried out in 1950 by Green *et al.* (1951). Other studies (e.g. Pearson & Wilkinson, 1952, and Green, 1956) supplemented this work, plus some collecting by the author more recently, with identifications carried out by A. Fowles of CCW. In total over 200 species have been identified, including four "Notable A" species (those found in fewer than thirty 10km squares in Britain) and 20 "Notable B" species (found in 30 - 100 of 10km squares). Many of them were found hiding beneath loose stones. The proportion of plant-eating (phytophagous) beetles was small, presumably limited by the relative sparsity of the vegetation, whereas those feeding on dung and carrion were well-represented (there was a flock of Soay sheep and numerous goats at the time of the major surveys). Representatives of these two groups are frequently seen – the minotaur beetle *Typhaeus typhoeus*, and *Aphodius ictericus*, both of which collect rabbit dung, and three of the true burying beetles, namely *Nicrophorus humator*, *N. investigator* and the "local" species *N. interruptus* on corpses of rabbits and birds (and frequently caught in light-traps put out to attract moths) – all are large and very obvious species. The flowerheads of hogweed *Heracleum sphondylium* attract many soldier beetles *Cantharis* spp. that hunt other insects that visit the flowers.

The small size of the island would make the dangers of over-collecting very real, particularly for flightless species (e.g. *Chrysomela populi* found only on a small patch of creeping willow *Salix repens*) which would be unlikely to be supported by colonization from the mainland.

Ecological studies have been carried out on a few species, for example by Green (1951), who investigated the distribution of the devil's coach-horse beetle *Staphylinus ater*. It was discovered that all records of this rove beetle were from beneath stones part-way down the cliffs, and frequently with one or other of two ground beetles, *Abax parrallelopidedus* or *Agonum ruficorne*. It was well known that *S. ater* is predominately a coastal species, but on Skokholm the restriction was extreme, with only a very narrow belt on the cliffs being occupied. Other Staphylinids were found and their distribution mapped, but no further study made into their ecology.

A number of scarce beetles have been recorded, associated with a variety of habitats. About 25 species are regarded as nationally scarce (1981), including *Trox scaber*, which is abundant in birds' nests (particularly those of the wheatear *Oenanthe oenanthe*), and the tortoise beetle *Cassida hemisphaeria*, which is found on sea campion *Silene maritima*. The 11-spot ladybird *Coccinella 11-punctata* is restricted to coastal areas in western Britain (though inland in the south-east), and has been recorded on just two occasions on Skokholm (in July 1977 and on 23rd April 1999). It is regarded as "uncommon" in Pembrokeshire. The rare 13-spot ladybird *Hippodamia tredecimpunctata* has been recorded once, on 5th July 1997, on Northern Plain, and is usually found in marshy areas. No systematic survey has ever been carried out. The 24-spot ladybird *Subcoccinella 24-punctata* has been seen on numerous occasions, usually single animals, but on occasion in large numbers e.g. July and August 1948, and has been the most frequently encountered species. The second most commonly recorded is the 7-spot ladybird *Coccinella 7-punctata* and surprisingly a find of 54 adults and 75 larvae/pupae on a small patch of bracken in South Haven on 11th August 2000 (pers. obs.) comprises the only listed breeding record.

Several local or rare invertebrates have been found on Skokholm. For example, the only Welsh records of the beetle *Graptodytes bilineatus* are found in Pembrokeshire, including on the island. A close look at the seashore occasionally reveals the ground beetle *Aepus robini*, a very small (2.5 mm) species that lives in sandstone crevices, and preys upon maritime springtails, retreating into air-filled crevices at high tide.

One particularly conspicuous species is the "celery leaf beetle" *Phaedon tumidulus*, not only because of its striking bronze colouration, but because of the occasional defoliation it brings about of the few stands of hogweed *Heracleum sphondylium* that exist on the island. A beetle less likely to be seen, but interesting because of the habitat it frequents, is *Laemostenus terricola*, which inhabits rabbit burrows on Skokholm, but is elsewhere often synanthropic in cellars and out-houses, sometimes under bark or stones, but most often in badgers' setts. The species is generally widespread but rare across Britain. The masses of sea mayweed on the coastal slopes on the island are home to the tiny "black seed weevil" *Diplapion confluens*. It bores into lower stems and rootstocks of mayweeds *Matricaria* and *Tripleurospermum*, mainly but not entirely on the British coast.

A number of female glow worms *Lampyris noctiluca* were introduced to South Haven in July 1946, transported from neighbouring Skomer Island (where there is a thriving population), but there have been no subsequent records.

Order: Trichoptera (caddis flies).

Ten species were recorded in 1955 - 56 by Fox (1957). Intensive searches were made for larvae, pupae and cases, and adults were caught by using a net or by the use of "treacle-licks" at dusk. He noted that North and South Ponds were fouled with bird excreta, and that East Pond had become covered with pond weed *Potamogeton* sp., resulting in the absence of a species of caddis fly that had previously been found there. South Haven Stream was apparently the most productive site during his searches. Static waters, often most affected by fouling by birds, were least productive. Since the survey, the number of gulls *Larus* sp. have increased substantially, and it would be worthwhile repeating the work. Various species are frequently caught in the light-traps used to sample moths, but have not been identified.

Order: Lepidoptera (butterflies and moths).

About 200 species of macrolepidoptera have been recorded on Skokholm. Notable A species (those found in fewer that thirty 10km squares in Britain) are Barrett's marbled coronet *Hadena luteago* ssp. *barretti*, black-banded *Polymixtis xanthomista* and thrift clearwing *Bembecia muscaeformis*. Notable B species (found in 30 - 100 of 10km squares) are square-spot dart *Euxoa obelisca grisea*, crescent dart *Agrotis trux lungera*, hoary footman *Eilema griseola* and marbled green *Cryphia muralis*.

Species typical of cliff vegetation on rocky western coasts include the thrift clearwing and black-banded, and species dependant on saxicolous lichens, such as the marbled green and hoary footman. Various species have their larval foodplant as campion *Silene* sp., including pod lover *Hadena perplexa* ssp. *capsophila*, and Barrett's marbled coronet. Species new to the island are recorded in most years. Others that had until recently not been recorded for many years have seemingly become re-established, as their larval foodplant has again become more widespread, for example true lover's knot *Lycophotia varia*, which feeds on heather *Calluna vulgaris*.

Loxton (1995) analysed the records of resident Lepidoptera for Skomer and Skokholm, and noted great differences between the two islands despite their close proximity to one another. He also found that the majority of species were common or unspecialized, which reflected the composition of the vegetation. The few nationally-scarce species present are not thought to be under threat from current management practises. Indeed, many habitats are unchangeable and hence beyond the need for management, e.g. sea-cliffs. In any case, conservation of island invertebrates should primarily be concerned with the maintenance of plant communities.

The most frequently encountered moth is the yellow shell *Camptogramma bilineata*, a day-flying species that inhabits the masses of bracken *Pteridium aquilinum* across the island. The most conspicuous though, by way of the action of its caterpillars in completely defoliating hogweed *Heracleum sphondylium* plants, are the *Depressaria* species. The pale, dark-spotted larvae form silk tents in which they gain a degree of protection from potential predators. The adult moths are on the wing from late-summer through to the spring, and are to be found during the winter months hiding between the pages of library books —as their name and habits would imply, they are somewhat flattened.

There are frequent "falls" of migrant moths such as silver-y *Autographa gamma* and rush veneer *Nomophila noctuella* throughout the late-summer period, following southerly or south-easterly winds. The 5-spot burnet moth *Zygaena trifolii* is common in most years, its larvae feeding on the extensive greater bird's-foot-trefoil *Lotus pedunculatus* in the marshy areas, whilst the cinnabar *Tyria jacobaeae* undergoes typical cycles of boom and bust.

Downhill (1961), Scott (1968), Lawman (1977) and Betts & Price (1995) compiled lists of the macro-moth species recorded on Skokholm. The "light-trap" was first used in 1960 and, coupled with visits to areas with flowering plants armed with a sweep-net at night, resulted in many new records beng obtained that year. Reference collections were made in 1959 - 60 by Downhill (1961), by Scott (1968) and Lawman (1977), the last of which is currently kept in the island laboratory but is in dire need of restoration. Amazingly, new species to the list are caught in most years – despite extensive trapping in 1961, seven years later 15 of the 77 species caught were firsts for the island; in addition, 7 species that had previously been recorded only rarely suddenly appeared to have established thriving populations on the island (Scott, 1968). Then in 1970 a further 23 new records of moths were obtained out of a total of 77 species, of which 7 were species caught for the first time in 1968 and 6 that had not been seen since first being recorded in 1961. However, comparisons must be made with caution, for 15 of those caught in 1970 were obtained without the light-trap (Neale, 1970). Undoubtedly there are repeated extinctions and recolonizations due to the extreme environment on Skokholm and the close proximity of the nearby mainland respectively. The cinnabar moth is a classic example of this, with many bumper years and complete defoliation of the larval foodplant (ragwort *Senecio vulgaris*) followed by years of absence. The micro-lepidoptera has been grossly under-recorded, though Smith (1951) made a special effort to survey previously-neglected orders and included it in his week-long study in June 1950; an unknown author listed 13 species that were found in September 1956.

There are no "notable" butterfly species recorded. There are resident breeding populations of small copper *Lycaena phlaeas* (two, sometimes three generations are recorded annually) and meadow brown *Maniola jurtina* (flying in late-June and throughout July), small numbers of common blue *Poliommatus icarus*, and breeding of "immigrant" species such as large white *Pieris brassicae*, small white *Artogeia rapae*, small tortoiseshell *Aglais urticae*, red admiral *Vanessa atalanta*, peacock *Inachis io* and painted lady *Cynthia cardui* recorded in most years. Others recorded in small numbers but quite frequently in the last three decades include speckled wood *Pararge aegeria*, grayling *Hipparchia semele*, ringlet *Aphantopus hyperantus*, comma *Polygonia c-album*, clouded yellow *Colias croceus*, orange tip *Anthocharis cardamines* and dark green fritillary *Mesoacidalia aglaja*, the last-named previously a fairly common breeding species (its foodplant, violets *Viola* spp. being widespread on the island) but having since met its demise through apparent over-collecting (Fowles, 1986). There is one record of silver-studded blue *Plebejus argus*, in July 1995, a single insect presumed to be carried on the wind from a breeding population on the mainland coast nearby, and identified by the author after it had been caught.

A westerly movement of large numbers of butterflies, mainly consisting of the large white *Pieris brassicae*, was monitored from Skokholm in late-August 1947 (Conder 1949b), following the first reports of large numbers passing the small island of Grassholm, some 8 miles to the west of Skokholm, on 9th August. One particularly impressive wave involved about 300 butterflies across a 20-yard front within a 10-minute period. Observations showed that butterflies did not solely go in the direction that the wind was blowing (from east to west), but mainly with the wind in the morning and against it in the afternoon (presumably having found the open sea not to their liking). Such migrations of large numbers of butterflies are rarely encountered today, undoubtedly due to habitat loss and the over-zealous and completely ridiculous use of pesticides in farming (and nowadays in public parks and even the tiniest private gardens) across Western Europe.

A butterfly transect is walked weekly from 1st April to 30th September, as part of the Institute of Terrestrial Ecology's national monitoring programme, and has been carried out since 1977. Totals for each species observed are included in Appendix X. The route was altered slightly in 1997, so that a gull colony could be avoided – it is unlikely that a recorder could have paid much attention to any butterflies in that section whilst fending off the attacks of gulls.

Brooke *et al.* (1985) studied the variation in the number of hind-wing spots on the meadow brown butterfly *Maniola jurtina* in populations of South Wales, including Skokholm. The usual situation in Britain is for males to have the spot distribution unimodal at two spots, though on Skokholm many have 3 spots. Females in South Wales were unimodal at zero spots in the east of the study area, with spotting increasing westwards and then showing virtually equal numbers of those with zero, one and two spots on Skokholm and the nearby mainland. Brakefield (1983) suggested that more highly-spotted meadow brown butterflies have high flying (and dispersal) ability, a factor that would be of use in a windy, maritime climate such as that encountered on the island, although Brooke *et al.* (1985) did not find such a relationship when studying three populations on Skokholm that were separated by areas of short, grazed open grassland known to form an obstacle to the dispersal of the butterfly (Dowdeswell, Fisher & Ford, 1949).

Order: Diptera (true flies).

F.W. Edwards (1934) collected free-living Diptera on Skokholm and identified about 60 species. Then K.G.V. Smith (1951) collected from 3rd - 9th June 1950 and identified a further 40 species new to the island list. Three main sampling techniques were utilized: 1) sweeping areas of vegetation with a net; 2) examination of flower heads; and 3) netting of specimens that were in flight. The areas supporting the most-varied fly fauna were in the mouth of a large Heligoland trap (Syrphids or hoverflies predominating), the marshes with *Juncus* sp.

(mainly Tipulids or craneflies, Asilids or robber-flies, Sciomyzids or marsh flies, and Muscids or house flies and kin) and areas of hogweed *Heracleum sphondylium* (representatives of all of those families previously listed were found, plus Empidids or robber-flies and Sphaericerids or dung flies).

Family: Syrphidae (hoverflies). These have received some attention in recent years, since the imagos are highly visible and identification is relatively straightforward, but great caution must be exercised by the newcomer to this field. Frequent studies of population structure on Skokholm have demonstrated that it is comprised of just a few fairly common, large species (for example *Eristalis tenax*) and a large number of smaller species. Nectar plants available to these flies are few, though ragwort *Senecio jacobaea* produces flowers profusely in some years (its distribution changes dramatically), and goldenrod *Solidago virgaurea* is becoming more widespread in the east, both of which flower primarily in July and August. A feature of the Syrphidae in general is that they resemble various bees and wasps in their colour patterns and body shape. A striking degree of polymorphism has been observed in *Eristalis tenax*, the "drone fly", a species which has one morph that is said to mimic the hive bee drone. On Skokholm, there are no hive bees, so the mimic presumably has little or no advantage as an anti-predation measure. The success of this morph of *E. tenax* would therefore suggest that there is little in the way of predatory pressure on the island population.

In late-summer of most years there seems to be a large influx of migrant hoverflies, coinciding with the arrival of migratory butterflies from southern Europe, such as clouded yellow and painted lady. In addition, local movements are undoubtedly made as the result of windy conditions – a species known to have its larval stage feed exclusively on cow dung, *Rhingia campestris*, has been recorded on the island on two occasions (both in July 1998), and is known to exist on the nearby mainland where cattle graze extensively.

The familiar aquatic but air-breathing larvae of some species and known as "rat-tailed maggots" are numerous in the oxygen-deficient waters of stagnant pools.

Family: Hippoboscidae (louse-flies or flat-flies). These are flattened blood-sucking parasites of birds and mammals. *Ornithomyia fringillina*, a species recorded on Skokholm on numerous occasions, has been the subject of a study on Fair Isle (Corbet, 1956). It is known to parasitize numerous passerine birds that breed on Skokholm. Stansfield (1954) made a qualitative study by examining every bird that had been caught for ringing purposes. The majority of birds caught were the first broods of the pipits and wheatears, giving rise to considerable numbers of flat-flies (all but one of which were *O. fringillina*, the other being *O. avicularia*) and fleas. The survey was repeated in the following year (Stansfield, 1955) to ascertain whether there was any variation in the infestation of birds in successive years. Numbers were broadly similar, and all records were of *O. fringillina*.

Family: Tipulidae (craneflies). These are the familiar long-legged flies commonly known as "daddy-long-legs" (as are harvest-spiders Opiliones and Pholcid spiders). The larvae feed as scavengers in soil or decaying organic matter, including in water, and are a favoured food of choughs (Meyer *et al.*, 1994). The adults of various species are on the wing throughout the summer and autumn, but particularly so during the latter part of the year, with the commonest species being *Tipula paludosa*, of which very many thousands can be flying at one time (pers. obs.). The cranefly *Limonia (Geranomyia) unicolor* is believed to breed in lichens on rocky coasts, and is locally frequent on the coast around Britain, and found on Skokholm. The beautiful orange and black cranefly *Ptychoptera albimana* is a small species, found on muddy margins of ponds and streams, mainly in late-summer. *Dicranomyia chorea* is a common cranefly found in the vicinity of damp grassland on Skokholm. It has been seen forming mating swarms before sunrise and sunset near the Well Pool in August – large numbers of males gyrate and dance, females enter the swarm and the mated pairs drop to the ground (all pers. obs.).

Family: Tabaniidae (horse-flies). The cleg-fly *Haematopota pluvialis* is widespread on the island throughout the summer, much to the discomfort of the island's human visitors (and its rabbits!), particularly on hot, breezeless days.

Family: Calliphoridae (blow-flies). Another family with a number of highly-visible species, particularly the various green- and blue-bottle flies. They are particularly common during midsummer on the flowerheads of ragwort and hogweed, and throughout the autumn, when they can be thousands strong on the sunny walls of the observatory buildings (when they form the bulk of the diet of migrant flycatchers, warblers and other birds).

Family: Dolichopododae (long-headed flies). The Dolichopodid *Aphrosylus celtiber* is a "local" fly of rocky-shores, where the larvae predate barnacles.

Family: Tephritidae (picture-winged flies). *Acanthiophilus helainthi* is associated with species of thistle of the family Cardueae. It is very rare and recently recorded only from Hampshire, Kent, London and Pembroke. The Skokholm record is an old one, alongside those from the Isle of Wight and Dorset.

Family: Sciomyzidae (marsh flies). Pupae of the snail-killing fly *Colobaea punctata* have been found in shells of *Lymnaea peregra*, *Planorbis corneus* and *P. planorbis*, whilst adults have been found next to drying-out ponds and ditches on Skokholm. There are just scattered British records, all in England and Wales.

Family: Sphaeroceridae (dung flies). The lesser dung fly *Copromyza equina* is found nationally on the dung of horse, sheep, cow, and dog, but on rabbit dung on Skokholm, also on carrion and compost heaps.

Order: Siphonaptera (fleas).

The flea fauna of West Wales has been little studied, but this is not the case on Skokholm, mainly due to the long-term bird-ringing programme, but those of mice and rabbits have also been ascertained. Six species have been found on birds and another in bird nests (nest samples made within 24 hours of their desertion by the fledgling birds). The first British record of the "stick-tight" flea *Echidnophaga gallinaceus* was found on a female white wagtail *Motacilla alba alba* (Thompson, 1952). Not strictly a bird flea, it is recorded from numerous wild and domestic mammals and man, commonly in tropical and subtropical regions of the Old World, so it was thought unlikely that it would become established in the country. The flea *Ceratophyllus borealis* was identified by Thompson (1951) following its discovery in the nests of wheatears *Oenanthe oenanthe* – the flea's apparent preferred host – on Skokholm. The pupae of the flea overwinter in the old nests and adults emerge to coincide with the return of the birds in springtime. It is interesting to note that only a small number of fleas were present at the time of young leaving the nest compared to those subsequently bred from the nest material by Thompson (1954).

Systematic checking of birds for fleas was carried out by Stansfield (1957) during the period April to October in 1954 and 1955, using "the Fair Isle apparatus", where chloroform was passed through the birds' feathers and caused parasites to drop out. In addition, nests were taken within 24 hours of the fledglings leaving them. As in

1951, *C. borealis* was found to be particularly common on the wheatear *Oenanthe oenanthe,* whereas a similar species, *C. gallinae* was only found on two non-resident birds (ascertained from the date of capture) and was clearly not an established species on Skokholm, whereas on Fair Isle both fleas were common. Both are strongly associated with the nests of their hosts, reinfesting the birds as they return to their nest-sites each spring. Stansfield surmised that the difference in the status of *C. gallinae* was due to the difference in the population of starlings *Sturnus vulgaris* – the main host of *C. gallinae* – on the two islands. On Fair Isle in 1955 there were about 100 breeding pairs of starlings, whereas Skokholm had just five. Another flea, *Dasypsyllus gallinulae* – common on wheatears on Fair Isle but only recorded twice on migrant birds passing through Skokholm – is not a "nest species" but rather a body species. It was clearly not present amongst the Skokholm breeding population of wheatears, and Stansfield suggested that it was the blackbird *Turdus merula* migration that occurs only on Fair Isle (that is, not seen on Skokholm) that results in their presence, since the flea was commonly found on them. Of course, Bird Observatories can today be extremely useful in the study of Britain's flea fauna due to the systematic trapping of birds that takes place.

The Manx shearwater *Puffinus puffinus* has a host-specific flea in the form of *Ornithopsylla laetitiae,* and this was found in a number of nests that were examined. The same flea was found once on a rabbit *Oryctolagus cuniculi,* though this would not be entirely unexpected given the competition for (and even sharing of) burrows between rabbits and the shearwaters. It has an interesting evolutionary aspect, being a rare example of a bird-parasite belonging to a family of mammal fleas having evolved from a rabbit flea.

Three other species of flea have been found, all on house mice (R.A. Davis, 1957a), namely *Ctenopthalamus nobilis, Nosopsyllus fasciatus* and *Hystricopsylla talpae* (the mole flea). The rabbit flea *Spilopsyllus cuniculi,* the vector for the *Myxomatosis cuniculi* virus, has not been found on Skokholm, despite intensive investigations by Stansfield (1957), and later by Betts (1988) when the disease was discovered on the island (see pages 91 - 92) . This is somewhat surprising given the presence of breeding buzzards *Buteo buteo* that undoubtedly make occasional trips to the nearby mainland.

Order: Hymenoptera (bees, wasps, ants).

Suborder Symphyta (sawflies)

There are just two definite records of sawflies on Skokholm. This is probably a group of insects that has been overlooked.

Suborder Apocrita (bees, wasps, ants); section Aculeata.

The most obvious sign of a member of this family is the presence of the "lighthouse gall", found on ground ivy *Glechoma hederacea*, and caused by larvae of the gall-midge *Dasyneura glechomae*.

Family: Apidae (bees).

Bees were collected to allow a check for acarine infestation and nosema infection in 1950. No infected animals were found.

[Acarine is an infestation by the mite *Acarapis woodi*. The life of an infected bee is shortened, though it usually has little effect in the active season. The mite is passed on from old bees to very young ones. A severe winter may cause an infected colony to dwindle in the spring. Nosema infection is caused by *Nosema apis*, a spore-forming protozoan. The protozoa multiply in the ventriculus and malpighian tubules (30 - 50 million spores) and impair the digestion of pollen, thereby shortening the life of the bee. The spores are excreted by the bee. Confirmation of nosema is by microscopic examination (400x): 30 bees are crushed in water and a droplet is examined for white, rice-shaped bodies.]

A.E. Brown (1975) investigated community structure of bumblebees and cuckoo bees. Various habitats that possessed a large number of flowering plants were sampled, and five species of bumblebee recorded (plus two cuckoo bees). Two species were far more common than the others, namely *Bombus lucorum* and *B. terrestris*. A check on the seminal receptacles of the queens of both species established that *B. lucorum* emerged from hibernation earlier than *B. terrestris*. Most workers were found taking nectar from heather *Calluna vulgaris* flowers, a plant with a long corolla tube, whereas drones were found on "daisy" flowers (Compositae). Judging from the number of individuals caught, and knowing the number that one nest would contain on average, Brown estimated that between 15 and 25 nests were present on the island.

Family: Chrysididae (ruby-tailed wasps)

There is currently much debate about the taxonomy of the ruby-tailed wasp *Chrysis ignita*, but nevertheless, an inability to put a correct name to one does not detract from its incredible beauty. Splendidly-coloured metallic blue-green on the thorax and, as their name implies, ruby-red on the abdomen, they are seen annually on Skokholm if the time is taken to sit on a sun-drenched rocky slope where they may be found seeking the nests of various mason bees, which they parasitise.

Family: Formicidae (ants)

Six species of ant have been recorded on Skokholm. The undertaking of their nuptial flights in late-summer brings about a feeding frenzy amongst the gulls and corvids, and causes great discomfort to human visitors.

Lasius flavus, the yellow meadow ant, is a common species, and the high density of large nests in some areas on Skokholm indicates long-undisturbed grassland.

Lasius alienus appears to require bare ground to provide warm enough conditions in Britain so it is generally associated with early successional stages on heathland, and rabbit-grazed turf on Skokholm. Nests are single-queened and mating swarms occur in August. This species has recently been reassessed and split into two species, the other being *Lasius psammophilus*. This means that the Skokholm records now need reassessing.

[In 1992, Seifert published details of the revision splitting *L. alienus* into *L. alienus* (sensuo stricto) and *L. psammophilus*. All previous records can now only be given the status *sensuo lato*. The pair is difficult to separate morphologically and useful keys have been produced by Blacker & Collingwood (2002) and Czechowski et al. (2002). A useful starting point for identification is the habitat from which ants are collected. *L. alienus* seems to favour dry, sparse grassland where there will be minimal competition from *L. flavus* and *Myrmica* species and *L. psammophilus* will be located in acid heathland. Both habitats exist on Skokholm, and it might be that both species will be identified.]

Myrmica scabrinodis tends to hunt in short vegetation on or near the ground, and it also removes the flesh from the carcasses of dead birds and mammals, which are widespread on the island. Unlike many ants, a large number of workers remain active on the surface during cold weather and even in winter. Each nest usually contains two or three queens and mating flights occur during August.

The turf ant *Tetramorium caespitum* is a particularly small but robust black ant, with a local distribution in Britain. Despite their diminutive size, the workers have a surprisingly powerful bite when disturbed (pers. obs.).

The small black ant *Lasius niger* inhabits grassland where there are stones of the mounds of *Lasius flavus*. However, this species too has undergone revision by Seifert (1992), as with *L. alienus* (above), into *L. niger* (sensuo stricto – s.s.) and *L. platythorax*. All previous records can now only be given the status sensuo lato (s.l.). The pair is difficult to separate morphologically and again, valuable keys are provided by Blacker and Collingwood (2002) and Czechowski *et al.* (2002). *L. niger* prefers relatively-dry situations in grassland or under stones and slabs in gardens whilst *L. platythorax* is found in wet, boggy places.

Lasius mixtus is a nest-parasitic ant, the queen invading nests of *Lasius niger* and *L. alienus* and eventually replacing the entire colony. It is widely distributed in Britain, but very local. It is almost completely subterranean, so easily overlooked unless nests are investigated.

Williamson (1949) studied the distribution of some ants and discovered that the "ant community" consists of species that overlap little in their habitat, with *Tetramorium caespitum* beneath stones on cliff edges, with sea campion; *Lasius alienus* only on the cliffs; *L. niger* on rabbit-grazed turf, along with *L. flavus* (this, the famous "mound-building ant", generally nests beneath stones on Skokholm). *Myrmica scabrinodis* was not studied.

Family: Andrenidae

Solitary mining bees frequent south-facing slopes with shallow soils, and also the lime mortar of the old walls in the proximity of the farm buildings and of the lime-kiln. *Andrena nigroaenea* is one of the first to be found on the wing in the spring, nesting in shallow, bare soils on sunny south-facing slopes. Individuals visit a wide range of flowers, with ground ivy *Glechoma hederacea* being the commonest plant in flower then (April), but the bees also seem to show a liking for the few dandelions *Taraxacum* spp. present in the Skokholm garden (pers. obs.).

Family: Halictidae

Sphecodes monilicornis is a solitary bee listed in the published Red Data Book as "rare". It is kleptoparasitic on other bees, laying its eggs in their nests. *Lasioglossum fulvicorne* and *L. fratellum* have been recorded as hosts elsewhere (not yet recorded on Skokholm), but other *Lasioglossum* species, namely *L. albipes* and *L. smeathmanellum* (status unknown in Britain) have both been found in recent searches by the author (in 2003). There is a large population of *L. smeathmanellum* in The Quarry, home to various other solitary bees.

Family: Eumenidae

The mason wasp *Ancistrocerus scoticus* is a locally-common species known to build its cells on rocks. Usual prey-items are small caterpillars, but it has also been found on chrysomelid beetle larvae. It is found throughout the UK, but is commoner in the north and west and especially by the sea.

Family: Anthophoridae

Gooden's nomad bee *Nomada goodeniana* is splendid in its yellow and black attire, and is easily mistaken for a wasp. It is kleptoparasitic on the very common mining bee *Andrena nigroaenea* and has been observed in mating swarms in late-April, most commonly at the top of North Haven where they nest in a sandy and stony bank (pers. obs.).

Family: Vespidae (Social Wasps)

Amazingly, there is just a single record of the common wasp *Vespula vulgaris*, of a single dead animal found by the author on a cliff-top. The only other social wasp recorded is the tree wasp *Dolichovespula sylvestris*, of which there are few, widely-scattered records, but were numerous in July 1995 (pers. obs.) feeding on flowers of figwort *Scrophularia nodosa* in the vicinity of the observatory buildings.

Order Hymenoptera; Sub-order Apocrita; section Parasitica.

Family: Ichneumonidae

This huge family of parasitic wasps requires expert knowledge to enable proper identification. Various specimens were collected by the author (mainly from ruderal vegetation) in the summer of 2003, and very kindly identified by Dr. M. Shaw, Keeper of Geology & Zoology for the National Museums of Scotland. Numerous other species are listed on the island record cards (1950's), but some of them have been untraceable in modern literature. The most obvious species in recent years has been *Enicospilus ramidulus*, a large, orange-yellow insect, which was frequently observed searching amongst the fronds of bracken *Pteridium aquilinum* for an unidentified prey species. *Diplazon laetatorius* is a handsome insect, its body black with yellow markings, its legs red with white bands. It is an oligophagous parasite of hoverfly larvae and has been reared from *Episyrphus balteatus*, *Sphaerophoria* spp, *Melanostoma* spp. and *Metasyrphus corollae*, laying its own eggs into the host eggs or young larvae. *Pimpla hypochondriaca* is very common in Britain, especially in hedgerows, gardens and similar situations, and widely-distributed in the British Isles. It attacks the naked or cocooned pupae of butterflies that settle above ground, particularly on tall vegetation, bushes, fences, and so on, and hence is frequently found in the vicinity of the cabbage patch in the Skokholm garden where "cabbage white" butterflies *Pieris* spp. abound.

Chapter 4: Factors that may affect the Features – an overview

Introduction

The island's ecology – how the species interact with each other – is still quite a mystery in most respects, apart from with the more obvious "feature" species. The interactions of the major factors (physical and biological) with these features have been well documented, some already mentioned in the species sections, and these are further explained below.

Section 1: Internal natural factors and environmental relationships

These factors are many, from climate, weather, soils and hydrology to degree of exposure, grazing by rabbits, burrowing and manuring by both birds and rabbits, and so on. Past human land-use will also have had a significant effect.

a) Habitats and plant communities

There are various biotic and physical factors that have the potential to affect each of the features. These have been studied in some detail by Gillham (1954 - 56) and Goodman & Gillham (1954), their findings published in a series of papers titled "The Ecology of the Pembrokeshire Islands", covering in particular the main environmental factors which influence Skokholm as a plant habitat. Work included the following topics:

1.   The effects of grazing by rabbits;
2.   The effects of trampling and burrowing by birds and animals;
3.   Manuring by birds and animals.

A summary of these factors, with updates where necessary, now follows.

1. <u>The effect of grazing by rabbits *Oryctolgus cuniculus*</u>.

Skokholm is home to up to an estimated 10,000 rabbits, since their introduction sometime in the late 12th Century when their fur and meat was of considerable economic importance (Stanbury, 1997). For years their distribution would have been restricted by stone-lined earth banks to prevent them from damaging the island's agricultural fields, but they were probably set free by rabbiters in order to encourage them to multiply (when a period of farming had come to an end). They would then have begun to have a great influence over the island's vegetation. Despite some determined attempts since then to destroy them, they remain a dominant factor that continues to shape the ecology of the island today.

Gillham (1955) demonstrated that grazing by rabbits was the dominant biotic factor in deciding the composition of the vegetation. She did this by preventing rabbits from entering areas of thrift *Armeria maritima* (the "Armerietum"). Within a few months to several years, a tall growth of red fescue grass *Festuca rubra* (a Festucetum) developed similar to that found on the nearby ungrazed island of Grassholm. The fescue is regarded as a "non-aggressive species", yet it was able to overgrow the thrift. Gillham surmised that in such exposed positions, grazing was a "deflecting factor", i.e. that the Armerietum was a biotically-induced plagioclimax and that the climatic climax vegetation-type, the Festucetum, was unable to develop. The rate of growth of the fescue was shown to be dependent upon the presence of suitable germination niches for grass seeds, its spread being far greater if new propagules were present.

Results along similar lines, but on a far-greater scale, resulted from Lockley's attempts to wipe out rabbits on Skokholm in 1939 - 40. The use of "cyanogas" removed practically the entire population, and the Armerietum of The Neck (a low-lying, fairly sheltered area at the eastern end of the island, of area 15 acres) began to degenerate – being overrun by those species that were able to flourish with the removal of grazing pressure.

Calluna vulgaris heath was once widespread in relatively-sheltered parts of the island (Goodman & Gillham, 1954). The plants were probably the remnants of the community that found the formerly-cultivated area – denuded of nutrients – to their liking at the end of the 19th Century. Various growth-forms occurred, depending on the degree of exposure and the grazing-pressure. Invasion by bracken was noted, but this would probably have been a cyclical event, as described by Watt (1955, in Ninnes, 1998). In recent years, however, there has been a steep decline in the amount of *Calluna*. The classic signs of grazing damage were noted on otherwise-flourishing heather plants in 1977, but they subsequently went into decline. Gynn (1985) noted that following the removal of goats in 1981, heather seedlings were found, but did not become established (probably due to grazing by rabbits – pers. obs.). She also suggested that storm-force winds and associated salt-spray might have killed the already-weakened plants, though many of them might simply have reached senescence.

Today, rabbit exclosures still provide excellent examples of how the vegetation develops without grazing.

2. The effects of trampling and burrowing by birds and animals

In addition to accommodating up to 10,000 rabbits, Skokholm is the breeding ground of an estimated 50,000 pairs of seabirds, the vast majority of which are burrow-nesting. The island is only 100 ha in size, so trampling of vegetation and digging into the soil are major factors affecting the vegetation.

Trampling has been shown by Gillham (1956b) to restrict or eliminate many species of plant of the coastal grassland, particularly in areas around the entrances to the burrows of puffins and Manx shearwaters and around the larger rabbit warrens. Tall-growing species have their meristematic regions exposed and thus easily damaged, so plants with a creeping habit or a rosette growth-form are more likely to survive. The effect is very similar to grazing. However, annual species are best-adapted, for example autumn and winter annuals such as mouse-ears *Cerastium* spp., chickweeds *Stellaria* sp., and annual meadow grass *Poa annua*. These are successful in the regions of the bird colonies, since they are able to germinate, grow and set seed whilst the birds are away at sea.

Trampling prevents the growth of bracken on footpaths, and in gull colonies areas are opened up as a result of bird activities, particularly in the vicinity of nests of pairs that successfully raise young, since the adults remain at the site for longer than those pairs that fail to reproduce, and the chicks put even more pressure on the plants.

Burrowing is of major importance in the initiation of soil erosion. In some areas there does seem to be a great loss of material, particularly on cliff-top slopes. Excavation of burrows was shown by Gillham (1956b) to continue throughout the birds' breeding season at least, with neighbouring plants frequently being smothered by ejecta, but with the fresh earth also initiating a vast number of small secondary plant successions as seeds germinated. Plant roots are also affected by the burrowing, as they become exposed to the air and light; anchorage to the soil is lost, further accentuating erosion. Drainage is also increased, and so in the most exposed areas deep-rooted plants such as sorrels *Rumex acetosa* and *R. acetosella* and thrift *Armeria maritima* predominate, better able to escape the drought conditions in the surface layers of the soil, as well as being better anchored against disturbance by the digging activities of animals and birds.

Wholesale burrowing into areas of thrift accentuates their typical hummocky nature. The disintegrating remains of dead plants situated between the living ones is excavated far more easily than the fibrous roots of the plants themselves, which leads to the formation of open channels between the individual hummocks. Displaced earth is thrown or blown up onto the tops of the *Armeria* and results in the further raising of that level. Burrows are formed within the tussocks, then undermining of the hummock eventually results in its collapse. Regeneration of the *Armeria* takes place as young plants become established between the old ones. In non-burrowed areas, the *Armeria* forms a flat or slightly-undulating turf, where the boundaries of the individual plants are not apparent (Gillham, 1956b).

There is concern about the stability of soil in areas where there is a high density of burrows and hence little vegetation to bind the soil, particularly on cliff-top slopes, although recent wet summers have encouraged some plant-growth in these areas and so monitoring continues by way of fixed-point photography (Warden's Annual Report, 1998). This could be an entirely natural sequence of events. It has been suggested that sea campion *Silene uniflora* seedlings could be planted in these areas to help bind the soil. Trampling has also been shown to bring about consolidation of some types of soils (Norman, 1970), and was even proposed on Skokholm, but this would hardly be of benefit to Manx shearwaters, at least not in the short-term for the nest burrows would be destroyed – it was for this reason that the author initiated the fixed-point photography, to demonstrate that such areas were not destined to become devoid of all soil. Between 1996 and 1999, many areas of bare soil on cliff-slopes were colonised by *Matricaria maritima*, possibly encouraged by relatively-wet summers. Subsequently, *Silene uniflora* also seems to have gained a foothold (pers. obs.).

3.   Manuring and regurgitations

On the whole, manuring is diffuse and less-important than grazing in shaping the vegetation on Skokholm. However, in localised areas, for example where seabirds nest colonially, or in roosts, the levels of guano have a significant part to play. Bird droppings are rich in "plant nutrients" (nitrates, phosphates, and others), and in addition to these there are concentrations of pellets regurgitated from the crops of gulls that contain indigestible remains of food items in the form of bones, fur, feathers, shells and plant-remains (and containing viable seeds of weed species – see below). Of course, not all plants can tolerate these nutrients in the high levels encountered, and in some areas angiosperms are completely eliminated, but they are stimulatory in moderate amounts – nitrophilous plants such as chickweed *Stellaria holostea* can become dominant (Gillham, 1956c). This is not always obvious except on the ungrazed, untrodden and unburrowed cliff-slopes to which nutrients sometimes drain, where buck's-horn plantain *Plantago coronopus* is the most characteristic nitrophile. In slightly more-favourable environments, where trampling is less severe, sea campion *Silene uniflora* typically dominates. Following the birds' departure and the dying-back of bracken in the early-autumn, non-flowering *Rumex acetosa* and ground ivy *Glechoma hederacea* produce large, fleshy foliage, this often being interspersed with chickweed *Stellaria media*, and most noticeable on the main trackway between South Haven and Crab Bay (pers. obs.).

In the case of lichens, communities become simplified or even eliminated where manuring is intense, although some species seem to benefit (Fletcher, 1997). Rabbit pellets are probably of little-importance to the levels of soil nutrients except in non-organic cliff soils newly exposed by erosion.

The defaecation habits of different seabird species vary. Areas most-affected in the gull-colonies are the feeding, preening and observation areas (which are often rock-outcrops), with defaecation in the immediate vicinity of the nest being less. With the puffin *Fratercula arctica* there are three main areas: 1) in the communal "standing ground" along the cliff-edge; 2) outside the burrow entrances; and 3) latrines situated within each burrow. Gillham (1956c) investigated the last of the aforementioned three, and it became obvious that the chamber could be located from the surface above by observation of the overlying vegetation, generally consisting of an unusually dark-green clump of sorrels *Rumex acetosa* and *R. acetosella*. These deep-rooted nitrophiles were obviously greatly-stimulated in those regions. Bluebells *Hyacinthoides non-scriptus* are also greatly-stimulated by guano and robust plants grow where manuring is at suitable levels. Grasses are also encouraged to grow, but since rabbits graze these they cannot dominate and are unable to suppress bluebell growth.

During periods of drought, many plants are likely to suffer in areas with high levels of nutrient-rich bird guano, particularly in the vicinity of the inland bird colonies. Gillham (1956c) observed the effects during the dry summer of 1949, when mesophytic species in the region of an inland gull colony were replaced by salt-loving species more typical of the cliffs. Bracken was unaffected, probably due to it possessing a deep root system. It was suggested that the capacity that enables plants of the cliff-edges to grow in saline soils also enables them to withstand high concentrations of nitrate and phosphate in the soil.

There has been a general loss of the amount of "marshy grassland" dominated by purple moor-grass *Molinia caerulea*, and this has been attributed to the drop in acidity due to manuring by gulls. Water-quality, also affected, is important too. In addition, gulls in roosts in places other than the nesting areas have probably been responsible for a change from *Festuca rubra* to *Agrostis capillaris*, through soil-enrichment. Conversely, the decline of *Holcus lanatus* in dry grassland and its replacement by *Festuca* and *Agrostis* is consistent with an assumed impoverishment of the soils since agricultural activity ceased.

Gillham (1952) studied the distribution of seeds by gulls. Regurgitated "corn pellets" were composed chiefly of the indigestible remains of oat *Avena sativa* and barley *Hordeum vulgare*, mainly only the chaff, and were found from May - November. However, in August of that year, the majority of pellets found contained viable seed (as a test, these were sown and did germinate in 9 days). Gillham found many oat and barley seedlings within rock crevices, which went on to form mature flowering plants the following summer, and this still continues today, with cereals and even tomato *Lycopersicon esculentum* found (pers. obs.). Other pellets in 1952 were found to contain the seeds of various other plants, typically "weed" species, which included the now "nationally-scarce" corn spurrey *Spergularia arvensis*. Also contained were the remains of beetles and other insects, but it was unclear if the birds had been primarily foraging for these animals and had incidentally picked up bits of plants and seeds that they could not digest or *vice versa*.

There is a tendency towards a zonation of communities depending on their tolerance to wind and salty sea-spray. For example, the Pteridietum, dominated by bracken *Pteridium aquilinum*, occurs in three main situations (Goodman & Gillham, 1954; Ninnes, 1998):

- Long-established stands in deep soils of the sheltered south-eastern side of the island.
- Where it has recently invaded and replaced moribund *Calluna vulgaris* heath, again in sheltered areas in the east.
- As sparse stands with fluctuating cover extending to the limits of its edaphic and climatic tolerances towards the western end of the island.

This distribution clearly demonstrates the negative impact of salt-spray upon bracken.

Bracken is highly associated with bluebells, on both Skokholm and Skomer, and these are of great interest. Ecologically speaking, the bracken effectively acts as a shade-giving woodland canopy, preventing the growth of other competitors to the bluebells, thus the asynchronous phenologies of the two species allow them to occupy the same piece of ground, the bluebells flowering just before the bracken erupts.

b) Species and assemblages

<u>Biotic factors affecting, or which have the potential to affect, feature species and assemblages</u>

There is currently no threat to the nesting seabirds from mammalian ground-predators (they are absent). The accidental introduction of any of these could decimate the bird population, and is perhaps potentially the most significant threat to breeding seabirds, so vigilant management programmes must be employed on those islands which are currently unaffected, in particular with regard to the transportation to the island of materials by boat (Dale Sailing Co. and THLS) and helicopter (THLS). The unofficial berthing of private boats carries a very real threat also. Removal programmes have commenced and even succeeded (after much effort) on some of the Welsh islands (e.g. rats on Ramsey). The impact of introduced mammalian predators on seabirds is reviewed by Burger & Gochfeld (1994).

Intra- and inter-specific predation is commonplace, particularly involving gulls. Great black-backed gulls are also significant predators of Manx shearwaters and occasionally of storm petrels, but this is (currently) accepted. This gull also preys upon rabbits. Some lesser black-backed and herring gulls carry out kleptoparasitism on puffins, seeming to specialise in this activity for the whole of the puffin chick-rearing period. A reduction in gull numbers may be to the advantage of breeding waders and auks. Predation of storm petrels by little owls *Athene noctua* and short-eared owl *Asio flammeus* has been significant in the past, but there are currently no owls breeding on Skokholm. They are both, however, breeding species on Skomer.

Any reduction in the level of grazing by rabbits would be likely to reduce nesting opportunities for species such as oystercatcher. In addition, foraging for invertebrates by choughs would be severely hampered. On the other hand, *Calluna* heath would benefit (see above). From time to time there has been discussion about making the 15 ha of The Neck rabbit-free in order to study this to a greater degree. This could have significant effects upon breeding puffins and shearwaters, and on some flowering plants. Invertebrates inhabiting this area might include rare species (the purse-web spider *Atypus affinis* is present there), so necessitating detailed survey prior to any decision being made. It would surely be better not to interfere with it at all.

Competition for burrows between Manx shearwaters and puffins has been studied on Skomer (Ashcroft, 1976; Davidson, 1994). A count of burrows on Skokholm, followed by tape-playback to estimate shearwater numbers, and a subjective view of puffin distribution would indicate that there is little competition for burrows between these species on the island, since the majority of shearwaters are found further inland.

A decline in rabbit numbers might be deleterious for these burrow-nesting birds, particularly Manx shearwater.

Physical factors with an affect, or the potential to affect, the feature species and assemblages

The fact that Skokholm is an island means that it is sufficiently isolated from the mainland (by way of a physical barrier, the sea) to prevent colonization by mammalian ground-predators. Conversely, some rare species which are present on the island but not on the nearby mainland are unlikely to be able to spread there, e.g. three-lobed crowfoot *Ranunculus tripartitus*, even if suitable habitat existed. It is similarly so with many invertebrates. Other than seabirds, there are few birds that do not also occur on the nearby mainland. Skokholm's populations of these species can therefore be considered as units of "metapopulations" within the locality (Loxton & Jones, 1995 and 1996).

The differential erosion of the cliffs by the sea (caused by geological differences, degree of exposure to large waves, and so on) around the island's coastline means that some areas are more suitable than others for the various seabirds to nest on. Ancient rockfalls have given rise to suitable nesting areas for storm petrels, but these could be just as easily lost again due to further collapses of the cliffs above.

Section 2: Internal human-induced factors

It has been suggested that the wildlife habitats on the Welsh islands are cultural formations, shaped by occupation by people over the last 12,000 years (Arnold, 1997). Rabbit-hunting and egg-collecting were commonplace in the recent past, to varying degrees, and these must have had some effect on the gull populations in particular, albeit in the short-term. Grazing too was extensive, with sheep and goats present, but at these times rabbit numbers were kept down by hunting. Certain lichens have benefited from the removal of a flock of goats in 1981, but sea campion – a favoured food of the goats (and of Caroline the cow in 1946, see Fursdon, 1983) – might have increased to the detriment of thrift (Ninnes, 1998).

Active management

Given that the site is a SSSI, there should be no deliberate management or intervention without the agreement of CCW. There is also a management plan that has been in existence and followed since 1980, and which has recently been completely overhauled and installed on the new computer programme Countryside Management System (CMS) developed for all SSSIs by CCW, which will allow for easy access to all of the required information and ease of reporting. The National Park authority regulates any building works. The very presence of people on the island, necessary to manage it as a nature reserve, means that time and financial resources are required, and that a degree of disturbance is inevitable.

There are potential conflicts from some management. For example, spraying of bracken with the herbicide asulam may bring about damage to other ferns, grasses, herbs and lichens. Flightless gull chicks are present when the spraying is carried out in July and August, but the low toxicity of the chemical means that it is unlikely to harm them. A worker walking across the fragile terrain with a large weight of liquid in a knapsack-sprayer leads to collapses of burrow roofs and birds being killed underfoot. Asulam itself can severely check the growth of Yorkshire fog *Holcus lanatus*, and temporarily affect bent grasses *Agrostis* spp. In addition, plantains *Plantago* spp. and docks *Rumex* spp. are deleteriously affected by the chemical. Any significant increase in the destruction of bracken could threaten lesser black-backed gull breeding success and distribution (this was recently used on a limited basis to control the distribution of gulls near to human habitation).

Gull nest-counting involves traversing the area of the colony on foot, using a line of people (up to 15 have been used – the more counters involved, the faster the task is completed). This causes a variable amount of damage to shearwater burrows, depending upon the weight and agility of the individual counters, and frequently results in birds being killed underfoot (pers. obs.). Since 1996, areas known to be fragile have been counted using a method developed on Skomer Island and adapted by the Skokholm Warden (Thompson, 1996a). Over the years, the effect of trampling is likely to have been significant. In addition to counting gulls, ringing activities prior to 1976 involved large numbers of people walking across the main colony of shearwaters in order to catch fledglings, and much damage was caused as burrows were destroyed underfoot (Lawman, 2000; and personal communications with visitors who were involved).

Until recently, many of the island's lesser black-backed gull nests were raked, i.e. eggs and nests destroyed. The effect was to contain the population in a few well-defined areas. In addition, the reduction in productivity undoubtedly resulted in less inter- and intra-specific predation, with fewer chicks to be fed.

Human visitors

Visitor access is controlled on Skokholm. There is a system of compulsory footpaths and visitor numbers are restricted to 15 at any one time (though for some years prior to and including 2000, up to 30 day-visitors were given a guided tour on Mondays between June and mid-August, though due to rough seas many did not take place). Some seabird species are particularly sensitive to disturbance by people situated on land or sea. For example, guillemots will leave their ledges in a panic if they are surprised, or not used to seeing people at all, i.e. at those sites well away from footpaths where people should not be, or boats at the foot of a nesting cliff (pers. obs.). If guillemots are forced to leave their nests, the eggs and chicks can be lost as they are dragged off the ledges by the fleeing adults, or are taken by predators (pers. obs.). Puffins may also desert their burrows if disturbed during incubation. Predation can also be exacerbated during even the briefest period of disturbance (e.g. wader chicks by corvids/gulls). The path system has been designed accordingly, but undoubtedly leaves some birds vulnerable, e.g. those oystercatchers with territories that are crossed by paths.

Grey seals show worried reactions to the sight and/or sound of people walking the cliff-top paths on Skokholm at all times of year, a factor that is probably most worrying during the pupping season, but must also result in the animals being injured at any time of year in their panic to reach the safety of the water.

Some of the human visitors to Skokholm wish to put greater demands upon the water supply, by installing showers to allow bathing. Freshwater issues forth from a number of freshwater springs located on a fault-line orientated approximately N - S from Orchid Bog to Crab Bay. A few ponds have been excavated on the spring line, providing a range of habitats, and one spring is already tapped for drinking and cooking, as it has been for many years. Further abstraction of water from this very-limited supply would necessitate damming of other streams, and they would dry-up far sooner than they may otherwise do in the summer months. The waterfalls formed undoubtedly contain a flora and fauna found nowhere else on the island. The island's hydrology may also be fundamentally altered by further tinkering with the delicate balance.

Trinity House Lighthouse Service (THLS)

Although the lighthouse is automatic (unmanned since the mid-1980's), there are frequent visits by THLS staff-members or contractors carrying out maintenance. The lighthouse and helipad are situated in the most densely - populated area of Manx shearwater burrows. There have been many occasions when these burrows have been affected by THLS operations, e.g. accidentally flooded with diesel fuel, filled with building rubble, collapsed underfoot, and covered over with helicopter nets or huge and extremely heavy diesel-filled fuel bags that have been left sitting about for days at a time, often leaking their contents. Staff members do have "spare" time, of course, and some seek to entertain themselves by fishing. Finding a site from which to fish without entering seabird nesting-colonies is impossible during the breeding season, yet some have tried anyway, and their sport even included the casting of baited hooks, along with a large lead weight, right in the middle of rafts of puffins. Staff-members jogging around the island have caused panic amongst the nesting birds, the joggers unconcerned about their actions. The THLS vehicle, an "all-terrain" petrol-engined affair, has been a source of amusement for some personnel, being driven up and down the main trackway at speed, and occasionally off the tracks and even at night. THLS is of course bound by the conditions of the SSSI notification, but staff members did not always

Opposite: Figure 32. Theresa Thompson shows her dismay at Trinity House fuel bags being scattered over Manx shearwater burrows. Note their distance away from the area of "hard-standing" around the helipad, where all of such activities should be restricted to.

adhere to its guidelines, often having to be reminded (or even made aware) of their existence by the Island Warden despite the production by him of "Guidelines for THLS staff visiting Skokholm" that should have been circulated to all personnel by THLS before they even arrived on the island.

In order to prevent disturbance to breeding birds, THLS has agreed not to fly the helicopter across the island during the period from March to October inclusive, "unless it is absolutely necessary from a safety point of view". The aircraft needs to land facing in to any wind that is blowing, so there will always be occasions when the pilot has no option but to fly across a part of the island, but this can be minimised with a little care, since the helipad is situated at a corner of the island where the open sea is not far away in any direction apart from to the east. There have been occasions when the island was crossed in conditions that were in the author's opinion not at all dangerous to their operations (with a gentle breeze blowing), but to fly around the perimeter of the island obviously takes more time and uses more fuel than it does to cross it. Bad positioning of refuelling vessels has been to blame on at least one occasion, for example being moored in South Bay, at the eastern end of the island, whereas the lighthouse is situated at the south-westernmost tip. A helicopter taking off from a ship whilst carrying a heavy load (a fuel bag) generates a lot of noise (full-power being required), and flying low over the whole length of the island causes a huge amount of disturbance to birds (pers. obs.).

Fire

Lockley experienced the danger of fire on Skokholm in 1934, when a number of turf fires smouldered for days underground (Lockley, 1947). Effects on the tinder-dry leaf litter of bracken would be catastrophic, exposing the mineral soil and leaving it vulnerable to erosion. Fire is most likely to occur during the dry summer months, when it could have major effects on the breeding birds (most are burrow- and ground-nesting species). It could be the result of natural events, but is far more likely to be caused by human practises.

Observatory staff members burn any rubbish that cannot be composted or sent off for recycling (this practise commenced in the late 1990's). Great care must be taken on breezy days since there is a huge amount of dry plant material right across the island.

Section 3: External natural factors

The migratory seabirds which breed on Skokholm are particularly affected by external factors, both natural and man-made (next section). These are generally beyond the control of island managers, but many are of fundamental importance in ensuring the survival of all life on Earth.

Climatic changes are known to occur naturally and on a cyclical basis. Resulting sea-temperature changes are likely to bring about an alteration in the availability of fish for seabirds to feed on. This is of particular importance within the geographical area in which the species breed, for birds that are feeding chicks must be able to forage relatively close to the nest-site.

There is currently inadequate knowledge of fish stocks and how these interact with seabird populations, but this of course will bring little weight to bear should bird conservation become an issue in these times when man continues to fish at an unsustainable rate. The importance of both the Celtic and Irish Sea "fronts" for feeding Manx shearwaters has been demonstrated (Stone *et al.*, 1994).

Prolonged spells of inclement weather have deleterious effects on many island species. Wet weather results in flooding of Manx shearwater and puffin burrows, and all breeding bird species are likely to lose eggs and young through chilling or drowning. Hot, dry weather can result in the death of chicks on the island plateau. Long, cold spells during the winter can result in the loss of the small island populations of land birds, for example the blackbird. Rough seas prevent auks from foraging successfully (Birkhead, 1976; Davidson, 1994). This could have a deleterious effect on egg-production in females, resulting in smaller eggs and lower breeding success (Lloyd, 1979).

Determination of the annual survival rates of adult seabirds does give an indication of the effects of the various external factors, and annual productivity monitoring probably reflects the availability of food within the breeding season. But given the wide range of factors, it is difficult to say with certainty that any one is having a particular effect.

Section 4: External human-induced factors

Skokholm is situated in an area where the oil, fishing and tourism industries all have a prominence: although we can protect seabirds (to a degree) whilst they are breeding, outside this season they are subject to factors beyond an island manager's control. Moreover, different species will migrate, overwinter, or spend their pre-breeding years in various parts of the world. Even during the breeding season, seabirds will naturally leave the island to feed, each species in different areas that may change over time. Conditions in the marine environment are ultimately of greater potential impact – oil or chemical pollution, over-fishing, recreation and so on, could all affect bird populations.

Oil and shipping

Milford Haven is home to two major oil refineries and one storage facility. There is regular tanker traffic past the southern side of the island between the estuary and an area of temporary anchorage in St. Bride's Bay. Occasionally smaller ships pass between Skokholm and Skomer in Broad Sound. A Resolution made by the International Maritime Organization (IMO) on 4th March 1993 states that laden tankers should not use the channel between Grassholm and The Smalls unless they are moving to or from an anchorage in St. Brides Bay and Milford Haven. This came about following a number of spillages, and in particular the grounding of the oil tanker *Christos Betas* on the Hats and Barrels reef (off The Smalls rocks) in 1978.

The islands of Skokholm and Skomer and their seabird populations are considered to be one ecological unit. An oil-pollution incident in the vicinity could therefore affect the whole unit, with catastrophic consequences, particularly if it occurred during the breeding season. Efficient shipping management is therefore of great importance for the well-being of the island's inhabitants.

The International Convention for the Prevention of Pollution from Ships (MARPOL) is the main international convention covering prevention of pollution of the marine environment by ships from operational or accidental causes. It is a combination of two treaties adopted in 1973 and 1978 respectively and updated by amendments through the years. In its original form it covered pollution by oil, chemicals, harmful substances in packaged form, sewage and garbage. The Protocol of 1978 was adopted at a Conference on Tanker Safety and Pollution Prevention in February 1978 that was convened following a number of tanker accidents in 1976 and 1977.

In 1992, MARPOL was amended to make it mandatory for tankers of 5,000 dwt or more ordered after 6th July 1993 to be fitted with double hulls, or an alternative design approved by IMO (Regulation 13F in Annex I of MARPOL 73/78). The requirement for double hulls that applies to new tankers has also been applied to existing ships under a programme that began in 1995 (Regulation 13G in Annex I of MARPOL 73/78) – all tankers have to be converted when they reach 30 years old, or be taken out of service. Sadly, because shipyard capacity is limited, this measure is being phased in over a number of years.

The oil tanker *Braer* spilled 84,000 tons of crude oil after running aground in the Shetlands in 1993. After the disaster, a report by Lord Donaldson titled "Safer Ships, Cleaner Seas" (May 1994) made more than 100 recommendations in order to prevent further accidents. Most of these were accepted and implemented, but they still failed to protect the South Wales coastline because inadequate tug cover was provided for "the western approaches" despite Donaldson's recommendation.

In February 1996, the oil tanker *Sea Empress* ran aground at the mouth of the Milford Haven estuary, just a few kilometres from Skokholm. Around 72,000 tonnes of light crude oil of the "Forties Blend" were spilled at the mouth of the waterway, the majority of which was carried away from the island by the prevailing northerly and then westerly winds, ruining long lengths of the south Pembrokeshire and Gower coastlines. Thousands of duck (mainly common scoter *Melanitta nigra*) were killed in Carmarthen Bay. Few breeding seabirds had returned to Skokholm at this time, although guillemot numbers dropped dramatically in the area and those missing were undoubtedly amongst those birds found dead or dying as a result of oil contamination (see Parr *et al.* 1997). Critically, the vessel had no protective outer hull. A full report on the effects on the wildlife in the area affected can be found in the Sea Empress Environmental Evaluation Committee report (1998). The full details of the whole "incident" can be found in the Marine Accident Investigation Branch's report (MAIB, 1997).

Following the Erika incident off the coast of France in December 1999, IMO Member States discussed accelerating the phase-out of single-hull tankers. As a result, IMO adopted a revised phase-out schedule in April 2001, which entered into force on 1st September 2003 (the 2001 amendments to MARPOL 73/78). The new MARPOL regulation 13G set out a stricter timetable for the phasing-out of single-hull tankers, the final date for Category 1 tankers (pre-MARPOL tankers) now being 2005. The final phasing-out date for category 2 and 3 tankers (MARPOL tankers and smaller tankers) is brought forward to 2010 from 2015.

The grounding of the *Sea Empress* tanker should have been avoided. A report by the Environment Data Services shortly afterwards revealed how the Department of Transport refused to implement many of the recommendations made in The Lord Donaldson Report following the grounding of the *Braer* off the coast of Shetland in 1993. It said that the Department of Transport had "... proved reluctant to upset the ports and shipping industries which it sponsors", and "... has succumbed to short term financial expediency." The Donaldson Report specifically stated that a levy should be imposed on the shipping companies to raise the £10 million needed each year to provide the salvage tugs. The government said, however, that "unilateral action could adversely affect the competitiveness of UK ports and industry". There were a number of other factors which did not help the salvage operation of the *Sea Empress* – strong winds combined with the largest spring tides of the year severely hindered the rescue attempt, and also kept much of the crude oil lost from the tanker inshore. But ultimately this was a disaster that could have been prevented if the best interests of the natural environment had not been sacrificed for short-term gain.

In 1995, just months before the grounding of *Sea Empress*, the Milford Haven Port Authority apparently objected to the SAC designation (see pages 37 - 39), stressing that it might interfere with the port's commercial viability. This would have required it to reach a management agreement with conservation bodies to reconcile differences of opinion between those involved with fisheries, recreation, wildlife and the commercial traffic. Safety in shipping practises would have to have been addressed in these discussions, as would the specific issue of why the practise of escorting laden tankers into the Haven with tugs had been abandoned several years previously.

It is now almost 11 years since the *Sea Empress* disaster, and the Government has still to provide adequate emergency tug cover for the western approaches. In 1998, the shipping minister announced in the House of Commons that "the Government was satisfied that the trials carried out since 1994 by the Coastguard Agency had demonstrated the capabilities of emergency towing vessels in preventing or lessening such risks". Despite lobbying by Milford Haven Port Authority, local MP's and conservation and other bodies in the voluntary sector, no emergency tug has been provided for the Irish Sea area. This leaves Milford Haven badly exposed, with the Falmouth tug being about 14 hours steaming-time away and the Minches tug around 24 hours away.

However, the environmental significance of the Pembrokeshire coast and the threats posed by shipping were recognised recently by Government as the Department of Transport announced that the Pembrokeshire Islands are to be given the status of Marine Environment High Risk Areas (MEHRAs). This follows a recommendation made by Lord Donaldson in his report "Safer Ships, Cleaner Seas" (May 1994) into the Braer oil-spill off the Shetland Islands in January 1993. The following quote was taken directly from the DTI's website:

"The area's sole MEHRA is at the Pembrokeshire Islands and is followed by a number of low- and medium-ranked cells, ending with two high ranked cells at the Gower Peninsula. There is a 'Traffic Separation Scheme' west of The Smalls, with an 'Area to be Avoided' between The Smalls and Grassholm Island. All tankers, gas carriers, chemical tankers carrying noxious liquid substances should avoid the 'Area to be Avoided'. Laden tankers over 10,000 gross tonnage are also recommended not to use the channel between Grassholm and Skomer Islands unless moving between the anchorage in St Bride's Bay and Milford Haven. The Pembrokeshire Islands are at the limit of the area of operation of the MCA Emergency Towing Vessel stationed in the Western Approaches but could be covered by the proposed Irish Sea Emergency Towing Vessel.

"Pembrokeshire Islands have underlying statutory designations on wildlife, landscape and geological grounds. They have a high concentration of vulnerable seabirds with low to very low offshore fishing. The Traffic Separation Scheme off The Smalls and the Area to be Avoided provides a significant level of protection and MCA radar surveys have shown that vessels abide by the restrictions. Other than monitoring the continuing effectiveness of the IMO routing measures, no further protective measures are considered necessary."

Smaller-oil spills from shipping are probably less frequent than in the past. Certainly, Lockley (1958) attributed much of the post-war decline of guillemots to pollution from this source. Small numbers of oiled seabirds and grey seals are recorded almost annually from the island, presumably as a result of spillages elsewhere, but also because of illegal tank washing and discharges.

Current oil- and gas-exploration in the Irish Sea potentially poses a significant threat to marine life. Recent opposition to this was relatively successful, resulting in a number of blocks in most of the identified environmentally sensitive areas off West Wales not being offered to the oil companies by the DTI. In 1979, a monitoring programme titled "Seabirds at Sea" was established by the Nature Conservancy Council, sponsored by Governmental departments and oil companies. This effectively identified all of those areas containing high concentrations of seabirds that were potentially vulnerable to oil pollution, including the Irish Sea, and listed the vulnerable species present in the area in each month of the year (Tasker et al. 1990). Skokholm birds featured highly in the report.

Other pollution

There are many insidious chemical pollutants known to be present in the Irish Sea (Irish Sea Forum, 1997). As well as foraging in local waters during the breeding season, the three auk species are known to over-winter in the area also. Residues from anti-fouling agents such as organotins become concentrated in these top predators through bioaccumulation, and are embryotoxic, i.e. they reduce hatching success and fertility and affect enzyme and hormone activity in adult birds (Linley-Adams, 1999). Other insidious chemicals, such as Polychlorinated Biphenyls (PCBs) are widespread. These may cause little direct harm, but because they concentrate in fat reserves they may become a problem if a stressed bird has to draw on these energy stores (Davidson, 1994). They are also thought to have been responsible for the impaired immune system of common seals *Phoca vitulina* in the North Sea, 70 percent of which had fallen prey to a distemper virus in 1988.

Fishing and fisheries

Every day, lobster-pots are set all around the island and there are frequent incidences of disturbance to cliff-nesting seabirds, particularly guillemots, as boats – particularly the noisy ones – come close to the shore. Rod-and-line fishing is common from boats during the summer months. Relatively small numbers of sand-eels are sought by humans in the local waters, mainly for use as bait for bass-fishing.

There is an offshore fishing industry based around the Norway lobster *Nephrops norvegicus* in the region of the "Smalls Grounds", situated some 80 km to the south-west of Skokholm. Numbers of lesser black-backed gulls increased dramatically on the island (and on Skomer) in the 1980's, a change attributed to the availability of food, with gull chicks being provisioned with discards from trawlers. Gull numbers have since declined, but Dunn (1993) states that the fishery remains active and discard levels remain high. However, fishing vessels have become larger but fewer, perhaps resulting in discards of larger quantity but over shorter periods of time and at fewer locations, and hence less-available to the gulls. The fishing operation has also become a night-time one, further reducing the availability of by-catch to diurnal birds. In this intensively-fished western Irish Sea *Nephrops* ground, a comparison of the benthos near to and distant from shipwrecks suggests that trawling may have reduced the overall diversity and biomass, as well as the occurrence of a range of larger-sized mollusc and echinoderm species (Lindeboom & de Groot, editors, 1998). This would agree with the observations of Hensley (1996) in a wider benthic survey of the area, who suggested that bioturbation or trawl-induced disturbance might be responsible for the impoverished fauna of muddy sediments.

Concern over the effects on the benthos of commercial fishing activity has heightened in recent years in response to an increase in fishing effort and in the deployment of larger and heavier gear. Much of the Irish Sea is potentially vulnerable to occasional fishing-induced disturbance but, in practise, fishing activity tends to be concentrated in smaller geographical areas where returns are highest. Seabirds in west Wales do not seem to be at risk from the current level of fishing activity (Moore *et al.* 1996), but both seals and birds are perceived by some fishermen to be competitors for fish stocks.

Fishing activities have both negative and positive impacts on bird populations. The negative impacts on seabird populations are two-fold: firstly, the short-term effects of direct mortality due to seabird entanglement in fishing gear; secondly, the long-term interactions at the population level, i.e. competition for one food resource. There is currently inadequate knowledge of fish stocks and how these interact with seabird populations, but this of course will bring little weight to bear should bird conservation become an issue in these times when man continues to fish at an unsustainable rate. Offsetting these factors are the benefits to some seabird species of the ready-availability of food arising from fishing boat discards of by-catch and offal (see above). Another major factor is the change in fish stock structure, where the depletion in number of larger individuals of predatory commercial species which prey on "whitefish" juveniles has led to a greater availability of these smaller fish for birds. Thus, recent increases in number of some bird species on Skokholm, e.g. razorbills and guillemots, could be the result of an unnatural glut of sand-eels *Ammodytes* spp., young herring *Clupea harengus* and young gadoids due to an imbalance in the marine ecosystem. Apart from sand-eels, there are commercial fisheries for all of these within the Celtic Sea region. There is no industrial fishery taking small fish specifically for fish-meal.

Within the Irish Sea, discards from the fisheries during the early 1980's were estimated to be capable of supporting 153,000 seabirds, and offal 58,000 seabirds (Furness *et al.*, 1988). The discards generated by the fleets sampled in the Irish Sea in 1996 totalled over 7,500 tonnes. This figure may be a considerable underestimate as not all fleets were sampled during all quarters and no record was made of discards of invertebrates. Offal may represent a further food source for scavenging birds. In the Celtic Sea, birds scavenging around boats operating in the hake fishery (where relatively-few undersized fish are caught), feed primarily on offal (Pollock, 1994).

Entanglement of seabirds in nets is widely reported, with diving species being particularly prone to capture, with monofilament gill- or tangle-nets being the principal culprits. Large mortalities have been recorded in such gear in the Kattegat (Olden *et al.*, 1985) and in certain areas of the English Channel. The use of monofilament nets is considered to be the principal cause of death among auks, especially in the seas around Britain and Iberia (ICES, 1992). As another example, drift-net fishing for salmon was identified as a potential problem after large numbers of guillemots and razorbills were recovered or reported trapped in Galway Bay (Whilde, 1979). A large proportion of the birds were juveniles, the impact of which is not seen at the breeding colonies for three to five years, at which time they are recruited into the breeding population. Recent legalisation of monofilament net for salmon drift-netting in the Republic of Ireland may serve to increase the extent of seabird entanglement. Irish legislation offers protection to the major auk colonies (Horn Head, Cliffs of Moher, and Old Head of Kinsale) by means of designating these areas as "Refuges for Fauna", within which netting is prohibited in the sea near to the cliffs.

Another cause of bird deaths is entanglement in "ghost nets", i.e. those lost (or abandoned) which continue to catch fish. On the west coast of Ireland in areas where bottom-set gill-nets are used to catch demersal fish, simulated ghost nets were shown to catch significant numbers of diving seabirds (Anon., 1996a), but no attempt was made to quantify the extent of the problem in gear being operated commercially. Despite the evidence of localised events of bird-entanglement in drift and gill-nets, there have been population increases over the last 25 years of the species of diving birds most likely to be affected by such activity, so the impact of this source of mortality may not be as important as feared, at least as far as the total population is concerned, at the present time.

A number of recent studies have attempted to quantify the mortality of small cetaceans due to incidental entanglement in fishing gear. A programme to assess the marine mammal by-catch of the Irish and UK bottom-set gill-net fisheries (that are primarily targeting hake) on the Celtic Shelf to the south-west of Britain and Ireland was conducted from 1992 - 1994 (Berrow et al., 1994; Tregenza et al., 1997). Forty-three harbour porpoises and 4 common dolphins were caught, with the majority between 49° and 52°N and 5° and 10°W (ICES Divisions VIIj, g, h). Of the total number caught, 63 percent were caught in static nets, 29 percent in tangle nets and the remainder in nets set over shipwrecks. The estimated total annual by-catch is 2,200 harbour porpoises and 200 common dolphins. This estimate of annual by-catch represents 6.2 percent and 0.3 percent respectively of their estimated population (Hammond *et al.* 1995) in the Celtic Sea. (The study did not include an estimate of the impact of UK gill-netters below 15 m, Irish gill-netters below 10 m, or French gill-netters operating in the southern part of the Celtic Sea.)

Recent estimates of the natural rate of increase of otherwise unaffected populations of harbour porpoises are 4 to 5 percent (e.g. Caswell *et al.*, 1995). The IWC (International Whaling Committee) and ASCOBANS (Agreement on Small Cetaceans of the Baltic and North Sea) have agreed that an annual by-catch rate of 1 to 2 percent of the estimated abundance is considered to be a level causing concern about the ability of the harbour porpoise population in the Celtic Sea to maintain itself (Anon., 1996 b). Other fishing methods used within the area which are known to cause mortality of harbour porpoises include bottom-set gill-nets and fixed nets in the inshore waters of the Irish Sea (Thomas, 1992).

Also implicated in the entanglement of cetaceans are trawl and purse seine nets. In a three-month period in early-1992, 118 dolphins (mainly common dolphins) were stranded on the coast of Devon and Cornwall (Kuiken et al., 1994). They had a number of skin lesions that are characteristic of capture in small-meshed nets and the recently-ingested mackerel Scomber scombrus and pilchard Sardina pilchardus found in their gut strongly suggested that they may have been caught in trawl or purse seine nets deployed to catch these fish. The size of the net opening and the towing speed of trawlers greatly affect whether they will be likely to catch cetaceans (Waring et al., 1990). The value of acoustic deterrents in reducing harbour porpoise by-catch in the bottom-set gill-net fishery for hake is being investigated.

Grey seals may become trapped in towed and fixed-type gears. In certain parts of Britain up to 2 percent of tagged seal pups have been returned from fishing gear (Sea Mammal Research Unit, unpublished). An annual catch of 60 grey seals was estimated during a study of Irish trawlers that were targeting herring in the inshore spawning grounds of the Celtic Sea during the 1994 - 95 season estimated. This was based on an actual catch of four seals during 78 fishing days, 7 percent of the total effort (Morizur et al., 1997), and equates to approximately one seal caught in every 25 hours of trawling (all of those caught were near the Saltee Islands colony in County Wexford). The impact of this level of seal by-catch on seal populations is unknown at present, but grey seals that breed around the Pembrokeshire islands are known to travel widely, and could certainly be affected by fishing practises around Ireland.

Fixed nets used near major seal colonies are believed to pose a greater threat than those that are towed, because fish caught in such nets are tempting to seals, which become tangled whilst feeding. By-caught seals have been reported from the gill-net fishery for cod in north Mayo. Fifty-one seals (mostly juveniles) were taken as by-catch over three years by vessels participating in a seal-fishery interaction study off the Mayo coast from 1994 to 1996 (BIM, 1998). A "ghost-fishing" experiment on the west coast of Ireland (Anon, 1996a) showed that discarded gill-nets at a depth of 45 - 50 m caught seals. The limited data available suggest that the by-catch in fishing operations is an important potential threat to seals, but without accurate information on seal population-dynamics and true by-catch levels it is difficult to determine its true effect.

Further information on this vast subject can be found at the website of the Department of the Environment, Food and Rural Affaires (DEFRA) at www.defra.gov.uk/marine/index.htm.

Tourism and recreation

Each year there are many occasions when rafting and cliff-nesting seabirds and basking grey seals are disturbed by recreation-orientated boating activities in the waters around Skokholm. The wildlife in the waters is quite unprotected, unlike those around Skomer, which comprise a Marine Nature Reserve. Operators of "sea safari" boats – a recent means of intrusion into the sea around Skokholm – have all been "accredited" under a "WiSe" scheme (Wildlife Safe) and are active members of the Pembrokeshire Marine Code group (the accreditation was given on the strength of operators having attended a "classroom" course, despite poor behaviour where it counts, on the sea in the previous year). As such they are expected to **voluntarily** adhere to the codes of conduct developed to protect the marine wildlife of Pembrokeshire whilst providing patrons with knowledge of the species being observed, but the author's personal observations (and video evidence) show that this was far from the case in the spring, summer and autumn following (and of course before) the accreditation. Puffins, guillemots, razorbills and grey seals are worst affected by them, but there is great concern that their speed (maximum of about 40 knots) will result in collisions with porpoises and dolphins in the cetacean-rich waters around the Pembrokeshire islands. In addition, the noise emitted by these craft is extremely loud (an observer on Skokholm can hear the engine noise emitted from as far away as Grassholm), causing annoyance to other people and scaring the wildlife that the users hope to see. Quieter craft are just as harmful, if they are operated without due care and attention – canoeists frequently steer their boats into secluded bays for a lunch stop and scare the breeding birds off the cliffs above (pers. obs.). Despite the recent designation of the seas around Skokholm as an SAC, and the establishment of a Management Scheme in order to "secure and maintain the favourable conservation status of the SAC by ensuring that human activities coexist in harmony with the species and habitats of the site", the aim of "avoiding unnecessary regulation" is undoubtedly where it will fail the wildlife. Those responsible for such schemes are clearly not thinking far enough ahead. Laws provide real penalties (as long as they are enforced), and certainly set real boundaries for the many unacceptable activities that are becoming commonplace, and which need to be stopped before they really become established.

There are frequent unauthorised landings from private boats. The wardening staff-members must always be vigilant, and visitors are encouraged to report any such activities to them. The sensitivity of the breeding birds is a prime consideration, but perhaps more so is the fact that the widely-scattered Manx shearwater burrows are very easily destroyed underfoot – those people landing without authorisation have not had the benefit of a guided tour and a briefing from the Warden about where they can and cannot go.

Low-flying aircraft

Until very recently, there were numerous incidences where low-flying military aircraft caused significant disturbance to nesting birds, particularly guillemots. Although "seasonal avoidance" was granted, with the skies over the island a "no fly" zone from 1st March to 31st July, there were many occasions when pilots somehow overlooked this. In 1998, following numerous complaints from the Wildlife Trust and CCW, the island was granted year-round avoidance by the Royal Air Force within the Ministry of Defence's Low Flying System with regards to aircraft training exercises, following numerous occasions when breeding birds were disturbed by jets. Since 2002, there seems to have been an upsurge in the number of light aircraft operators providing "pleasure trips", some of which are out over the Pembrokeshire islands (pers. obs.).

Climate and weather

Any factor that influences meteorological conditions, and particularly climate, will be likely to have an affect on the various features. For example, Manx shearwaters, puffins and rabbits rely on the burrows drying out sufficiently during the spring to facilitate a successful breeding attempt. There is now undeniable proof that man's activities are currently bringing about global warming at an unprecedented rate. This is predicted to bring about far more rainfall – in the form of deluges during storms – and this could lead to unseasonable flooding of burrows. The plant communities would undoubtedly change too as temperature rises, but this is assuming that such heat-tolerant species exist locally and can reach the island.

Disease

Outbreaks of botulism amongst the *Larus* gulls in south-west Wales in the 1980's coincided with the introduction of black refuse sacs in households. It was suggested that the sacks provided the right conditions for growth of the bacterium responsible, *Clostridium botulinum*. This coupled with the slow rate of covering the rubbish once it reached the landfill site resulted in poisoned food becoming available to the most competitive adult birds.

The build-up of insidious man-made chemicals in the marine environment is known to reduce the immune response in birds and mammals, making them more susceptible to disease.

Chapter 5: Evaluation for nature conservation

Having described the primary and secondary habitats and species, and the factors affecting them, a brief process of evaluation is invaluable in order to put into context all of the main points of this information. These will directly relate to recommendations for future island management and give a better picture of exactly what the island's fauna and flora has to face up to.

Size

Skokholm is considerably smaller than many of the other Welsh islands, e.g. Skomer, Ramsey and Bardsey. Although it is interesting to compare the size of a site with others, size as a criterion must be linked to quality.

- The size of certain components of the seabird assemblage (in particular the Manx shearwater and possibly the storm petrel population) indicate that the site possesses a quality that is of the utmost importance to these species. The lesser black-backed gull colony accounts for approximately 3 - 4 percent of the world population of race *graellsii*. The island also holds significant proportions of Welsh and English-breeding razorbill and puffin.

- The small extent of most types of habitat means that "landbird" species are relatively few in number (Loxton & Jones, 1995), and populations experience large fluctuations in size and even periods of presence and absence typical of an ecological isolate. For example, blackbirds *Turdus merula* were absent from Skokholm (as a breeding species) between 1936 and 1969 (Loxton & Jones, 1995; also see Loxton & Silcocks, 1996).

Diversity

- There is a relatively small range of habitats present on Skokholm. This is usual, considering that it is a small island situated in an extremely exposed situation. The following types do exist, however: maritime grassland; marshy grassland; heathland; wet heath; bracken; inland rock; ponds, flushes and streams; rocky, shingle and sand beaches; sea-cliffs, caves and crevices. Many of these habitats are in a complex mosaic and can be said to be somewhat dynamic – over the last 50 years significant changes in distribution of the various plant species has taken place, with no clear reason (Ninnes, 1996). Diversity of wetland vegetation has decreased, and although some efforts have been made to prevent gulls from roosting in such areas, this habitat has not been considered as important as the seabird assemblage.

- The flora is perhaps far from "outstanding" (from a botanist's point of view), but continuous grazing by rabbits maintains considerably more diversity than would otherwise be the case. In bracken-dominated areas the springtime flora is reminiscent of some deciduous woodlands, the asynchronous phenologies of the herb species (bluebells, red campion) and bracken allowing their coexistence in the same area of ground.

- The diversity of lichens on Skokholm is exceptional, the site being listed in a report to the Nature Conservancy Council as a site of national/international importance (James and Rose, 1978).

- There is a diverse and rich assemblage of invertebrates, particularly within the Coleoptera and Lepidoptera, although the Invertebrate Site Register (1993) evaluation lists Skokholm as a Grade C site. The site is nationally important for the conservation of harvestmen (Opiliones) (Invertebrate Site Register).

- Compared to neighbouring Skomer, a considerably larger island of volcanic rock, there are fewer seabird species breeding (no shag *Phalacrocorax aristotelis*, cormorant *Phalacrocorax carbo* or kittiwake *Rissa tridactyla*). This is probably due to a lack of suitable nest-sites. Also, few parts of the island's coastline provide suitable nesting ledges for guillemots and razorbills, so numbers of these species are limited (the whole length of the southern coast is virtually devoid of ledges and embayments, for example). Breeding landbirds are also significantly less diverse, but do include oystercatcher *Haematopus ostralegus*, peregrine *Falco peregrinus*, buzzard *Buteo buteo*, wheatear *Oenanthe oenanthe*, rock pipit *Anthus petrosus*, chough *Pyrrhocorax pyrrhocorax* and previously lapwing *Vanellus vanellus*.

- There is relatively little management required or even possible to maintain or increase diversity, with the exception of control of bracken and excavation of ponds, though rejuvenated *Calluna* heathland may shortly require management due to the lack of grazing in a rabbit-exclosure, as *Festuca* grass becomes dominant.

Naturalness

Generally, the more natural a site, the greater its nature conservation value.

- Skokholm appears to be a wild and therefore natural place, but due to a fairly long history of human occupation, the introduction of rabbits *Oryctolagus cuniculus,* and commencement of farming practises, the site has undoubtedly been modified to a large degree. But probably the most important consideration is the rabbit population. Since their introduction, burrowing, grazing and manuring by them has considerably modified the vegetation, soil moisture content, temperature and structure (Gillham, 1956b).

- Some changes in the vegetation are thought to be attributable to the effects of nutrient-enrichment by seabirds, and in particular the lesser black-backed gulls, which grew in number considerably in the 1970's and 1980's, thought to be due to the availability of discards from fishing vessels.

- An attempt was made on Skokholm to improve about ten acres of pasture on the western half of Northern Plain in 1962 - 63 by the spreading of fertilizer (Lloyd, 1964). This was in an attempt to assess whether the quality and abundance of food has an affect upon reproduction in rabbits. It is unlikely that there were any long-lasting effects upon the vegetation, and certainly nothing is obvious today.

- Some aspects of the flora are reminiscent of that more typical in a woodland habitat, and it could be that the island was once wooded. Tree cover might have been a hindrance to Manx shearwaters at that time, if it existed, so its removal (due to felling by man and/or grazing by rabbits and stock animals) has probably been beneficial to this species. However, it should be noted that some procellariids do nest in such habitats in other parts of the World.

- Although numbers of visitors are not large and far less than most other island nature reserves, there is a degree of erosion on pedestrian routes, especially the cliff-top paths; the erosive effect of trampling feet is exacerbated by shallow, often skeletal soils, rain and in particular, wind. In other areas the vegetation is modified by moderate trampling (Gillham, 1956b). The majority of human activity is confined to the area around the living-quarters at the observatory. The lighthouse, built in the early 1900's, is no longer manned (automated in 1985), although service crews visit frequently. In addition, the provision of safe landing areas for the service boat and the "improvements" of tracks and paths from these shoreline areas by the application of cement is a major alteration of the natural situation.

- Various plant species have been introduced to the island, particularly in the gardens.

- Very little vegetation management is carried out, with bracken control being the most significant.

- All of the bird species currently found on the island are considered to be a natural component of the fauna, though Canada goose *Branta canadensis* has bred since 1999. Little owls *Athene noctua* are rarely recorded now. Gulls have been controlled in the past, with little noticeable effect on numbers in the long term. However, raking of a varying percentage of the nests of lesser black-backed gulls continued until recently, in order to confine the birds to areas where they a) cause little damage to fragile vegetation and b) do not impose on visitors (the birds have since been given priority over people).

- The vegetation of the steeper cliffs is doubtless little modified by the activities of man and grazing animals, at least currently (the last goat flock was removed in 1981).

Rarity

- Islands around the British Isles that are free from mammalian ground-predators – and therefore suitable for breeding seabirds – are rarities themselves.

- The Manx shearwater has a particularly restricted breeding distribution, with 90 percent of the world population nesting around the coast of Britain and Ireland. They have specialised habitat requirements (adjacent to the sea and free of mammalian ground-predators), which few sites provide.

- Other rare breeding birds on Skokholm are chough and peregrine. Lapwings have declined by 79 percent in Wales since 1987 (Bullock, 1996). There were 7 pairs on Skokholm in 1998, 25 percent of the Pembrokeshire breeding population that year, but none have bred since 2000. However, there is the potential for their return, as long as their favoured habitat on the island (marshy grassland) is unaltered by man's activities – the hydrology of the site could be severely threatened by any further abstraction in order to provide shower-facilities and the like. Lapwings are to be found elsewhere in Britain and are therefore considered to be less important than the seabird assemblage.

- The lichen community contains the golden hair lichen *Teloschistes flavicans* (part of one of 12 "core sites" in the United Kingdom – Gilbert and Purvis 1996). *Rocella fusiformis* is listed as "near-threatened" (found in 15 or fewer 10km squares in the UK).

- Skokholm's vegetation communities are possibly unique. They do not match with any NVC community, this thought to be due to a combination of factors, namely the long history of grazing by rabbits, the abundance of seabird burrows, the manuring and trampling by roosting gulls and the recent decline of heathland (Ninnes, 1998). In any case, the maritime grassland of the plateau is a rare example of a rabbit-maintained vegetation.

- The only nationally-rare plant on the island is three-lobed crowfoot *Ranunculus tripartitus*, which is restricted to just one shallow ephemeral pool and the runnel that drains it. It is rare and declining throughout its range. There are several "locally scarce" plants (at the Pembrokeshire level). Divided sedge *Carex divisa* was discovered in 1997 amongst the extensive stand of sand sedge *Carex arenaria* to the north of North Pond (Evans, 1997). It is only the second known site in Pembrokeshire, the other being at nearby Dale.

- The house mice on Skokholm have developed a unique gene pool over the last century (Berry, 1996).

- Several local or rare invertebrates have been found on Skokholm. For example, the only Welsh records of the beetle *Graptodytes bilineatus* are found in Pembrokeshire. The spider *Clubiona genevensis* has been recorded just three times in Wales (at two localities), one of which was on Skokholm in 1935. Several "local" moths occur, mainly species of cliff vegetation on rocky western coasts, such as the thrift clearwing *Bembecia muscaeformis* and black-banded *Polymixtis xanthomista*. Also, species dependent on saxicolous lichens – the marbled green *Cryphia muralis* and hoary footman *Eilema griseola*, for example.

Fragility

Fragility implies that a habitat or ecosystem is vulnerable, difficult to recreate and might have become rare as a result of permanent damage elsewhere. With regard to species, changes in land use or habitat cover have often been linked to extinctions of land bird species. Note that this section contains more points than any other.

- Heather *Calluna vulgaris* has been reportedly suppressed by rabbits since at least 1954 (Goodman & Gillham 1954) and has displayed some of the distinctive signs of damage by grazing (MacDonald 1990, in Ninnes 1996). Until about 1980 a few continuous stands remained, with acid grassland associate species, but these had become fragmented less than a decade later (Ninnes, 1996). Gynn (1985) suggests that strong storms may have contributed to the decline of the already weakened plants.

- Weather-induced stress (e.g. drought, storms) occasionally results in other changes in vegetation.

- Fire is a hazard that could decimate ground and burrow-nesting birds, those burning or smouldering underground proving particularly long-lived and difficult to extinguish. Lockley experienced this in 1934, following the visit of many people during the 8th International Ornithological Congress (Lockley, 1947).

- The surface vegetation of marshy areas is extremely sensitive to physical damage from trampling, particularly by people, but more recently by Canada geese *Branta canadensis*.

- Vegetation is sensitive to manuring by seabirds. Also, some lichen communities become simplified or even eliminated where soiling is intense, although some species seem to benefit (Fletcher, 1997). Rabbit pellets are of little importance to soil nutrient content except in non-organic cliff soils newly exposed by erosion.

- There are local factors that influence some of the important species. Seabirds are vulnerable to human disturbance both from the land and sea. Breeding guillemots, razorbills, choughs, peregrines and grey seals are considered to be particularly sensitive to disturbance. If guillemots are scared from their nests, then eggs and chicks can be lost as they are dragged off the ledges by the fleeing adults, or taken by predators (pers. obs.). Puffins may also desert their burrows if disturbed during incubation. Breeding seabirds are vulnerable to disturbance by low flying aircraft. Grey seals show worried reactions to the sight and/or sound of passing boats and aircraft. Visitor management by way of a desirable footpath system can alleviate the affects of island-based disturbance, but water-borne persons are far more difficult (and at present, virtually impossible) to control. Predation can also exacerbate the fragility of some species (e.g. wader chicks by corvids/gulls).

- The burrows of shearwaters and puffins are very vulnerable to trampling. Drought or heavy rain may also cause burrow collapse. This is rare but can be great when it occurs. The success of the birds themselves can lead to their downfall – the once large puffin colony on Grassholm was thought to have met its demise as the mat of red fescue grass they had burrowed into became eroded away underfoot, leading to burrow-roof collapse. This was after its zenith in 1890 (in Lockley, 1938 and 1969). Cliff-top slopes where puffins nest have very little vegetation.

- Areas of boulder beach and rock-fall where storm petrels nest are quite unstable in places. Human access to such sites could result in catastrophic losses of breeding petrels.

- The distance from the mainland is of positive note, particularly with regard to the difficulty of access to the site for mammalian predators. However, things are changing: from 2001, a number of "sea safari" tour boats began operating in the waters around the island. As vessels of all types have become more seaworthy, more affordable and have more powerful engines, the number of SCUBA divers investigating the sea life and shipwrecks has also increased dramatically, and unfortunately they seek the more sheltered and remote bays to stop for lunch, lacking all regard for the nesting birds (pers. obs.).

- The accidental introduction of mammalian predators, particularly rats, is potentially one of the most significant threats to breeding seabirds. Removal programmes have commenced on some of the Welsh islands (and succeeded on Ramsey) and the impact of introduced mammalian predators on seabirds is reviewed by Burger & Gochfeld (1994).

- Although we can protect seabirds whilst breeding, outside this season they are subject to factors beyond our control. Moreover, different species will migrate, overwinter, or spend their pre-breeding years in various parts of the world. Even during the breeding season seabirds will naturally leave the island to feed, they may feed in different areas and these areas may change during the breeding season. Conditions in the marine environment are ultimately of greater potential impact. Oil- or chemical-pollution, over-fishing, human recreational activities and so on, could all affect bird populations directly or by influencing food-availability. The islands of Skokholm and Skomer and their seabird populations are considered to be one ecological unit.

- Oil spills from tankers have occurred in the local area and oil has impacted upon Skokholm and/or its birds, namely the *Benjamin Coates* (1962), and most recently the *Sea Empress* (February 1996). Following the latter, on Skokholm the number of guillemots decreased by some 26 percent from 1995 to 1996 (Skokholm

Warden's Annual Report to the Dyfed Wildlife Trust, 1996). The oil spilled was Forties Blend, a light form of crude oil. Smaller oil spills from shipping are probably less frequent than in the past, now that the source of any such oil is traceable. Certainly, Lockley (1958) attributed much of the post-war guillemot decline to pollution from this source.

- Lichens are generally dependant on an unpolluted atmosphere and can be affected by even a short term deterioration in air quality (*Teloschistes flavicans* is particularly sensitive, for example). Some important species on Skokholm are associated with seabird guano (e.g. *Rocella* spp.). Significant changes in the status of seabirds may affect these lichen assemblages. "Edge of range" species may be particularly vulnerable to small environmental changes.

- Three-lobed crowfoot *Ranunculus tripartitus,* a "pink list" species, is confined to just three sites on the island, two of which contain very few plants. If the prime pool were to be affected by a catastrophic event, such as a diesel-spillage from the nearby lighthouse, or a natural event such as a prolonged storm and its associated salt-laden winds, the outcome would be disastrous for it.

- Of the current management procedures, spraying of bracken with herbicide could threaten other features. Lichens are known to suffer (thallus breakdown) if emulsifying or detergent agents are added to the pesticide to assist with its distribution. Current practise is to mix the asulam with water. Asulam itself can severely check the growth of Yorkshire fog grass *Holcus lanatus,* and a temporary check to bents *Agrostis* spp. In addition, plantains *Plantago* spp. and docks *Rumex* spp. are controlled. Any significant increase in bracken control could perhaps threaten lesser black-backed gull breeding success and distribution (this is currently being used on a limited basis to control the distribution of gulls near to human habitation).

Typicalness

- Skokholm is typical of the Welsh islands (excluding Anglesey), being situated close to the mainland and small in size, low-lying and lacking woodland (Reed & Parr, 1997). Typically, many taxa are poorly represented – few habitats and small size means that species-richness is relatively limited. This typically applies only to those islands that are nature reserves (Reed, 1983). The turnover of landbird populations is typical of other islands and of other ecological isolates in the mainland agricultural landscape, but where there are few data sets for the latter, unlike the islands (Williamson, 1981).

- The seabird assemblage is typical of an island without mammalian ground-predators (though Manx shearwater and storm petrel are "special"). Landbirds such as peregrine and chough are typical of the Pembrokeshire coast, whilst oystercatcher and lapwing are typical of undisturbed, unimproved habitats.

- The maritime grassland on Skokholm is atypical – it does not fit into any community currently listed in the NVC. However, in general the communities are typical of exposed cliffs on western coasts of Britain, e.g. MC1, the *Crithmum maritimum – Spergularia rupicola* maritime rock-crevice community; MC6, the *Atriplex hastata* agg. – *Beta vulgaris* ssp. maritima sea-bird cliff community; MC7, the *Stellaria media – Rumex acetosa* seabird cliff community; MC8, the *Festuca rubra – Armeria maritima* maritime grassland; and MC9, the *Festuca rubra – Holcus lanatus* maritime grassland.

Position in an ecological unit

- An obvious ecological unit is the island itself, isolated by the surrounding sea and instantly recognisable as such. When species from such an isolate are lost there are few chances of re-colonization, if any, so the island populations of immobile species are potentially threatened with extinction. This does not of course apply to the breeding seabirds that, it could be argued, are part of a far larger ecological unit. This includes the sea over which they range and the other islands of Skomer and Middleholm, with which Skokholm is included in a single Special Protection Area for wild birds under European law (European Community Directive 79/409/EEC on the Conservation of Wild Birds). There is considerable interchange of Manx shearwater and lesser black-backed gulls between the islands, for example, hence their grouping as a single colony. The Skokholm Manx shearwaters are of course a significant component of the World population. In addition, the islands of Grassholm and Ramsey can be considered to be part of the same ecological unit – the four islands together were considered together to be a Grade 1 Site in the Nature Conservation Review (Ratcliffe, 1977) – and doubtless interchange occurs here too in the case of gulls and auks.

- A grey seal population wanders throughout the waters surrounding the Pembrokeshire islands, with up to 25 seen daily basking on rocks around Skokholm. Pupping occurs in considerable numbers on Ramsey and Skomer and mainland sites, but with a few pups born on Skokholm each year. These animals are near to the southern limit of their range.

- On a broader scale, Skokholm is perhaps an important stopping point for passage bird migrants – no mammalian ground-predators and little in the way of disturbance – and some birds have been known to return to the island in consecutive winters, e.g. robin *Erithacus rubecula* (Betts, 1992).

Potential for improvement / restoration for conservation

Skokholm is of greatest importance for its breeding Manx shearwaters, storm petrels and lesser black-backed gulls. Given the large size of the populations of these species, the island is thought to be desirable to them in its present condition. However, there are some factors that do affect these "feature" species and so need further study, as follows:

- Although there is known to be competition for burrows between puffins and Manx shearwaters, a recent count gave the total number of burrows on Skokholm at 85,000 (Smith *et al.* 2001). The same census estimated about 46,000 pairs of Manx Shearwaters, an increase over previous estimates of 35,000 pairs. The breeding population of puffins is estimated at approximately 2,000 pairs (a stable figure), but was previously up to 5,000 - 10,000 pairs at the time when shearwater numbers were first calculated. Therefore, although competition for burrows undoubtedly exists, there are plenty more available and even though they may be considered "sub-optimal" (when compared to those currently in use), they were probably used in the past. Given sufficient food, the potential for increase in number of nesting seabirds would ultimately be limited by the availability of nest-sites.

- There is concern about the stability of soil in areas where there is a high density of burrows and hence little vegetation to bind the soil, particularly on cliff-top slopes, although recent wet summers have encouraged some plant growth in these areas and continue to be monitored (Warden's Report 1998). This could be an entirely natural sequence of events. It has been suggested that sea campion *Silene uniflora* seedlings could be planted in these areas. Footpaths could perhaps be closed temporarily, or re-routed where possible.

- Bracken has long been thought to impede the passage of Manx shearwaters and bring about their predation by gulls (Lockley, 1942, and recent Warden's Reports) and the spraying (with herbicide) of swathes through the vegetation has undoubtedly provided more opportunities for adults and particularly fledglings to reach safety.

- Bracken has been encroaching onto cliff-top slopes used by puffins for nesting. The herbicide *Asulam* has been sprayed onto the bracken in these areas, resulting in the successful check of its growth and puffins have again been observed entering the burrows in this area (Warden's Annual Report, 1998).

- *Calluna* heathland has been in decline on Skokholm since before 1964, and by 1989 heather remained only as tiny shoots within a single area of short grassland, but following exclusion of rabbits in 1991 bushes have developed quite readily (Ninnes, 1996). Extension of the rabbit-exclosure in 1997 has resulted in further growth of *Calluna*, but it is still far less abundant and widespread on the island than before. Further fencing could be considered, though this is likely to take its toll on nocturnal birds that frequently fly into it (pers. obs.). Collection of seed and its subsequent sowing onto specially-prepared areas of soil could encourage the spread of heath.

- The three-lobed crowfoot *Ranunculus tripartitus* is restricted to one seasonal pool on Skokholm, but was once recorded in another nearby. There are other "apparently suitable" sites on the island, so plants could be transplanted.

- Many shrubs and trees have been planted in recent years, to create cover for migrant birds, mainly in the vicinity of the buildings where there is some shelter from salt-laden winds. Cuttings could be taken and planted along the few walls that have no cover. However, this might mean a loss of lichens or other plants which inhabit the walls, due to increased shading.

- Great black-backed gulls *Larus marinus* are the top predators on Skokholm, and currently number 71 breeding pairs (2004). Numbers of Manx shearwater corpses over the island and nest-site pellet studies have shown that they take a large toll on these birds and occasionally storm petrels (Warden's Reports). Losses of these species could be reduced if a gull-control programme were undertaken. However, on balance the gulls seem to be having a minimal effect on the populations of any species on Skokholm.

- Although different survey methods were used, the results of the various storm petrel population studies strongly suggest that there has been a decline in the number of pairs nesting in the island walls. These structures have become derelict in many places, due to the ravages of time, and the excavations of rabbits and Manx shearwaters. They are also sites for an array of lichens. They could be rebuilt, but obtaining the necessary stone would mean destruction of other natural rocky areas. Currently there are many natural nest-sites not being used.

- There is a potential for improvement in island water-bodies. The larger ponds are eutrophicated to some degree. However, in order to improve the freshwater habitats, there would have to be a reduction in gull numbers to reduce the incidence of bathing and manuring. But lesser black-backed gulls, which comprise the bulk of gulls on the island, are a main feature of the reserve.

Evaluation for research/study

The change in conditions in the lease in 1976, forbidding the trapping of any animal, meant that many long-term bird studies came to an abrupt halt (very many seabird studies have since been carried out on neighbouring Skomer Island). The Edward Grey Institute of Ornithology from Oxford University vacated Skokholm and the bird-related scientific guidance it had provided was gone. The island also lost its official Bird Observatory status due to the cessation of ringing, which could potentially be re-established. However, the erection of netting of any description will put Manx shearwaters and storm petrels at risk.

- There are currently other projects taking place on Skokholm which do not rely on trapping of animals. They include the installation of storm petrel nest-boxes in a number of suitable locations, in order to achieve the aim of having a "more accessible" breeding population for study; a long-term botanical study, looking at changes in the vegetation over many years; monitoring of the rare golden-hair lichen; and the relationship between bracken distribution and nesting gulls.

- There are a number of other subjects requiring further study, each of which will not require any trapping:

1. Status of invertebrate species, last studied in some detail for some groups in the 1950's, particularly the aquatic fauna of ephemeral pools, and rare species. Many have been recorded only once, over 40 years ago.
2. Status of fungi, last studied in the 1950's.
3. Distribution of saxicolous lichens in relation to aspect, manuring by seabirds, etc.
4. The rate of soil erosion and loss.
5. Influence of bracken and gull distribution on occupancy of burrows by Manx shearwaters (utilising the shearwater study-plots that are already in existence).
6. Changes in vegetation as gull populations continue to decline.
7. An NVC study to ascertain whether communities are indeed "unique".

The results of such studies are all of considerable use in making management decisions. Despite the previous restrictions on the trapping of animals and the cessation of much of the bird research, there are some continuing long-term studies involving the vegetation (e.g. Ninnes 1998). Fixed-point photography is an integral part of this and other studies, including monitoring of lichen populations e.g. *Teloschistes flavicans*, monitoring of gull distribution, and so on.

Management recommendations

Following on from the descriptions and evaluation procedure, all that remains is to make a brief list of the management prescriptions that have actually resulted from these deliberations. Mention has already been made of some aspects of these in the habitat and species descriptions.

- Key species and habitats should be monitored on a regular basis. Details will vary with each species. The presence of rare and scarce species should be confirmed. Checks, repairs and repainting and or replacement of all survey marks should be carried out annually.

- Bird monitoring methods require further development so that disturbance is reduced.

- A system of terricolous lichen monitoring still needs to be established. It is not known if the assemblage is in a favourable condition.

- Monitor the effects of the many "factors" that could prove detrimental to the island's wildlife and habitats, for example, human visitors on the island, boats that are increasingly present around the island, lighthouse operations, and so on.

- Control the many man-made factors. It would be folly to construct more landing-sites for boats in order to bring about a very slightly-increased chance of the boat mooring at Skokholm when a landing at South Haven is temporarily impractical – the costs in the form of destruction of valuable habitat, exclusion of breeding birds from their nest-sites and the increase in unauthorised landings would hugely counteract any small advantage that might be gained. Ensure that visitors remain on the footpaths at all times. Ensure that water-use is sensibly controlled, thus negating the need to take more from sources that can ill-afford it.

- Continue to control natural factors such as bracken.

- Any proposed habitat or species management should be considered very carefully bearing <u>all</u> of the habitats and features in mind.

With the Wildlife Trust now having ownership of the island, it will be feasible to repeat many of the past population studies and to initiate new ones. However, studies of adult survival, reproduction success and so on, of seabirds are currently carried out on Skomer, where a suitable infrastructure – currently being modernised thanks to a huge investment of money – already exists. The island, of such huge "stature" thanks to its breeding seabirds, would benefit more if its inhabitants were left unmolested, and efforts put in to controlling the growing number of human factors that are likely to bring about their demise.

The burden is a heavy one in these rapidly-changing times. I desperately hope that The Wildlife Trust of South & West Wales is prepared to put the well-being of the wildlife as its priority, rather than concede to a handful of vociferous groups of "users" all with their own selfish agendas (and perhaps offering financial incentives) that will lead to tougher times for the things that really need the island to remain as it is – the animals.

Appendices

Appendix I: H.M. Meteorological Office summary of Skokholm data

Appendix II: An annotated list of higher plants

Appendix III: A list of Bryophytes

Appendix IV: A list of lichens

Appendix V: A list of fungi

Appendix VI: Birds first recorded in the UK/Wales/Pembrokeshire on Skokholm

Appendix VII: The Island Year

Appendix VIII: Birds

Appendix IX: A list of invertebrates

Appendix X: Butterfly transect totals, 1977 - 2001

Appendix I: H.M. Meteorological Office summary of Skokholm data

Month :	Jan	Feb	Mar	April	May	June	July	Aug	Sept	Oct	Nov	Dec	Mean
Variable													
Maximum Temp ° C	8.2	7.7	9.1	11.3	13.8	16.6	18.4	18.6	16.7	14.2	11.0	9.3	12.9
Minimum Temp ° C	4.3	3.7	4.5	5.8	8.3	10.9	12.7	13.0	12.0	10.1	6.9	5.5	8.1
Mean Temp ° C	6.3	5.7	6.8	8.6	11.0	13.7	15.6	15.8	14.4	12.1	8.9	7.4	10.5
Temperature Range ° C	3.9	4.0	4.6	5.5	5.5	5.8	5.7	5.5	4.7	4.1	4.0	3.8	4.8
Highest Maximum ° C	13.0	13.0	17.0	21.0	25.0	29.0	29.0	29.0	26.0	21.0	16.0	14.0	
Lowest Minimum ° C	-8.0	-6.0	-4.0	-1.0	1.0	5.0	8.0	7.0	5.0	2.0	-2.0	-5.0	
Lowest Max. ° C	-2.0	-1.0	2.0	4.0	7.0	11.0	12.0	13.0	11.0	9.0	5.0	0.0	
Highest Min. ° C	10.0	10.0	10.0	11.0	16.0	18.0	19.0	20.0	17.0	16.0	14.0	12.0	
Grass Min. ° C	2.7	2.1	2.7	3.5	6.1	8.9	10.8	11.3	10.1	8.5	5.1	3.6	6.3
30 cm soil temp ° C	6.2	5.7	6.9	9.4	12.3	15.3	16.9	16.7	14.9	12.4	9.3	7.4	11.1
Sunshine hr/day	2.0	2.9	4.3	6.5	7.6	7.4	7.3	6.7	5.2	3.4	2.5	1.7	4.79
Rainfall (mm)	90.0	63.0	66.0	52.0	49.0	52.0	45.0	67.0	73.0	94.0	97.0	100.	Tot 849
Max. hourly RH (%)	88.0	87.0	88.0	88.0	89.0	90.0	91.0	91.0	90.0	89.0	88.0	88.0	89.0
Min. hourly RH (%)	85.0	83.0	80.0	76.0	76.0	76.0	76.0	76.0	79.0	82.0	82.0	85.0	80.0
Wind at 10 m (knots)	15.8	14.9	14.2	12.1	11.7	10.6	10.2	11.1	12.5	14.3	15.1	15.8	13.2
Air frost days	3.3	3.4	0.9	0.1	0	0	0	0	0	0	0.1	1.6	9.4
Grass frost days	6.7	7.5	5.8	3.7	0.5	0	0	0	0	0	2.3	5.5	Tot 32
>= 0.2mm rain (days)	19.4	14.8	16.3	12.2	13.3	11.8	10.3	13.3	14.0	17.9	19.1	19.1	Tot 181
>= 1mm rain (days)	15.6	11.4	11.8	9.0	9.7	9.1	7.8	9.6	10.8	14.1	15.2	15.0	Tot 139
>= 10mm rain (days)	2.6	1.8	2.1	1.5	1.2	1.6	1.4	2.3	2.5	2.9	3.4	3.5	Tot 27
Snowfall (days)	0.4	0.8	0.2	0.2	0	0	0	0	0	0	0	0.3	1.9
Sleet/snowfall (days)	1.4	1.7	0.6	0.3	0	0	0	0	0	0	0	0.5	4.5
Snow lying (days)	0	0	0	0	0	0	0	0	0	0	0	0	0.01
Hail (days)	3.7	2.4	2.4	1.4	0.6	0	0.1	0	0.3	1.3	3.1	2.8	Tot 18
Thunder heard (days)	0.6	0.3	0.1	0	0.5	0.3	0.5	0.7	0.3	1.0	0.7	0.7	5.8

Sequence, English and Latin follow Stace (1991). This is an update of "Flora of Skokholm" produced by E. Gynn in 1995. The symbol "⊛" indicates that the species is represented in Mary Gillham's Skokholm and Grassholm Herbarium, held at National Museum of Wales, Cardiff (photocopies on Skokholm). There have been periods of plant-recording e.g. 1947-60, and these are reflected in the text below.

OPHIOGLOSSIACEAE

Adder's-Tongue *Ophioglossum vulgatum* L.
A small population was first discovered at East Bog in 1981, but no plants have been seen there since 1997. This follows the establishment of a gull roost at the site, the possible cause of the plant's demise. Larger populations have been found to the north and east of North Pond (over 10,000 plants estimated here in 1989), with a new location (but within the same general area) discovered in 1997. Scarce in Pembrokeshire.

OSMUNDACEAE

Royal Fern *Osmunda regalis* L.
A single plant, partially grazed and non-sporing, grew at the edge of East Pond between 1948 and 1954.

DENNSTAEDTIACEAE

Bracken *Pteridium aquilinum* (L.) Kuhn. ⊛
Dominant over most of the more-sheltered localities. It increased in extent once farming ceased, initially by encroaching on former field areas. Rather intolerant of wind and salty sea-spray, so seldom reaches the cliff-edge. No ground flora beneath the denser stands, otherwise Bluebell, Ground Ivy, Yorkshire Fog and Common Sorrel are associated species, and more recently Sea Campion where Bracken has invaded the coastal grassland. Presumably due to the harsh conditions, its spread is vegetative rather than via spore production. Controlled in certain areas through hand-scythe and herbicide. Bracken was previously limited in its distribution by ploughing (pre-1900) and by trampling and grazing (a flock of Soay Sheep once consisted of about 90 animals).

ASPLENIACEAE

Black Spleenwort *Asplenium adiantum-nigrum* L.
A single plant was recorded on a vertical wall of a rabbit burrow to the north-east of Gate Rock in 1954, amongst the moss *Dicranella heteromalla*; and another in 1980, on a North Haven promontory, with ripe sori.

Sea Spleenwort *Asplenium marinum* L. ⊛
Common in ungrazed cliff crevices, and in the lime kiln in South Haven

BLECHNACEAE

Hard Fern *Blechnum spicant* (L.) Roth.
A record of two small patches in East Bog in 1949, but these had apparently disappeared by 1960.

WOODSIACEAE

Hart's-tongue *Phyllitis scolopendrium* (L.) Newm.
Recorded on an eastern cliff prior to 1947. Three plants grew on a wall in the Wheelhouse courtyard in 1981, but did not persist past 1984.

Lady-fern *Athyrium filix-femina* (L.) Roth. ✿
Abundant in East Bog, along the banks of the stream from the Well Pool, and on the lee side of inland walls, including that of the cottage garden.

Maidenhair Spleenwort *Asplenium trichomanes* L.
One plant on a chimney of "The Wheelhouse block" from 1980 until about 1990.

Rustyback *Ceterach officinarum* DC.
On the wall beside the laboratory during and around 1967.

DRYOPTERIDACEAE

Male-fern *Dryopteris filix-mas* (L.) Schott. ✿
A few plants at East Bog and in the rabbit-exclosure by The Well; previously recorded on some cliff-faces (presumably in the east), and one in the courtyard behind the Sycamore trees in the late-1980's.

Broad Buckler-fern *Dryopteris dilatata* (Hoffm.) A. Gray
A few recorded in East Bog in 1980 and 8 plants in a clump there in 1993. May still be present.

Narrow Buckler Fern *Dryopteris carthusiana* (Villars) H.P. Fuchs
A deporporate specimen was apparently referable to this species, on a wall behind the Sycamore trees in the courtyard in 1990. A single specimen grew on the wall running from the Observatory towards North Pond in the period 1993 - 94.

PINACEAE

Norway Spruce *Picea abies* (L.) Karsten
Introduced into the garden in 1966, but died in 1976.

Bishop Pine *Pinus muricata* D. Don
Introduced into the garden in 1966, but died in 1976.

RANUNCULACEAE

Meadow Buttercup *Ranunculus acris* L. ✿
Occasional in marshland (e.g. particularly within rabbit-exclosures at Orchid Bog and The Well), rare in grassland. Not recorded prior to 1947.

Creeping Buttercup *Ranunculus repens* L. ✿
Frequent throughout most communities, particularly damp grassland and marshes.

Lesser Spearwort *Ranunculus flammula* L. ✿
Abundant in moist grassland, marshes, flushes, ponds and streams.

Celandine *Ranunculus ficaria* L. ✿
Frequent on the coastal slopes in a variety of plant communities, e.g. on the relatively-sheltered slopes above South Haven where Bracken forms a dense canopy in the summer, but also persists where Bracken has been eradicated by spraying of herbicide; in coastal grassland dominate by the grasses Red Fescue and Common Bent on the north and west coasts, e.g. above The Dents. Produces a spectacular floral display in late-March.

Ivy-leaved Crowfoot *Ranunculus hederaceus* L. ✿
A colony in the spring-fed Well Pool and the stream draining it into South Haven; also in Orchid Bog Pool and the stream that drains it into North Haven.

Three-lobed Crowfoot *Ranunculus tripartitus* D.C. ✿
A flourishing colony in a small spring-fed pool and drainage stream at The Dip, first discovered in 1949. A nationally-scarce species confined to the south and south west of Britain, and the island's rarest plant. Described as a "winter annual", strangely it has been recorded flowering and fruiting in all months March to October on Skokholm during the period 1997 - 2003 (personal observations), particularly so during wet summers, and it is suspected that this resulted from the development of a good seed bank (Evans & Lansdown, 2000).

Pond Water-crowfoot *Ranunculus peltatus* Schrank. ✿
Intermittently recorded from North Pond, perhaps overlooked, but no records between 1947 and 1960, nor since 2000.

Old man's Beard *Clematis vitalba* L.
Planted in the Observatory garden in 1982, but did not survive.

Pheasant's Eye *Adonis annua* L.
Eight plants were in the Observatory garden in 1950.

PAPAVERACEAE

Common Poppy *Papaver rhoeas* L.
A weed of cultivation, it was occasional in the Observatory garden up to the 1950's.

FUMARIACEAE

Common Fumitory *Fumaria officinalis* L.
One plant was found flowering on The Neck in May 1991.

URTICACEAE

Small Nettle *Urtica urens* L.
Locally frequent around the Observatory buildings and in gull colonies on the sheltered south- and east-coasts, occasionally elsewhere.

Common Nettle *Urtica dioica* L.
Abundant around the Observatory and locally frequent in the shelter of walls or tall Bracken. Although nitrophilous, it is only rarely found in the gull colonies, with the exception of the area to the immediate west of Orchid Bog (where this plant is the dominant species, affording excellent concealment to incubating birds and also chicks).

BETULACEAE

Silver Birch *Betula pendula* Roth.
A single tree was introduced to the courtyard early 1980's, but was dead by 1996.

Alder *Alnus glutinosa* (L.) Gaertn.
Five saplings were planted in the rabbit-exclosure by The Well in 1976, with three surviving in 1983, but none by 1987.

Hazel *Corylus avellana* L.
Seedlings were planted in the cottage garden in 1982, and one small tree survives (2004).

CHENOPODIACEAE

Good-King-Henry *Chenopodium bonus-henricus* L.
Found at the lime kiln and around the Observatory buildings in the 1990's. A scarce plant in Pembrokeshire.

Red Goosefoot *Chenopodium rubrum* L. ✲
A dwarf form is the first and most abundant coloniser of the dry pond-beds and depression pans in early-summer. It is very tolerant of exposure and is found scattered along the cliff-edge. Found at very few other sites in Pembrokeshire.

Nettle-leaved Goosefoot *Chenopodium murale* L. ✲
Frequent near the lighthouse, and in East Bog and South Pond areas. At very few other sites in Pembrokeshire.

Fat-hen *Chenopodium album* L.
Sparsely distributed on ungrazed cliffs.

Spear-leaved Orache *Atriplex prostrata* L.
Abundant on all cliffs, occasionally in gardens.

Babington's Orache *Atriplex glabriuscula* Edmonst.
A characteristic nitrophile of bird colonies where grazing is slight or absent, e.g. rocky slopes at Blacksmith's Landing, and the gull-dominated promontory of Little Neck. One record of it in dry pond-beds (1949).

Common Orache *Atriplex patula* L.
Frequent on cliffs and as a weed of cultivation. Recorded in the period 1947 - 60, in 1984, and again after 1987, e.g. at the edges of South Haven stream at its lowermost reaches.

Shrubby Orache *Atriplex halimus* L.
Two seedlings were planted in the cottage garden in 1982, but both had died by the following year.

Sea-purslane *Atriplex portulacoides* (L.)
One or two plants have persisted on two small sea-stacks in Obione Bay since the species was first seen in 1947. Herring Gulls have occasionally built a nest on top of the plants in the 1990's and at least up to 2004, with no really detrimental effects exhibited. Better-known as a salt-marsh plant, this is one of several cliff sites in West Wales.

Sea Beet *Beta vulgaris* L. ssp. *maritima* (L.) Thell.
An obligate halophyte. Common in cliff-crevices where grazing is absent.

Atriplex prostrata L. x *Atriplex glabriuscula* Edmonst.
Identified on The Stack in 1950.

PORTULACEAE

Blinks *Montia fontana* L. ⊛
A dwarf form is occasional to frequent in moist, closely-grazed turf. Larger plants are abundant in marshes, streams and cliff flushes.

CARYOPHYLLACEAE

Common Chickweed *Stellaria media* (L.) Vill. ⊛
Abundant in heavily-manured areas and on recently-bared soil. Nitrophilous and shade-tolerant. It is one of the most characteristic species of burrow entrances and is dominant in the Lesser Black-backed Gull colonies and on footpaths from autumn through until spring, once trampling pressure from human visitors has ceased. Was the dominant plant of the lairs of the Soay Sheep that were kept on Skokholm in the past.

Lesser Stitchwort *Stellaria graminea* L. ⊛
Scattered among sheltered grass and Heather, e.g. the rabbit-exclosures.

Bog Stitchwort *Stellaria uliginosa* Grimm. ⊛
Once frequent in sheltered streams, marshes and cliff flushes, but in recent times only found in the Well Pool, in the stream draining Orchid Bog and on the banks of the stream down into South Haven.

Common Mouse-ear *Cerastium fontanum* Fr. ⊛
Scattered throughout all communities, but commonest in grassland.

Sticky Mouse-ear *Cerastium glomeratum* Thuill.
On southern and eastern cliffs, uncommon; also found amongst Sand Sedge *Carex arenaria* southwest of North Pond in 1982.

Sea Mouse-ear *Cerastium diffusum* Pers. ⊛
Abundant as dwarf, ephemeral plants on cliffs and on coastal grassland and in Thrift, and on the top of the wall between the Cottage and the Middle Block.

Heath Pearlwort *Sagina subulata* (SW.) C. Presl. ⊛
Common in the heavily-grazed grassland in the east (e.g. Home Meadow and Northern Plain, and on footpaths between the Observatory and Crab Bay; also on the slopes of Crab Bay). Also on walls, rock outcrops and in dry pond-beds in summer.

Procumbent Pearlwort *Sagina procumbens* L. ⊛
Commonly distributed throughout tall communities but generally replaced by *Sagina maritima* in the most-exposed habitats.

Annual Pearlwort *Sagina apetala* Ard.
Unconfirmed sightings between 1947 and 1952. Recent records of plants on a wall near the laboratory in 1981 and in 1993.

Sea Pearlwort *Sagina maritima* Don. ⊛
Abundant in closely-grazed maritime swards. Also found in cliff crevices and on inland rock-outcrops. Has been confused with Thyme-leaved Sandwort *Arenaria serpyllifolia* when in later stages of disintegration.

Corn Spurrey *Spergula arvensis* L.
In the Observatory garden prior to 1946, then in gull-roost areas on cliffs at Dumbbell Bay in July 1950. Seeds have been identified in gull pellets found on the island (Gillham, 1952), and this species' absence now is probably a reflection of the increased use of herbicides in modern farming practises.

Rock Sea-spurrey *Spergularia rupicola* Lebel ex Le Jolis. ⊛
Common on all cliffs and in coastal Thrift, forming mats in exposed places with shallow soils e.g. Twinlet Bay, and to the south and west of the lighthouse. Tolerant of extreme exposure to wind and salt-spray.

Ragged-Robin *Lychnis flos-cuculi* L.
A cluster of flowering plants was amongst rushes to the south of East Bog in 1998. How did it suddenly appear and then disappear?

Sea Campion *Silene uniflora* Roth (*S. maritima* With.) ⊛
Dominant on cliff-top slopes except in the most exposed sites. Seems to be favoured by manuring; is tolerant of partial burial, and of shading by coastal Bracken. Many plants lack the red pigment in the calyx (so are pale-green and white). Not grazed by rabbits and affected in some seasons by the fungi *Uromyces behenis* (D.C.) Unger and *Ustilago violacea* (Pers.) G. Deml & Oberw. In the last few decades it has made huge advances into areas previously covered by Thrift, and is even found on walls and earth-banks towards the centre of the island, e.g. at North Pond, completely away from areas that one would normally consider to be its "proper" habitat.

White Campion *Silene latifolia* Poiret
Rare in the Observatory garden, not seen since the early-1950's.

Red Campion *Silene dioica* (L.) Clairv.
Previously rare amongst Bracken in the east and not recorded in the period 1950 to 1975. Since then, it has been expanding to the east and south of The Well in South Haven Basin and there are scattered clumps by the Observatory, in the yards, and stands amongst Bracken to the south of The Bog. Also, previously recorded on the eastern-most end of The Neck (1982).

POLYGONACEAE

Amphibious Bistort *Persicaria amphibia* (L.) Gray
Dominant in North Pond, South Pond and some of the depression pans. Occasional in damp grassland.

Redshank *Persicaria maculosa* Gray
Frequently recorded, with scattered plants in the cliff-top gull colonies, depression pans around North Pond, and in the gardens.

Water-pepper *Persicaria hydropiper* (L.) Spach
Locally dominant in the wetter areas of springs, marshes and depression pans, and the streams draining them, e.g. South Pond, Orchid Bog, North Pond, and the waterfall on the cliff in Hog Bay. The beautiful lime-green foliage turns an intense red in the early-autumn and is easily located then, before fading then withering away.

Knotgrass *Polygonum aviculare* L.
Scattered plants in the gull roosts on the cliffs and in the yard and gardens. The Knot Grass moth *Acronicta rumicis* L. is frequently recorded (although its caterpillars have also been recorded feeding on docks *Rumex* sp., and on Stinging Nettle).

Sheep's Sorrel *Rumex acetosella* L.
Common everywhere except in the wettest and most exposed habitats or beneath the denser stands of Bracken. Characteristically associated with Rabbit warrens.

Common Sorrel *Rumex acetosa* L.
Common everywhere and especially abundant in gull colonies, even on cliff-top slopes. More salt-tolerant, shade-tolerant and moisture-tolerant than *R. acetosella.* Produces particularly-lush foliage amongst the withering Bracken in the autumn.

Curled Dock *Rumex crispus* L.
Frequent on cliffs, amongst supralittoral boulders and in the seasonal ponds and ditches. Occasional in grassland.

Wood Dock *Rumex sanguineus* L.
There were two small clumps near sea level in South Haven and others on north-east coasts in 1950, and again in 1975.

Broad-leaved Dock *Rumex obtusifolius* L.
One plant on the wall of the workshop (now known as the Bullhouse) in the period 1980 to 1983.

PLUMBAGINACEAE

Thrift *Armeria maritima* (Miller) Willd.
The most resistant of all the island species to both salt-laden winds and biotic activity, it once dominated all of the most exposed areas around the island perimeter. It is rapidly overrun by *Festuca rubra* or *Holcus lanatus* when grazing is eliminated, and in recent years, some originally pure stands have been extensively invaded by Sea Campion *Silene maritima.* It is tolerant of medium to heavy manuring and trampling, but gives way to grasses and *Plantago coronopus* when either is excessive. It forms deep masses of "peat-like" material which are water-retentive in even the windiest situations and these are much burrowed into by birds and rabbits, giving the community a characteristic hummocky appearance.

CLUSIACEAE

Trailing St. John's-wort *Hypericum humifusum* L. ✤
Scattered in grass communities in the east, e.g. Gull Field, The Neck, but is easily overlooked; formerly found amongst Heather.

Marsh St. John's-wort *Hypericum elodes* L. ✤
Abundant in East Pond/E. Bog and now spreading westwards onto the marsh; long since extinct in South Pond.

MALVACEAE

Tree-mallow *Lavatera arborea* L. ✤
Rooted into crevices on sheer cliffs in sheltered eastern inlets, e.g. Crab Bay, Wreck Cove, Peter's Bay and formerly Hog Bay. Also found on the southern side of The Stack. Skokholm seeds were sown into the Observatory garden in 1953 (outcome unknown), and again into the Wall Garden during the 1990's, where

plants now appear intermittently following any digging, reaching huge proportions (up to 2m in height). It is a species restricted to south-western Britain.

VIOLACEAE

Common Dog-violet *Viola riviniana* Reichb.
Abundant in grassland and former heath; occasional to frequent in marshy grassland and amongst Bracken. Plants found above North Haven resembling *V. reichenbachiana* in the late 1980's were considered to show aberrant morphology due to stress.

Wild Pansy *Viola tricolor tricolor.* L.
Abundant on cliff-tops – generally amongst Sea Campion – in the vicinity of Crab Bay and Spy Rock / Wreck Cove, and a little at North Haven and towards the eastern-end of The Neck. A rare species in Pembrokeshire.

TAMARICACEAE

Tamarisk *Tamarix gallica* L.
A small bush was in the cottage garden from 1975 until the mid-to-late 1980's.

SALICACEAE

Silky-leaved Osier *Salix cinerea* x *S. viminalis* = *S.* x *smithiana*
Introduced into the rabbit-exclosure at The Well sometime in the 1960's/70's, and is still present. Growth is limited by the salty winds.

Goat Willow *Salix caprea* L.
Cuttings from plants on the mainland were introduced into the rabbit-exclosure at The Well and in the garden in 1980 - 81, but they were dead by 1987.

Grey Willow *Salix cinerea* L.
Cuttings were introduced to the Wall Garden, and to The Well and Orchid Bog rabbit-exclosures in the late-1980's and early-1990's, but only survived in the garden. Cuttings taken from the garden were planted in the Well Exclosure in 1994, where they continue to thrive despite the attentions of rabbits in the winter of 2001 - 02 when they breached the fence.

Creeping Willow *Salix repens* L.
There is a well-established wild population in East Bog, the major part fenced off from Rabbits, but it seems to grow equally well outside. Previously also found on the cliffs in Hog Bay (Gillham, 1953b).

BRASSICACEAE

Thale Cress *Arabidopsis thaliana* (L.) Heynh.
A single colony recorded on the sheltered North Haven cliff in 1947 - 53 (was mistakenly recorded as *Arabis hirsuta* (L.) Scop.)

Water-cress *Rorippa nasturtium-aquaticum* (L.) Hayek.
Occasional in East Pond and eastern spring-fed streams. Formerly dominant at The Well Pool. Rarely found in western cliff flushes.

Horse-radish *Armoracia rusticana* Gaertn., Mey & Scherb.
A single plant outside the wheelhouse, planted in 1976, disappeared by 1996. A part of the root was transplanted to the Wall Garden in 1995 and the resulting plant still flourishes, despite usually being defoliated by the caterpillars of Large White butterflies *Pieris brassicae*.

Cuckooflower *Cardamine pratensis* L.
Frequent in marshes and streams, particularly East and Orchid Bogs and the Well Pool, but has become far less-common in recent years.

Hairy Bitter-cress *Cardamine hirsuta* L. ✷
Rare in sheltered parts of cliff, grassland and garden.

Common Scurvygrass *Cochlearia officinalis* L.
Some on damp, shady cliffs e.g. Rat Bay, but in a persistently dense stand on the eastern cliff-top slope of Hog Bay which is heavily-manured by seabirds. Intermittently present and in varying abundance in other locations such as Theatre Cove and South Haven.

Danish Scurvygrass *Cochlearia danica* L. ✷
Scattered on cliffs and walls, but widespread amongst Sea Campion in all areas from The Neck to the westernmost end of the island.

Shepherd's-purse *Capsella bursa-pastoris* (L.) Medikus ✷
Very few records, e.g. in the Wheelhouse yard in July 1950; near the Gantry in 1979; occasional in yards and gardens since.

Lesser Swine-cress *Coronopus didymus* (L.) Smith ✷
Abundant in the gardens whenever soil is disturbed. Occasional in short grass on cliffs and paths.

Cabbage *Brassica oleracea* L.
There was one plant on the promontory between Peter's Bay and Dumbbell Bay in May 1950, and another in Bracken to the south of Hog Bay (near Little Split) in June 1950.

Charlock *Sinapis arvensis* L.
Rare, flowering in the Observatory garden in June 1950, near North Pond in July 1980, and one plant flowering in a gull colony on a slope west of Wreck Cove in 1983.

ERICACEAE

Heather *Calluna vulgaris* (L.) Hull

Formerly widespread in the eastern-half of the island, but by the 1980's restricted to the two fields immediately west of the Observatory buildings. Bushes were stunted by grazing and by salt-damage from wind-borne sea-spray. It is intolerant of manuring and trampling and has been overrun by Bracken in places. A rabbit-exclosure was installed east of North Pond in 1991 at the last active site, to immediate and dramatic effect, with an extension to the fence erected in 1997 further encouraging its growth and spread.

Bell Heather *Erica cinerea* L.

There were formerly a few plants scattered among the Heather in the north-east, extinct by the mid-1980's.

PRIMULACEAE

Primrose *Primula vulgaris* Huds. ⊛

Abundant in moist, sheltered soils in South Haven, above North Haven and in Windmill Gully, and on earthy cliff slopes in Rat Bay.

Cowslip *Primula veris* L.

One or two plants amongst the Bracken of South Haven before 1949.

Primula vulgaris x *P. veris* = *P. polyantha* Miller

One or two plants previously recorded by the South Haven stream.

Bog Pimpernel *Anagallis tenella* (L.) L. ⊛

Frequent to locally-dominant in moist grassland and flushes across the island, but particularly common at East Bog (on a little-used trackway), in grassland between North Stream and The Jogs, and at The Dip.

Scarlet Pimpernel *Anagallis arvensis* ssp. *arvensis* L. ⊛

Frequent throughout, in all communities, particularly grassland and thrift and often associated with rabbit warrens. The pink flowered form is found in various locations, e.g. beside the main trackway that runs between South Haven and Crab Bay, and amongst Sea Campion at The Dents.

Blue Pimpernel *Anagallis arvensis* ssp. *caerulea* Hartmann

First found on the north coast in 1947, and frequently on Northern Plain and annually amongst Thrift by Long Low since the 1980's.

Chaffweed *Anagallis minima* (L.) E.H. Krause ⊛

Locally-frequent in closely-grazed grassland, and seasonally-flooded areas in the east. Scarce in Pembrokeshire.

Sea-milkwort *Glaux maritima* L. ⊛

A small population at the seaward end of North Pond Stream, about 30m above sea-level. Normally a plant of salt-marshes, the seed may have been brought to Skokholm by birds.

Brookweed *Samolus valeriandi* L. ✤
Frequent in streams, ditches and damp areas in the south and east, becoming rarer in the west.

HYDRANGEACEAE

Hydrangea *Hydrangea* sp.
One plant in the cottage garden from about 1975. Flowered irregularly in the 1980's, but annually since.

GROSSULARIACEAE

Escallonia *Escallonia* sp.
Six were planted in the cottage garden and Wheelhouse courtyard in 1983, with just one surviving in the following year and supplemented by new cuttings, but all were gone by 1988.

Red Currant *Ribes rubrum* L.
Two bushes were planted in the cottage garden in 1982. Extinct by 1987.

Black Currant *Ribus nigrum* L.
Previously planted in the cottage garden, heavily grazed by goats prior to 1981. One large bush and two cuttings were planted in 1982, but were dead by 1987. Two more were subsequently planted, and these continue to survive (but not thrive) within a rabbit-exclosure.

CRASSULACEAE

Navelwort *Umbilicus repestris* (Salisb.) Dandy
Frequent in cliff-crevices and on ungrazed rocks and walls and, rather unusually, on an earthy Bracken-dominated slope in South Haven.

English Stonecrop *Sedum anglicum* Huds. ✤
A plant common in crevices of cliffs, walls and inland rock outcrops, frequent in grassland and especially among moribund Thrift.

ROSACEAE

Meadowsweet *Filipendula ulmaria* (L.) Maxim. ✤
Once rare beside the lower part of the sheltered stream leading into South Haven. Last recorded in 1953.

Bramble *Rubus series Glandulosi* Wimmer & Grab.
Numerus low bushes in the sheltered parts of the island, particularly since the removal of sheep (in 1939 - 40) and goats (in 1981). There is an expanse of large plants behind The Wheelhouse and also in the rabbit-exclosure at East Bog. Small patches exist within the lime kiln and the old well. Introduced into a rabbit-exclosure in the

247

cottage garden in 1994 - 95, where plants have since slowly become established amongst a dense mat of Red Fescue grass.

Raspberry *Rubus idaeus* L.
Two plants appeared in the cottage garden in 1982, but they never thrived and were dead before 1990.

Silverweed *Potentilla anserina* L. ⊛
Abundant in damp grassland, marshes, ditches and shallow ponds, and wholly dominant in places, e.g. immediately east of Winter Pond.

Tormentil *Potentilla erecta* (L.) Raeusch. ⊛
Abundant in short grassland and heathland, mostly in the east. Occasional in marshy areas and under the sparser Bracken.

Trailing Tormentil *Potentilla anglica* Laich. ⊛
Once rare in grass and heath, e.g. on The Neck, and west of the buildings, in the 1940's. Not recorded since 1950.

Creeping Cinquefoil *Potentilla reptans* L.
Once rare in the central grasslands, but not recorded since 1960.

Burnet Rose *Rosa pimpinellifolia* L.
There were previously a few plants on North Haven cliffs, and one in the cottage garden in 1960.

Blackthorn *Prunus spinosa* L.
A small population on a spur of the North Haven cliffs. Introduced into the cottage garden, and Well and East Bog exclosures 1988 - 1991, but only two of the introductions survive, both in the garden.

Hawthorn *Crataegus monogyna* Jacq.
Five plants were introduced into the cottage garden in 1982, extinct by 1987. One introduced into the same site in 1995 was dead the following year.

FABACEAE

Kidney Vetch *Anthyllis vulneraria* L. ⊛
Rare on inaccessible parts of the more sheltered cliffs, e.g. Peter's Bay, South Haven.

Common Bird's-foot-trefoil *Lotus corniculatus* L. ⊛
Abundant in grassland, occasional to frequent amongst Thrift and Heather. A small patch persists (2004) in a crevice on the southern side of Sugar Loaf, out of the reach of grazers and which flowers profusely each year.

Greater Bird's-foot-trefoil *Lotus pedunculatus* Cav. (*L. uliginosus* Schk.). ⊛
Abundant in marshland, and frequent in grassland and amongst Heather, it seems to benefit from exclosure protection from grazing by rabbits, although in some years does flourish outside these too. Not recorded before 1947.

Tufted Vetch *Vicia cracca* L.
One plant was at East Bog in 1949.

Common Vetch *Vicia sativa* L.
Recorded by Lockley. Subsequently there were single plants at Orchid Bog (1977) and on Sugar Loaf (1983).

HALORAGACEAE

Alternate Water-milfoil *Myriophyllum alterniflorum* DC. ⊛
Common in North Pond.

LYTHRACEAE

Water-purslane *Lythrum portula* (L.) D. Webb (*Peplis portula* L.) ⊛
Frequent in shallow ponds and depression pans, e.g. Winter Pond, South Pond.

ONAGRACEAE

Great Willowherb *Epilobium hirsutum* L.
A clump in the Wall Garden from 1999, possibly introduced in a birdseed mix, and fast-establishing itself there.

Short-fruited Willowherb *Epilobium obscurum* Schreb. ⊛
Occasional in the eastern marshes; noted in 1975, 1983 and 1991 (at Orchid Bog) and 1993 (at East Bog).

Marsh Willowherb *Epilobium palustre* L.
In marsh and bog in the 1940's.

Fuchsia *Fuchsia magellanica* Lam.
In the garden in 1953. None in 1981. Reintroduced in 1990 into two rabbit-exclosures on the eastern side of walls around the observatory buildings. Cuttings were successfully planted in the Wheelhouse Yard in 1998-99.

EUPHORBIACEAE

Annual Mercury *Mercurialis annua* L.
One plant in the cottage garden in 1954.

Sun Spurge *Euphorbia helioscopia* L.
Once frequent in the Cottage Garden (1950).

Dwarf Spurge *Euphorbia exigua* L.
Recorded on the edge of the lighthouse track before 1947, but not since.

Petty Spurge *Euphorbia peplus* L.

An occasional weed in the Observatory garden prior to 1940 and again in 1953.

LINACEAE

Allseed *Radiola linoides* Roth

Abundant and often locally-dominant in short turf, e.g. Northern Plain, Green Heath.

POLYGALACEAE

Heath Milkwort *Polygala serpyllifolia* Hose

Recorded on heathland in the 1940's and 1950's. Very occasional since among short grass and Heather of sheltered situations, e.g. Green Heath Rabbit Exclosure.

ACERACEAE

Sycamore *Acer pseudoplatanus* L.

Six in the Observatory garden where they are afforded some shelter by the low walls, three of which are "mature" but very stunted. There are small trees in the rabbit-exclosure by The Well. Several seedlings were planted in the garden in 1982 and many more in the shelter of walls around the Observatory (rabbit-exclosures erected) in the late 1980's and 1990's, which are flourishing. Two or three plants growing "as one" in the Wheelhouse yard have flourished since the 1970's, setting seed annually, and now constitute by far the largest "tree" on Skokholm. Their size is limited by the height of the walls and buildings, with summer growth quickly killed back by autumn gales. Very popular with migrating birds, undoubtedly due in part to the relative scarcity of cover elsewhere on the island.

GERANIACEAE

Cut-leaved Cranesbill *Geranium dissectum* L.

A single plant was on Halfway Wall next to North Pond in 1987.

Sea Storks-bill *Erodium maritimum* (L.) L'Her. ⊛

Common in grassland on dry, shallow soils right across the island. Particularly characteristic of cliff-slopes and as an early colonizer of bare soil. A "nationally scarce" species.

ARALIACEAE

Ivy *Hedera helix* L.

On numerous parts of cliffs in North Haven and on the western face of Spy Rock.

APIACEAE

Marsh Pennywort *Hydrocotyle vulgaris* L. ⊛
Abundant to locally-dominant in marshland and damp grassland. Dominant in damp hollows in Bracken communities and abundant in shallow ponds, pans and cliff flushes; occasional among Thrift.

Sweet Cicely *Myrrhis odorata* (L.) Scop.
Planted in the Wall Garden in 1999.

Rock Samphire *Crithmum maritimum* L.
An obligate halophyte unable to withstand grazing, but abundant as a crevice plant on all ungrazed cliffs.

Hemlock Water-dropwort *Oenanthe crocata* L. ⊛
Locally dominant on steep, wet cliffs in Hog Bay where East Pond Stream flows over, in the exclosures at the Well and Orchid Bog, and occasionally recorded at South Pond. Requires protection from grazing by rabbits.

Hemlock *Conium maculatum* L. ⊛
Abundant around the Observatory buildings, rare elsewhere.

Fool's Water-cress *Apium nodiflorum* (L.) Lag. ⊛
Common in the semi-permanent spring-fed streams draining East Bog and the Well Pool.

Lesser Marshwort *Apium inundatum* (L.) H.G. Reichb.
Found in the still waters of the ponds, depression pans and ditches, and in the stream draining the The Dip pool. On the muddy margins of summer pools within the expanse of an otherwise dry North Pond basin. A scarce plant in Pembrokeshire.

Hogweed *Heracleum sphondylium* L. ⊛
Patches of considerable size in various locations: inland of The Oven, at Windmill Gully, Hard Point and on the north-eastern part of The Neck, to the north of North Pond, and around the Observatory buildings. Previously on the southern slopes of Hog Bay (pers. obs.). The flower umbels are visited by numerous insects in mid-summer, and plants are frequently defoliated by the larvae of the beetle *Phaedon tumidulus* and of caterpillars of moths such as *Depressaria* spp. In the autumn, migrant birds such as Willow Warblers seek those insects that live within the hollow stems.

Sea Carrot *Daucus carota* L. ssp. *gummifer* (Syme) Hook.
A small self-perpetuating population, in crevices high up on the relatively sheltered south-facing cliff face of Wreck Cove.

GENTIANACEAE

Common Centaury *Centaurium erythraea* Rafn. var. *capitatum* (Willd.ex Cham.)
Dwarf plants frequent in closely-grazed grassland, especially on the eastern, damper regions of Home Meadow near a spring. In the early 2000's a spread of Goldenrod across Home Meadow encouraged Centaury plants to advance alongside it, and many large specimens (for Skokholm) result from the sheltered conditions.

SOLANACEAE

Tomato *Lycopersicon esculentum* Miller (*L. lycopersicum* (L.) Karsten)
A few plants were well-established in the vicinity of gull colonies on the boulders and cliff-slopes in North Haven/Rat Bay and Peter's Bay in August 2003.

Black Nightshade *Solanum nigrum* L.
Locally frequent in the dry bed of South Pond, in gull colonies on sheltered cliffs, in the vicinity of the lime kiln, usually within Bracken and only really obvious once the *Pteridium* begins to wither in the autumn. Occasionally found around the buildings.

Bittersweet *Solanum dulcamara* L. ⊛
A few plants were recorded on a cliff in Hog Bay until at least 1956 (Gillham 1956a). In 1991, there were a few plants in The Bog, in Bracken situated between The Well and in South Haven, and one by South Pond in 1993.

CONVOLVULACEAE

Hedge Bindweed *Calystegia sepium* (L.) R. Br.
A single plant was in the cottage garden in 1983 - 84.

BORAGINACEAE

Borage *Borago officinalis* L. ⊛
Introduced to the cottage garden and where plants quickly appear following disturbance of the soil.

Water Forget-me-not *Myosotis scorpioides* L.
Occasional in damp places in the east.

Creeping Forget-me-not *Myosotis secunda* A. Murr. ⊛
Common in ponds, streams and ditches.

Field Forget-me-not *Myosotis arvensis* (L.) Hill
Occasional around the Observatory buildings.

Early Forget-me-not *Myosotis ramosissima* Rochel. ✲

Abundant on cliff-tops and walls, occasional as a weed of cultivation, and particularly common amongst Sea Campion and sorrels. Previously abundant amongst Thrift and Heather.

Changing Forget-me-not *Myosotis discolor* Pers. ✲

Occasional to frequent on cliffs, in grassland, on the edges of footpaths and amongst short Bracken.

LAMIACEAE

Betony *Stachys officinalis* (L.) Trev. St. Leon

A single plant on a sheltered cliff in North Haven in 1949.

Marsh Woundwort *Stachys palustris* L. ✲

A large colony in the cottage garden up to 1947.

Field Woundwort *Stachys arvensis* (L.) L. ✲

Recorded by Lockley, and reappeared in the cottage garden in 1954. A weed of cultivation.

White Dead-nettle *Lamium album* L.

A few plants in the Wall Garden from the year 2000.

Red Dead-nettle *Lamium purpureum* L. ✲

Frequent in the cottage garden.

Henbit Dead-nettle *Lamium amplexicaule* L.

Recorded by Lockley.

Common Hemp-nettle *Galeopsis tetrahit* L.

Recorded by Lockley.

Lesser Skullcap *Scutellaria minor* Huds. ✲

Once occasional to frequent in marshy grassland of the east and centre, also near Northern Rocks, but in recent years confined to East Bog. Its decline was thought to be due to the increase in numbers of Lesser Black-backed Gulls, though large numbers of these birds currently roosting at E. Bog do not seem to have affected it at all.

Wood Sage *Teucrium scorodonia* L. ✲

Patchily abundant in parts of the central fields (previously amongst the Heather that grew there) such as Gull Field, Isthmian Heath, the southern-most limits of Northern Plain, and on The Neck. Also amongst sparse Bracken in the same areas. Not grazed by Rabbits.

Bugle *Ajuga reptans* L.

Recorded by Lockley.

Cat-mint *Nepeta cateria* L.
One plant outside the "Middle Block" building between 1973 and 1975.

Ground-ivy *Glechoma hederacea* L. ⊛
Abundant beneath Bracken and also on heavily-grazed grassland and sheltered cliff-tops, previously amongst Heather. Typically the first plant to produce flowers (in March) and visited by queen bumblebees. Lush foliage is produced in the autumn by those plants growing amongst Bracken.

Selfheal *Prunella vulgaris* L. ⊛
Common in grassland and marshes, and on footpath edges.

Balm *Melissa officinalis* L.
Introduced into the Wall Garden in 1999.

Wild Thyme *Thymus polytrichus* A. Kerner ex Borbas (*T. drucei* Ronn.) ⊛
Formerly frequent among Heather, now scattered patches in grassland and on rocks and cliffs, e.g. cliff-top in Rat Bay, on Sugar Loaf, Spy Rock and The Cutting.

Gypsywort *Lycopus europaeus* L.
Three plants in the stream draining Orchid Bog, near to the cliff, in 1960; twelve clumps flowering on marshy ground to the north of North Pond in 2003.

Water Mint *Mentha aquatica* L. ⊛
Frequent in East Pond, Orchid Bog, marshes and streams. Rare further west.

CALLITRICHACEAE

Common Water-starwort *Callitriche stagnalis* Scop. ⊛
Abundant in all temporarily-submerged areas, ponds, pans, streams and ditches.

PLANTAGINACEAE

Buck's-horn Plantain *Plantago coronopus* L. ⊛
Minute plants dominate those areas of the cliff-tops that are subjected to intense grazing, burrowing, treading and manuring. Larger plants are found on walls and rocky outcrops. A broad-leaved succulent form *maritimum* occurs on inaccessible cliffs e.g. Little Bay, The Stack, and is characteristically nitrophilous and salt-tolerant.

Sea Plantain *Plantago maritima* L. ⊛
Large plants are frequent on inaccessible cliff-faces except the most windswept sites. Very intolerant of grazing.

Greater Plantain *Plantago major* L. ⊛
Frequent in garden and formerly frequent in gull feeding-grounds on the cliffs. Rare on footpaths.

Ribwort Plantain *Plantago lanceolata* L.
Occasional in yards and gardens. A few by a northern stream in 1951.

Shoreweed *Littorella uniflora* (L.) Asch. ⊛
Abundant in the shallow water and then the dry beds of all the temporary ponds and depression pans and in some of the streams and ditches.

BUDDLEJACEAE

Butterfly-bush *Buddleja davidii* Franch.
Planted in Observatory gardens in 1981, but gone by 1987. More planted around Observatory 1988 onwards, now thriving and providing nectar for butterflies and cover for birds.

OLEACEAE

Ash *Fraxinus excelsior* L.
Introduced into Observatory garden. Extinct by 1960.

Wild Privet *Ligustrum vulgare* L.
A few plants on a sheltered western cliff face in North Haven. Introduced into Observatory garden in 1982, still present 2004.

SCROPHULARIACEAE

Common Figwort *Scrophularia nodosa* L. ⊛
Once occasional among tall Bracken in South Haven basin, in recent years has appeared just to the east of the Wheelhouse.

Sharp-leaved Fluellen *Kickxia elatine* (L.) Dum.
A small colony flowered and fruited on a cliff face in Calf Bay in 1948.

Foxglove *Digitalis purpurea* L. ⊛
A few plants annually on the steep, sheltered cliffs of North Haven (occasionally on rockfall) and the walls of the Observatory gardens, very occasional in Bracken and on walls elsewhere in the east.

Thyme-leaved Speedwell *Veronica serpyllifolia* L.
Once occasional among the eastern Heather before its demise.

Heath Speedwell *Veronica officinalis* L. ⊛
Formerly frequent among Heather.

Germander Speedwell *Veronica chamaedrys* L. ⊛
One plant previously amongst the (now extinct) Heather on The Neck, and one plant within the rabbit-exclosure at East Bog in 1995.

Wall Speedwell *Veronica arvensis* L. ⊛
Occasional in yards and gardens, but not recorded since 1960.

Green Field-speedwell *Veronica agrestis* L.
Frequent in gardens and yards, and occasional amongst Bracken.

Common Field-speedwell *Veronica persica* Poir. ⊛
Occasionally abundant in the yards and gardens; once rare in the north-eastern grassland and Heather.

Ivy-leaved Speedwell *Veronica hederifolia* L.
Recorded by Lockley.

Eyebright *Euphrasia* sp.
The nomenclature changes within the eyebrights means that the species need(s) checking. Once abundant among short grass and heather, in recent years has been restricted to the top of a grassy mound within East Bog.

Marsh Lousewort *Pedicularis palustris* L.
Recorded by Lockley.

Lousewort *Pedicularis sylvatica* L.
Recorded by Lockley.

CAMPANULACEAE

Sheep's-bit *Jasione montana* L.
A few plants exist on the vertical western face of Spy Rock; on the eastern face of Crab Bay in 1989.

RUBIACEAE

Woodruff *Galium odoratum* (L.) Scop.
Recorded by Lockley.

Common Marsh-bedstraw *Galium palustre* L. ⊛
Frequent in marshes, ponds and streams.

Lady's Bedstraw *Galium verum* L. ⊛
Occasional to rare on sheltered rock-outcrops, among short grass and in North Haven (on the western cliff-face and central spur).

Heath Bedstraw *Galium saxatile* L. ✿
Abundant in grass- and Heather-communities.

CAPRIFOLIACEAE

Elder *Sambucus nigra* L.
Introduced into the Observatory gardens and appeared on a westerly rock outcrop in 1953. Subsequently grew in the Heligoland trap by the well, and after removal of goats in 1981, numerous bushes appeared among the Bracken to the east of the Observatory. Damaged by salty sea-spray and usually regenerating from the base each spring. Many small plants were introduced in the period 1988 - 95, with some around the Observatory reaching up to 12 feet tall in 2000. Continues to spread. The more-sheltered plants produce berries each year that are greatly relished by some warblers, Blackbirds and Starlings. Not grazed by Rabbits.

Honeysuckle *Lonicera periclymenum* L.
A few plants exist on sheltered cliffs in North Haven and Peter's Bay.

ASTERACEAE

Lesser Burdock *Arctium minus* (Hill) Bernh.
Frequent around the Observatory and Red Hut, previously around the lighthouse and amongst eastern Bracken. Notable for very occasionally ensnaring Storm Petrels *Hydrobates pelagicus* and other small birds (e.g. Sedge Warbler *Acrocephalus schoenobaenus*) in the burrs.

Spear Thistle *Cirsium vulgare* (Savi) Ten.
Scattered throughout all but the most-exposed and wet localities, and in 2002 great numbers of dwarf plants matured amongst the western-most Sea Campion, seeding profusely.

Marsh Thistle *Cirsium palustre* (L.) Scop.
Occasional to frequent in the more-sheltered marshy areas, particularly to the south and east of North Pond, though also amongst Bracken in places, and in some years tremendous numbers of flowering plants produce a breathtaking display amongst the sorrels of The Bog.

Creeping Thistle *Cirsium arvense* (L.) Scop.
Occasional to frequent around the buildings and among grass and Heather, with isolated stands as far west as Sugarloaf.

Greater Knapweed *Centaurea scabiosa* L.
Recorded by Lockley.

Common Knapweed *Centaurea nigra* L.
One clump previously in the cottage garden. Occasionally found at North Haven.

Chicory *Cichorium intybus* L.
Recorded by Lockley in the cottage garden.

Cat's-ear *Hypochaeris radicata* L.
Frequent on the more-sheltered of the inaccessible cliffs, e.g. South Haven.

Lesser Hawkbit *Leontodon saxatilis* Lam. (*L. taraxacoides* (Villars) Merat)
Locally frequent among eastern grass and Bracken, and on eastern cliffs, e.g. Crab Bay, North Haven.

Hawkweed Oxtongue *Picris hieracioides* L.
One clump flowering on North Haven cliff in 1950.

Perennial Sow-thistle *Sonchus arvensis* L.
Previously on sheltered inaccessible cliffs and in the yards of the buildings, and from 2000 a few plants have grown amongst the Sand Sedge to the north of North Pond. There was a single plant on a Sea Campion-covered cliff-ledge at The Dents in 2003.

Smooth Sow-thistle *Sonchus oleraceus* L.
Frequent on cliffs, occasional in coastal grassland, and in the garden.

Prickly Sow-thistle *Sonchus asper* (L.) Hill.
Distribution as *S. oleraceus*, but becoming far more common in recent years, particularly around the Observatory buildings and in scattered patches elsewhere, e.g. above The Dents.

Dandelion *Taraxacum sect. Rederalia.* Kirschner, Oellgaard & Stepanek
Occasional, usually on inaccessible cliffs, tops of walls and in gardens.

Dandelion *Taraxacum sect. Erythrosperma* (Lindb. f.) Dahlst.
Not recorded since 1960.

Marsh Cudweed *Gnaphalium uliginosum* L. (*Filaginella uliginosa* (L.) Opiz.)
A summer colonizer of dry ponds and depression pans.

Common Fleabane *Pulicaria dysenterica* (L.) Bernh.
Formerly found only at Orchid Bog, now flourishing also in and above South Haven (near to the hydraulic ram-pump).

Goldenrod *Solidago virgaurea* L.
Abundant among the sheltered eastern Bracken of South Bay and North Haven, eastward to Gull Field, with an outlying patch to the west of North Haven, and in recent years forming almost single species stands on the south side of Home Meadow (where it is currently spreading westwards at a rapid rate) and above the gantry. A nectar source favoured by insects, although perhaps less so than Ragwort *Senecio vulgaris*.

Daisy *Bellis perennis* L.
Local in the yard and gardens, but commonest in the moist turf and on the damp main-trackway near East Pond.

Feverfew *Tanacetum parthenium* (L.) Schultz-Bip.
Introduced into the cotage garden in 1982, but gone by 1987.

Tansy *Tanacetum vulgare* L.
A single plant by South Pond in 1981.

Yarrow *Achillea millefolium* L. ✿
Dwarf plants – rarely flowering unless within rabbit-exclosures – are locally-frequent in the sheltered grassland.

Corn Marigold *Chrysanthemum segetum* L.
Once "local" in cliff-located gull colonies and the cottage garden.

Oxeye Daisy *Leucanthemum vulgare* Lam.
A scattering of plants on the more-sheltered of the North Haven cliffs.

Pineappleweed *Matricaria discoidea* DC.
Local in gull colonies on cliff-slopes.

Sea Mayweed *Tripleurospermum maritimum* (L.) Koch
Widespread, abundant to locally dominant on coastal slopes (e.g. above Little Bay and near to the lighthouse), frequent amongst Sea Campion and exposed grassland. Salt-tolerant.

Scentless Mayweed *Tripleurospermum inodorum* (L.) Schultz-Bip.
Occasional in the cottage garden.

Common Ragwort *Senecio jacobaea* L.
An extremely mobile biennial that dominates the various grasslands and even Bracken in some years, especially in the east. May be heavily predated by caterpillars of the Cinnabar Moth *Tyria jacobaeae*, although extinctions of the moth subsequently occur and can go unrecorded for years at a time.

Groundsel *Senecio vulgaris* L.
Occasional in yards and gardens and on the tops of the higher walls around the Observatory.

Heath Groundsel *Senecio sylvaticus* L. ✿
Occasional in yards and gardens and on the tops of the higher walls around the Observatory.

Hemp Agrimony *Eupatorium cannabinum* L.
A few clumps in two locations: on the east-facing cliff in North Haven and in Hog Bay, where spring-fed streams flow over. Recorded from East Bog in 1989.

ALISMATACEAE

Lesser Water-plantain *Baldellia ranunculoides* (L.) Parl.
Once "occasional to frequent" in temporary ponds and depression pans as far west as The Dip. Not recorded in recent years, perhaps overlooked. The few Pembrokeshire sites are largely on the St. David's peninsula.

POTAMOGETONACEAE

Broad-leaved Pondweed *Potamogeton natans* L.
Recorded in the centre of North Pond in 1965.

Bog Pondweed *Potamogeton polygonifolius* Pourret ✸
Once abundant in the deepest water of North Pond and in the northern and easterly streams, it now seems restricted to a few pools in East Bog. Requires acid water, so gull droppings could be bringing about its demise.

ARACEAE

Lords-and-Ladies *Arum maculatum* L.
A number of clumped plants in the South Haven Basin and Hog Bay, within the Well exclosure, and in the Observatory small yard beneath the Sycamore trees. The spadix of the flowers is yellow.

LEMNACEAE

Common Duckweed *Lemna minor* L.
Nitrophilous. Frequent in most ponds, streams, ditches and on sheltered wet cliffs.

JUNCACEAE

Heath Rush *Juncus squarrosus* L.
Recorded by Lockley (1947).

Toad Rush *Juncus bufonius* L.
Small plants are frequent in depression pans, cliff-flushes and marshes.

Jointed Rush *Juncus articulatus* L.
Common in ponds, marshes and cliff-flushes e.g. the lowest reaches of South Haven stream. The gall-forming plant louse *Livia juncorum* has been recorded affecting plants on Skokholm.

Sharp-flowered Rush *Juncus acutiflorus* Ehrh. Ex Hoffm.
Dominant over much of the eastern marshes.

Bulbous Rush *Juncus bulbosus* L.
Common in ponds, marshes and cliff-flushes, often of minute size in heavily-grazed areas.

Soft Rush *Juncus effuses* L.
Common in the vicinity of South Pond, and with some at East Bog.

Field Wood-rush *Luzula campestris* (L.) DC
There are many tiny plants in the heavily-grazed grasslands of the east, e.g. Northern Plain.

CYPERACEAE

Common Spike-rush *Eleocharis palustris* (L.) Roemer & Schultes ✿
Frequent in the ponds and marshes, especially North Pond.

Bristle Club-rush *Isolepsis setacea* (L.) R. Br.
Frequent in wet grassland and cliff flushes, e.g. South Haven stream.

Slender Club-rush *Isolepsis cernua* (Vahl) Roemer and Schultes
Occasional to frequent in wet grassland and cliff flushes, e.g. South Haven stream.

Floating Club-rush *Eleogiton fluitans* (L.) Link
An "almost pure community" was present along the northern edge of North Pond in 1956.

False Fox-sedge *Carex otrubae* Podp. ✿
A small patch at the seaward end of South Haven stream.

Sand Sedge *Carex arenaria* L. ✿
Frequent to locally-dominant in the centre of the island all around North Pond, to the north of the island west of Bread Rock and rare on cliffs e.g. South Haven (stream-side). Also in a few crevices on Sugar Loaf rock. It occupies an unusually wide range of habitats, from seasonally submerged areas to dry shallow soils.

Divided Sedge *Carex divisa* Hudson
Sampled from amongst the Sand Sedge on the northern edge of North Pond in 1997. It is only the second known site in Pembrokeshire, the other being at Dale on the nearby mainland.

Star Sedge *Carex echinata* Murray ✿
Rarely recorded in the eastern marshes.

Glaucous Sedge *Carex flacca* Schreb.
Occasionally recorded in sheltered freshwater areas, e.g. East Bog.

Yellow-sedge *Carex viridula* Michaux ssp. *oedocaspa* (*C. demissa* Hornem.)
Frequent in sheltered marshes, streams and cliff flushes e.g. South Haven stream.

Spring Sedge *Carex caryophyllea* Latour.
Recorded by Lockley (1947).

Common Sedge *Carex nigra* (L.) Reichard
Occasional in eastern marshes and by North Pond.

Flea Sedge *Carex pulicaris* L.
Previously very rarely found in the ponds.

POACEAE

Red Fescue *Festuca rubra* L.
Occurs in all communities but is most abundant on exposed cliff-tops and amongst Thrift. It is very tolerant of manuring and treading and would dominate all of the more-exposed parts of the island (as it does on the ungrazed island of Grassholm) if it were not grazed by rabbits. This is demonstrated by the island's rabbit-exclosures.

Sheep's-fescue *Festuca ovina* L.
Much rarer than *F. rubra* and more with an inland distribution.

Perennial Rye-grass *Lolium perenne* L.
Previously abundant and mown for hay (Fenton, 1903) but confined to yards and gardens since the increase in rabbits from 1940 onwards. Not recorded at all in recent years, but may be non-flowering and thus overlooked.

Squirreltail Fescue *Vulpia bromoides* (L.) Gray
Frequent on walls around the buildings and on eastern grassland, and formerly on heathland.

Crested Dog's-tail *Cynosurus cristatus* L.
Rare, confined to ungrazed cliffs and the shelter of tall vegetation.

Annual Meadow-grass *Poa annua* L.
An abundant colonizer of bare ground and very tolerant of manuring and trampling.

Rough Meadow-grass *Poa trivialis* L.
Frequent in Observatory gardens and as small patches on ungrazed cliffs. Occasional in streams and marshes, otherwise rare.

Smooth Meadow-grass *Poa pratensis* L.
Locally "occasional to frequent" beneath Bracken, rare in grassland, marshes and formerly amongst heather.

Cock's-foot *Dactylis glomerata* L.
Common in the Observatory garden, locally frequent on ungrazed cliffs, very rare elsewhere.

Sea Fern-grass *Catapodium marinum* (L.) C.E. Hubb.
Local on cliffs and walls, e.g. on the lime kiln.

Floating Sweet-grass *Glyceria fluitans* (L.) R.Br.
Seasonally dominant during the wet phase in many of the temporary ponds, pans and marshes. Occasional in East Bog. Has been common in the Well Pool in recent years, causing open water to be quickly lost and necessitating its part-clearance.

Downy Oat-grass *Helictotrichon pubescens* (Huds.) Pilger
Recorded by Lockley (1947).

Meadow Oat-grass *Helictotrichon pratense* (L.) Besser ex Pilger
Recorded by Lockley (1934).

False Oat-grass *Arrhenatherum elatius* (L.) J&C Presl.
Locally frequent on the steeper, most sheltered cliffs and amongst tall Bracken. Very apparent around South Haven during a *Myxomatosis* outbreak in 1989, but also subsequently.

Yellow Oat-grass *Trisetum flavescens* (L.) P. Beauv. Ex J.S & C. Presl.
A few plants flowered near the Observatory in 1947.

Yorkshire-fog *Holcus lanatus* L. ✽
Abundant everywhere due to its unpalatability to Rabbits, but particularly so in the central Bog. In some years it becomes dominant amongst stands of Sea Campion, e.g. Western Plain.

Silver Hair-grass *Aira caryophyllea* L. ✽
Abundant on closely-grazed grassland and on walls, and previously amongst Heather.

Early Hair-grass *Aira praecox* L. ✽
Occasional to frequent on closely-grazed grassland, e.g. southern-most parts of Northern Plain, particularly on shallow soils.

Common Bent *Agrostis capillaris* L. ✽
The most abundant grass after *Holcus lanatus*, and replacing Thrift on sheltered cliff tops, usually with Sea Campion. Very tolerant of grazing, manuring and treading. Rarely flowers unless grazing is reduced.

Creeping Bent *Agrostis stolonifera* L. ✽
Widely distributed in all the marshes and pools, and cliff flushes e.g. South Haven stream. Replaces *A. capillaris* in the more-exposed grassland and Thrift.

Velvet Bent *Agrostis canina* L.
Occasionally recorded on cliff-faces.

Marsh Foxtail *Alopecurus geniculatus* L.
Occasional in the more-sheltered ponds and marshes, e.g. Well Pool, Orchid Bog.

Smooth Brome *Bromus racemosus* L.

Once abundant on the tops of high walls near the Observatory until the planting of trees and shrubs in the late-1980's – since these have grown to exceed the height of the walls the grasses have all but disappeared.

Soft Brome *Bromus hordeaceus* ssp. *ferronii* ⊛

Abundant on sheltered, ungrazed cliffs, e.g. Wreck Cove, Peter's Bay. Apparently encouraged by bird guano.

Barren Brome *Anisantha sterilis* (L.) Nevski ⊛

Introduced into the Observatory garden in 1982, but not recorded since 1987.

False Brome *Brachypodium sylvaticum* (Huds.) P. Beauv. ⊛

Locally abundant on the steep cliffs of North Haven.

Bearded Couch *Elymus caninus* (L.) L. ⊛

Twenty-four flowering shoots were in the cottage garden in 1954.

Common Couch *Elytrigia repens* (L.) Desv. Ex Nevski

Recorded by Lockley (1947); also in the Wheelhouse yard in 1975.

Purple Moor-grass *Molinia caerulea* (L.) Moench

Once common in the central marshes and East Bog, now restricted to a few small patches around North Pond and in the Orchid Bog and East Bog Rabbit exclosures. Its decline is possibly due to an increase in gull manuring.

Common Reed *Phragmites australis* (Cav.)Trin. Ex Steudel

One small clump on the cliff at the lower end of South Haven stream, which does not seem to spread, and another in the inlet stream to the Well Pool, which has moved into the pool itself in recent years, requiring frequent management to prevent further spread. Has attracted numerous Reed Warblers *Acrocephalus scirpaceus* during migration periods (e.g. August 2003).

Barley *Hordeum vulgare* L.

Found on various cliffs by Gillham (1956c), and more recently by the author. These probably arrive in the form of indigestible remains in regurgitated gull "pellets".

Common Oat *Avena sativa* L.

Found on various cliffs by Gillham (1956c), and more recently by the author, in a similar manner to barley *Hordeum vulgare*.

LILIACEAE

Spring Squill *Scilla verna* Huds. ⊛

Frequent to abundant in coastal grassland of medium to slight exposure, particularly near the north coast.

Bluebell *Hyacinthoides non-scripta* (L.) Chouard ex Rothm. ⊛
Seasonally dominant in most of the areas occupied later in the year by Bracken, isolated clumps further west being the latest to flower (in June).

Spanish Bluebell *Hyacinthoides hispanica* (Mill.) Rothm.
Introduced into the cottage garden, but not recorded since 1983.

Chives *Allium schoenoprasum* L.
Introduced into the cottage garden in 1982, now present in the Wall Garden.

Garlic *Allium sativum* L.
Planted in the cottage garden in 1982 - 83, but no longer present.

Snowdrop *Galanthus nivalis* L.
Introduced into the cottage garden, no longer present.

Bunch-flowered Daffodil *Narcissus tazetta* L.
Planted around the Observatory buildings, particularly next to the Wheelhouse block (presently the Warden's living quarters), where the sweet scent is much admired in late-March and early-April. Frequently visited by bumblebees *Bombus* spp.

Pheasant's-eye Daffodil *Narcissus poeticus* L.
A few plants introduced around the Observatory buildings, mainly in the cottage garden.

Daffodil *Narcissus pseudonarcissus* L.
Introduced around the Observatory buildings, where a fine display is produced in late-March and early-April.

IRIDACEAE

Yellow Iris *Iris pseudacorus* L.
Introduced into the Heligoland trap (at what is now known as "The Well") in 1954, where it has become strongly established and requires much in the way of control in order to maintain any open water there. Subsequently a number of rhizomes were transplanted to a few spots in and around North Pond, where it is spreading only slowly in the shallows. Some rhizomes were planted in Winter Pond, but subsequently removed when it was clear that the plant would quickly grow into all areas.

ORCHIDACEAE

Heath Spotted-Orchid *Dactylorhiza maculata* (L.) Soo.
A few flowering plants were discovered at East Bog by a group from the Royal Dutch Natural History Society in 1997. Persisted for just one more year before disappearing.

Southern Marsh-Orchid x Common Spotted-Orchid *Dactylorhiza praetermissa* x *Dactylorhiza fuchsii* = *D. grandis* (Druce) P. Hunt.

Common in Orchid Bog where it spread from a single plant in the 1930's to several hundreds from 1950-onwards. Grazed by rabbits and slugs. Usually fewer than a dozen have been found in recent years, amongst rushes at Orchid and East Bogs, and in a flush to the north of the Well rabbit-exclosure. None seen since 1999.

Early Purple Orchid *Orchis mascula* (L.) L.
Recorded by Lockley (1947).

Appendix III: A list of Bryophytes. List from Gillham (1954), Smith (1995) *, and Johnson (2002) **

MUSCI (mosses)

POLYTRICHALES

Polytrichaceae
Polytrichum piliferum Hedw.

P. juniperinum Hedw.

FISSIDENTALES

Fissidentaceae
Fissidens viridulus (Web. & Mohr) Wahl. *

F. pusillus Wils. ex Milde.*

F. bryoides Hedw. *

F. curnowii Mitt.

DICRANALES

Archidiaceae
Archidium alternifolium (Hedw.) Schp.

Ditrichaceae
Pleuridium subulatum (Hedw.) Lindb.

Ceratodon purpureus (Hedw.) Brid. *

Dicranaceae
Dicranella heteromalla (Hedw.) Schp. *

Campylopus fragilis (Turn.) B.& S.

Campylopus introflexus (Hedw.) Brid. **

POTTIALES

Pottiaceae
Tortula subulata (Wils.) Limpr. **Unconfirmed**

T. muralis Hedw.

Tortella nitida (Lindb.) Broth. *

T. flavovirens (Bruch) Broth. *

Pottia truncata (Hedw.) Farnr.

P. crinata Wils.

Pottia wilsoni (Hook) B. & S.

Phascum cuspidatum Hedw.

Barbula fallax Hedw.

B. cylindrica (Tayl.) Schp.

Trichostomum brachydontium (Mitt.) C. Jens.

Weissia microstoma (Hedw.) C.M.

GRIMMIALES

Grimmiaceae
Schistidium maritimum (Turn) Bruch & Schimp
Grimmia pulvinata (Hedw.) Sm. *
G. trichophylla Grev.

FUNARIALES

Funariaceae
Funaria hygrometrica Hedw.
F. attenuata (Dicks) Lindb.
F. obtusa (Dicks) Lindb.

EUBRYALES

Bryaceae
Bryum pallens (Brid.) Rohl.
B. pseudotriquetrum var. pseudotriquetrum
(Hedw.) Schwager. *
B. caespiticium Hedw.
B. erythrocarpum Schwaegr.
B. alpinum With.
B. capillare Hedw.

Mniaceae
Mnium hornum Hedw. *
Plagiomnium rostratum (Schrad) Kop.
Pohlia elongata Hedw.
P. annotina (Hedw.) Lindb.
Epipterigium tozeri (Grev.) Lindb. *

ISOBRYALES

Orthotrichaceae
Orthotrichum diaphanum Brid. *
Ulota phyllantha Brid.

Neckeraceae
Thamnobryum alopecurum (Hedw.) Gangulee.

HYPNOBRYALES

Hypnaceae
Campyliadelphus stellatus (Hedw.) Kanda
Calliergonella cuspidata (Hedw.) Loeske.
Hypnum cupressiforme Hedw. *

Campyliaceae
Campylium polygamum (Schimp. in B.S.G.) C. Jens.
C. chrysophyllum (Brid.) J. Lange
Drepanocladus aduncus (Hedw.) Warnst.
D. fluitans (Hedw.) Warnst.
D. revolvens (Sw.) Warnst.

Amblystegiaceae
Amblystegium serpens (Hedw.) Br. Eur.

Brachytheciaceae
Brachythecium albicans Hedw.
Brachythecium rutabulum Hedw. *
B. velutinum Hedw.
Isothecium myosuroides Brid. *
Homalothecium sericeum (Hedw.) B. S. & G.
Eurhynchium praelongum Hedw. *
Rhynchostegium riparioides (Hedw.) Cardot.

Plagiotheciaceae
Plagiothecium denticulatum (Hedg.) B.S.G.
P. nemorale (Hitt) Jaeg.

Hylocomiaceae
Rhytidiadelphus squarrosus (Hedw.) Wrnst.*

HEPATICAE (liverworts)

Jungermanniales

Sub-order Jungermannineae

Calypogeiaceae
Calypogeia fissa (L.) Raddi
C. arguta Mont. & Nees

Cephaloziellaceae
Cephaloziella starkii (Funck.)

Geocalycaceae (Harphanthaceae)
Lophocolea bidentata (L.) Dumort.
L. heterophylla (Schrad.) Dumort.
L. fragrans (Moris & De Not.) Gottsche, Lindenb. & Nees.
Chiloscyphus polyanthos (L.) Corda
C. pallescens (Ehrh. ex Hoffm.) Dumort.
Saccogyna viticulosa (L.) Dumort.

Jungermanniaceae
Lophozia sp.

Scapaniaceae
Scapania undulata (L.) Dumort.
S. irrigua (Nees) Nees

Jubulaceae (Frullaniaceae)
Frullania tamarisci (L.) Dumort.
F. microphylla (Gottsche) Pearson
F. dilatata (L.) Dumort.

Lejeuneaceae
Marchesinia mackaii (Hook.) Gray
Lejeunea lamacerina (Steph.) Schiffn.

Metzgeriales

Sub-order Metzgerineae

Pelliaceae
Pellia epiphylla (L.) Corda
P. endiviifolia (Dicks.) Dumort.

Pallaviciniaceae
Moerckia flotowiana (Nees.) Schiffn.

Mezgeriaceae
Metzgeria furcata (L.) Dumort.

Aneuraceae
Aneura pinguis (L.) Dumort.
Riccardia multifida (L.) Gray
R. chamedryfolia (With .) Grolle

Marchantiales

Conocephalaceae
Conocephalum conicum (L.) Lindb.

Ricciaceae
Riccia sorocarpa Bisch.

Appendix IV: Lichens

The classification of lichens is in a constant state of flux. The system used here can be found at http://indexfungorum.org

ARTHONIALES

Roccellaceae
Opegrapha caesariensis
O. varia
Roccella fuciformis
R. phycopsis
Sclerophyton circumscriptum

LECANORALES

Acarosporaceae
Acarospora fuscata

Bacidiaceae
Bacidia scopulicola
Cliostomum griffithi
Lecania baeomma
Lecania hutchinsiae
Solenopsora holophea
S. vulturiensis
Tephromela atra

Candelariaceae
Candelariella vitellina

Catillariaceae
Catillaria chalybeia
C. lenticularis

Cladoniaceae
Cladonia fimbriata
C. foliaceae
C. humilis
C. pocillum
C. pyxidata
C. rangiformis
C. subcervicornis
C. verticillata

Haematommataceae
Haematomma ochroleucum
Hypogymnia tubulosa

Lecanoraceae
Aspicilia caesiocinerea
A. cinerea
A. leprosescens
Lecanora actophila
L. campestris
L. dispersa
L. expallens
L. fugiens
L. gangaleoides
L. helicopis
L. muralis
L. poliophaea
L. polytropa
L. sulphurea
Lecidella scabra
Scoliciosporum umbrinum

Pannariaceae
Degelia atlantica

Parmeliaceae

Evernia prunastri

Neofuscelia verruculifera

Parmelia caperata

P. conspersa

P crinata Ach

P. delisiei

P. fuliginosa

P. loxodes

P. perlata

P. saxatilis

P. sulcata

Usnea subfloridana

Physiaceae

Anaptychia runcinata

Buellia aethalea

B. punctata

B. stellulata

B. subdisciformis

Diploicia canescens

Diplotomma alboatrum

D. chlorophaeum

Phaeophyscia orbicularis

Rinodina atrocinerea

R. confragosa

R. exigua

R. luridescens

Porpidiaceae

Porpidia albocaerulescens

Protoblastenia rupestris

Physcia adscendens

P. tribacia

P. caesia

P. tenella

Porpidia cinereoatra

P. tuberculosa

Ramalinaceae

Ramalina farinacea

R. lacera

Ramalina siliquosa

R. subfarinacaea

Rhizocarpaceae

Rhizocarpon geographicum

LICHINALES

Lichinaceae

Lichina confinis

Lichina pygmaea

OSTROPALES

Thelotremataceae

Diploschistes scruposus

PELTIGERALES

Collemataceae
Collema tenax

Peltigeraceae
Peltigera membranacea
P. britannica

PERTUSARIALES

Pertusariaceae
Ochrolechia androgyna
O. parella
Pertusaria amara
P. monogona
P. pseudocorallina

PYRENULALES

Pyrenulaceae
Pyrenula nitida

TELOSCHISTALES

Teloschistaceae
Caloplaca aurantia
C. ceracea
C. citrina
C. crenularia
C. flavescens
C. granulosa
C. isidigera
C. marina
C. verruculifera
Teloschistes flavicans
Xanthoria parietina
X. ectaneoides
X. candelaria

TRICHOTHELIALES

Trichotheliaceae
Porina curnowii

VERRUCARIALES

Verrucaraceae
Dermatocarpon miniatum
Staurothele rugulosa
Verrucaria maura
V. mucosa
V. viridula
V. muralis
V. nigrescens
V. macrostoma

Incertae sedis
Lepraria incana
L. lesdainii

Appendix V: Fungi found on Skokholm

FUNGI

BASIDIOMYCOTA

BASIDIOMYCETES

TREMELLOMYCETIDAE

AURICULARIALES

Auriculariaceae
Auricularia auricula-judae (Fr.) Quél

TREMALLALES

Exidiaceae
Sebacina incrustans (Pers.) Tul. & C. Tul.
Stypella subhyalina (A. Pearson) P. Roberts 1998

UREDINALES

Pucciniaceae
Euromyces behenis (D.C.) Unger

UREDINIOMYCETES

Incertae cedis

MICROBOTRYALES

Microbotryaceae

Microbotryum violaceum (Pers.) G. Deml & Oberw.

USTILAGINOMYCETES

Incertae sedis

Inc. sedis

Platygloeaceae
Platygloea effusa Schröt.

AGARICOMYCETIDAE: AGARICALES

Agaricaceae

Agaricus arvensis Sch. Horse Mushroom
A. avellaneus With.
A. bisporus (J.E. Lange) Pilàt
A. comtulus Fr.
A. fulvaster Berk. & M.A. Curtis
A. impudicus (Rea) Pilàt
A. lepiotoides Berk. & Broome
A. litoralis (Wakef. & A. Pearson) Konrad & Maubl.
A. nanus Cumino
A. porphyrizon P.D. Orton
A. semotus Fr.
A. silvaticus Schaeff.
A. silvaticus var. pallidus (F.H. Møller & J. Schäff) Maire
A. silvicola (Vitt.) Peck. Wood Mushroom
A. squamulosus Alb. & Schwein
A. straminus Scop.
A. xanthodermus Genev.
A. xantholepis (F.H. Møller) F.H. Møller
Lepiota clypeolaria (Bull.) Quél.
L. felina (Pers.) Karst.
L. oreadiformis Velen.
L. scobinella (Fr.) Gillet
Leucoagaricus georginae (W.G. Sm.) Cand.
L. leucothites (Vitt.) M.M. Moser ex Bon
Macrolepiota procera var. procera Scop.
M. excoriata (Schaeff.) M.M. Mosel
Postia stiptica (Pers.) Jülich

Bolbitiaceae

Agrocybe pediades (Fr.) Fayod
A. pusiola (Fr.) Métrod
Conocybe antipus (Lasch) Fayod
C. dumetorum (Velen.) Svrček
C. ochracea (Kühner) Singer
C. spicula (Lasch) Kühner
C. subovalis Kühner & Watling
Galerina embolus (Fr.) P.D. Orton
Naucoria tabacina (D.C.) Gillet
Panaeolina foenisecii (Pers.) Maire
Panaeolus acuminatus (Schaeff.) Quél.
P. ater (J.E. Lange) Kühner & Romaqn.
P. campanulatus (Bull.) Quél.
P cinctulus (Bolt.) Britzelm.
P. papilionaceus var. papilionaceus (Bull.) Quél.
P. phalaenarum var. phalaenarum (Fr.) Ew. Gerhardt
P. retirugis (Fr.) Gillet
P. semiovatus var. semiovatus (Sowerby) S. Lundell & Nannf.

P. semiovatus var. phalaenarum (Fr.) Ew. G.
Pholiota sphaleromorpha (Bull.) Quél
Pholiotina coprophila (Kühner) Singer

Clavariaceae

Clavaria fragilis Holmsk.
Clavulinopsis corniculata (Schaeff.) Corner
C. fusiformis (Sowerby) Corner
C. laeticolor (Berk & M.A. Curtis) R.H. Pet.
C. luteoalba (Rea) Corner
C. luteoalba var. latispora Corner
C. helveola (Pers.) Corner
C. helveola var. geoglossoides Corner

Coprinceae

Coprinus atramentarius (Bull.) Fr.
C. ephemeroides (DC.) Fr.
C. ephemerus (Bull.) Fr.
C. lagopus (Fr.) Fr.
C. niveus (Pers.) Fr.
C. papillatus (Batsch) Fr.
C. papillatus var. oxygenus Fr.
C. patouillardii Quél
C. plicatilis (Curtis) Fr.
C. radians (Desm.) Fr.
C. radiatus (Bolt.) Gray
C. urticola (Berk. & Broome) Buller
C. velox Godey
Psathyrella ammophila (Durieu & Lév) P.D. Orton
P. bifrons (Berk.) A.H. Sm.
P. bodiophylla (Romagn.) Park.-Rhodes
P. candonlleana (Fr.) Maire
P. fibrillosa (Pers.) Maire
P. prona f. prona (Fr.) Gillet
P. stercoraria (Kühner & Joss.) Arnolds

Cortinariaceae

Conocybe semiglobata Kühner & Watling
C. subovalis Kühner & Watling
C. tenera (Schaeff.) P. Kumm
Cortinarius cinnamomeus (L.) Fr.
C. incisus (Pers.) Fr.
Crepidotus variabilis (Pers.) P. Kumm
Galerina camerina (Fr.) Kühner
G. clavata (Velen.) Kühner
G. nana (Petri) Kühner
G. sideroides (Bull.) Kühner
G. tibiicystis (G.F. Atk.) Kühner
Pleurotellus dicyorhizus (DC.) Kühner
Tubaria anthracophila P. Karst.

Entolomataceae

Entoloma anatinum (Lasch) Donk
E. Byssisedum (Pers.) Donk
E. chalybaeum var. chalybaeum (Fr.) Noordel
E. conferendum var. conferendum (Britz.) Noord.
E. costatum (Fr.) P. Kumm
E. cuspidiferum (Kühner& Romagn.) Noordel
E. infula var. Infula (Arnolds & Noordel) Noordel
E. jubatum (Fr.) P. Karst
E. mammosum (L.) Hessler
E. papillatum (Bres.) Dennis
E. pleopodium (Bull.) Noordel.
E. porphyrophaeum (Fr.) Karst.
E. rhodopolium (Fr.) P. Kumm.
E. rufocarneum (Berk.) Noordel
E. sarcitum (FR. Noordel.
E. sericeum (Bull.) Quél
E. serrulatum (Pers.) Hesler
E. solstitiale (Fr.) Noord.
E. speculum (Fr.) Quél
E. verecundum (Fr.) Noord.
E. wynnei (Berk. & Broome) Sacc.
Nolanea juncea (Fr.) Gillet

Hygrophoraceae

Hygrocybe ceracea (Wulf.) Kumm.
H. chlorophana (Fr.) Wüncshe
H. coccinea (Sch.) Kumm.
H. conica (Scop.) Kumm.
H. lepida Arnolds
H. miniata (Fr.) Kumm.
H. nigrescens (Quél.) Kühn.
Hygrophoropsis aurantiaca (Wulf.) Maire

Lycoperdaceae

Bovista nigrescens Pers.
B. plumbea Pers.
B. polymorpha (Vitt.) Kreisel
B. pusilla (Batsch) Pers.
Calvatia candica (Rostk.) Hollós
C. utriformis (Bull.) Jaap
Handkea excipuliformis (Scop.) Kreisel
H. utriformis (Bull.) Pers.
Langermannia gigantean (Batsch) Rostk.
Lycoperdon ericetorum var. cepiforme (Bull.) Bowerman
L. molle Pers.
L. polymorphum Vittad.
L. umbrinum Pers.
Vascellum pratense (Pers.) Kreisel

Marasmiaceae

Flagelloscypha minutissima (Burt) Donk
Lachnella villosa (Pers.) Gillet
Marasmiellus candicus (Bolton) Singer
M. ramealis (Bull.) Singer
M. vaillanti (Pers.) Singer
Marasmius collinus (Scop.) Singer
M. graminum (Lib.) Berk
M. juncinus Velen.
M. oreades (Bolt.) Fr.
Micromphale brassicolens (Romagn.) PD. Ort.
M. foetidum (Sowerby) Singer
Nochascypha filicina (P. Karst.) Kuntze

Pleurotaceae

Pleurotus herbarum Velen.
P. pubescens Peck

Pluteaceae

Volvariella gloiocephala (DC.) Boek. & End.

Strophariaceae

Hypholoma ericaceum (Pers.) Kühner
Psilocybe bullacea (Bull.) P. Kumm.
P. callosa (Fr.) Gillet
P. coprophila (Bull.) P. Kumm.
P. inquilina (Fr.) Bres.
P. merdaria (Fr.) Ricken
P. moelleria Guzmán
P. montana (Pers.) P. Kumm
P. semilanceata (Fr.) Kumm.
P. semilanceata var. obtusata Bon
P. scocholmica Park.-Rhodes
P. strictipes Singer & A.H. Sm.
Stropharia cornilla (Bull.) Fr.
S. luteonitens (Vahl) Quél
S. semiglobata (Batsch) Quél.

Tricholomataceae

Calocybe carnea (Bull.) Donk
Calyptella capula (Holmsk.) Quél
C. griseopallida (Weinm.) Park.-Rhodes
Camarophyllopsis foetens (W. Phillips) Arn.
Collybia coracina (Fr.) Gillet
C. clusilis (Fr.) Sacc.
Clitocybe candicans (Pers.) P. Kumm.
C. diatreta (Fr.) P. Kumm.
C. fragrans Sowerby
C. phaeopthalma (Pers.) Kuyper
C. rivulosa (Pers.) Kumm.
Crinipellis scabella (Alb. & Schwein.) Murrill
Dermoloma cuneifolium (Fr.) Singer ex Bon
Gerronema ericetorum (Pers.) Sing.

Tricholomataceae (continued)

Gymnopus impudicus (Fr.) Antonin, Halling & Noordel.
G. ocior (Pers.) Antonin & Noordel.
Hemimycena cucullata (Pers.) Singer
Hygrocybe calyptriformis var. calyptriformis (Berk.) Fayod
H. conica var. conica (Scop.) P. Kumm.
H. irrigata (Pers.) Bon
H. lacmus (Schumach.) P.D. Orton & Watling
H. laeta var. laeta (Pers.) P. Kumm.
H. miniatus var. sphagnophilus (Peck) Hongo
H. mucronella (Fr.) P. Karst
H. pratensis var. pallida (Cooke) Arnolds
H. psittacina var. psittacina (Schaff.) P. Kumm.
H. psittacina var. perplexa (A.H. Sm. & Hesler) Boertm.
H. punicea (Fr.) P. Kumm.
H. russocoriaceae (Berk & T.K. Mill.) P.D. Orton & Watling
H. virginea var. virginea (Wulfen) P.D. Orton & Watling
H. virginea var. fuscescens (Bres.) Arnolds
H. vitellina (Fr.) P. Karst
Hygrophorus camarophyllus (A.-S.) Dum., Grandj. & R. Mre.
H. nigrescens (Quél) Quél
H. pratensis var. pratensis (Pers.) Bon
H. turundus var. sphaerosporus Rea
Lepista flaccida (Sowerby) Pat.
Leptotus glaucus (Batsch) Maire
Mycena adscendens (Lasch) Maas Geest.
M. aetites (Fr.) Quél.
M. alcalina (Fr.) Kumm.
M. amicta (Fr.) Quél.

Mycena. ammoniaca (Fr.) Quél.
M. amicta (Fr.) Quél.
M. arcangeliana Bres.
M. atromarginata (Lasch) Gillet
M. capillaripes Peck
M. cinerella (P. Karst) P. Karst
M. clavularis (Batsch.) Sacc.
M. corticola (Schumach.) Quél
M. debilis (Fr.) Quél.
M. filopes (Bull.) P. Kumm.
M. galopus var. galopus (Pers.) P. Kumm.
M. hiemalis (Obs.) Quél.
M. juncicola (Fr.) Gillet
M. leptocephala (Pers.) Gillet
M. metata (Secr. ex Fr.) Quél
M. olida Bres.
M. olivaceomarginata (Massee) Massee
M. polygramma (Bull.) Gray
M. pura (Pers.) Kumm.
M. pusilla A.H. Sm.M. sanguinolenta (Alb. & Schwein.) P. Kumm.
M. stylobates (Pers.) Kumm.
M. vitilis (Fr.) Quél.
Omphalina ericetorum (Bull.) M. Lange
O. retosta (Fr.) P.D. Orton
O. subhepatica (Batsch) Murrill
Panellus mitis (Pers.) Singer
Phaeotellus acerosus (Fr.) Gulden
Resupinatus applicatus (Batsch) Gray
Rickenella fibula (Bull.) Raithel.
R. swartzii (Fr.) Kuyper
Tricholoma album (Sch.) Kumm.
T. hygrophanum Velen.
Tricholomopsis rutilans (Sch.) Sing.

BOLETALES

Coniophoraceae
Coniophora puteana (Schum.) P. Karst.
C. arida (Fr.) P. Karst.
Leucogyrophana pinastri (Fr.) Ginns & Weresub

CANTHARELLALES

Botryobasidiaceae
Botryobasidium pruinatum (Bres.) J. Erikss.
Botryohypochnus isabellinus (Fr.) J. Erikss.

CERATOBASIDIALES

Ceratobasidiaceae
Thanatophorus cucumeris (A.B. Frank) Donk
T. terrigenus (Bres.) G. Langer

DACRYMYCETALES

Dacrymycetaceae
Dacrymyces stillatus Nees
Ditiola radicata (A. & S.) Fr.

HYMENOCHAETALES

Schizoporaceae
Hyphodontia pallidula (Bres.) J. Erikss.
Schizopora paradoxica (Schrad.) Donk

PHALLALES

Geastraceae
Sphaerobolus stellatus Tode

Gomphaceae
Ceratellopsis aculeata (Pat.) Corner

POLYPORALES

Atheliaceae
Amphinema byssoides (Pers.) J. Erikss.
Athelia arachoidea (Berk.) Jülich
Piloderma byssinum (P. Karst.) Jülich

Corticiaceae
Corticium farinellum (P. Karst.) Sacc
C. terrestre (Kniep) Kniep
Hyphodontia sambuci (Pers.) J. Erikks.
Tomentella microspora (P. Karst.) Höhn & Lit.

Cyphellaceae
Calyptella capula Holmsk.
Lachnella villosa (Pers.) Gillet
Radulomyces confluens (Fr.) M.P. Christ

Fomitopsidaceae
Postia caesia (Schrad.) P. Karst.
P. rancida (Bres.) M.J. Larsen & Lombard
Podoporia cincta (Berk.) Park.-Rhodes

Hyphodermataceae
Hyphoderma praetermissum (P. Karst.) J.
Erikss. & Å. Strid.

Meripilaceae
Rigidoporus sanguinolentus (Alb. & Sch.) Donk

Meruliaceae
Phlebia livida (Pers.) Bres.
P. ochraceofulva (Bourd. & Galzin) Donk

Phanerochaetaceae
Ceraceomyces tessulatus (Cooke) Jülich
Phanerochaete sordida (P. Karst) J. Erikss. &
Ryvarden
P. tuberculata (P. Karst.) Parmasto
P. velutina (DC.) Parmasto
Phlebiopsis ravenelii (Cooke) Hjortstam

Podoscyphaceae
Granulobasidium vellereum (Ellis & Cragin)
Jülich

Polyporaceae
Datronia mollis (Sommerf.) Donk
Trametes versicolor (L.) Lloyd

Sistotremataceae
Sistotrema diademiferum (Bourd. & Galzin)
Donk
Sistotremastrum niveocremeum (Höhn &
Litsch.) J Eriikss.
Trechispora clancularis (Park.-Rhodes) K.H.
Larss.
T. mutabilis (Pers.) Liberta
T. sphaerospora (Maire) Parmasto
Trechispora byssinella (Bourdot) Liberta

Xenasmataceae
Xenasma pruinosum (Pat.) Donk
Xenasmatella vaga (Fr.) Stalpers

THELOPHORALES

Thelephoraceae
Thelephora mucida Pers.
Tomentolla fuscocinerea (Pers.) Donk.
Xenasmatella vaga (Fr.) Stalpers

ASCOMYCOTA

ASCOMYCETES

EUROTIOMYCETIDAE

EUROTIALES

Trichocomaceae
Aspergillus fumigatus Fresen.
Paecilomyces lilacinus (Thom.) Samson

Appendix VI: Rare and scarce birds on Skokholm – the first records.

First records for Britain were: Olive-backed Pipit *A. hodgsoni*, Swainson's Thrush *Catharus ustulatus*, and Western Bonelli's Warbler *Phylloscopus bonelli*.

First records for Wales found on (or seen from) Skokholm are as follows: Black-browed Albatross *Diomedea melanophris*, American Golden Plover *Pluvialis dominica*, Semipalmated Sandpiper *Calidris pusilla*, Pectoral Sandpiper *Calidris melanotos*, Upland Sandpiper *Bartramia longicauda*, Short-toed Lark *Calandrella brachydactyla*, Tawny Pipit *A. campestris*, Red-throated Pipit *A. cervinus*, White-throated Robin *Irania gutteralis*, Aquatic Warbler *Acrocephalus paludicola*, Great Reed Warbler *A. arundinaceus*, Booted Warbler *Hippolais caligata*, Icterine Warbler *Hippolais icterina*, Subalpine Warbler *Sylvia cantillans*, Sardinian Warbler *S. melanocephala*, Yellow-browed Warbler *P. inornatus*, Radde's Warbler *Phylloscopus schwarzi*, Western Bonelli's Warbler *P. bonelli*, Red-eyed Vireo *Vireo olivaceus*, Lapland Bunting *Calcarius lapponicus*, Rustic Bunting *E. rustica*, Pine Bunting *E. leucocephalos*, Rose-breasted Grosbeak *Pheucticus ludovicianus*, Northern Oriole *Icterus galbula* and Bobolink *Dolichonyx oryzivorus*.

First records for Pembrokeshire were: Black Stork *Ciconia nigra*, Blue-winged Teal *Anas discors*, Kentish Plover *Charadrius alexandrinus*, Lesser Yellowlegs *Tringa flavipes*, Mediterranean Gull *Larus melanocephalus*, Little Swift *Apus affinis*, Shorelark *Eremophila alpestris*, Richard's Pipit *Anthus novaseelandiae*, Water Pipit *A. spinoletta*, Isabelline Wheatear *Oenanthe isabellina*, Desert Wheatear *O. deserti*, Melodious Warbler *Hippolais polyglotta*, Barred Warbler *S. nisoria*, Greenish Warbler *Phylloscopus trochiloides*, Firecrest *Regulus ignicapillus*, Red-breasted Flycatcher *Ficedula parva*, Common Rosefinch *Carpodacus erythrinus*, Ortolan Bunting *Emberiza hortulana*, Little Bunting *E. pusilla*, Black-headed Bunting *E. melanocephala*.

Appendix VII: A summary of the island year

Neither words nor photographs can truly convey the spirit of Skokholm, particularly when those very paragraphs contain rather detailed analytical descriptions such as many of those presented so far. It is perhaps easiest to understand what it is that brings regular visitors back to the "dream island" time and time again – and causes Wardens to remain entrenched for up to a decade – by way of a simple diary of the events, that repeat themselves year by year, without fail. Long may it remain this way.

January and February

There is little in the way of plant life above a few centimetres in height and, with the exception of the rich lichen flora, the colours are subdued – pale pastel greens, yellows and browns. Only in a few partly-sheltered hollows do the woody remains of previous year's Bracken stems persist, lying prone following many batterings by winter gales and driving rain. On the western cliff-slopes, mats of Sea Campion foliage have been torn up, rolled back and scorched by the salty winds.

Rabbits struggle to find enough grazing to maintain their number, and many perish through starvation, their corpses littering the plateau and providing sustenance for the resident Ravens, which are already building their nest on one of the traditionally-favoured cliff-ledges.

The three large, rain-fed ponds are overflowing, and adorned with various dabbling ducks – tens of Wigeon and Teal, a few Mallard and Shoveler and the occasional Gadwall – all finding plenty of food in the way of aquatic plants and the seeds of Amphibious Bistort. The excess water rushes seaward in streams where already the foliage of Creeping Forget-me-not and Blinks is expanding in readiness for the advancing spring. Meanwhile, in the Observatory yards, the leaves of various planted *Narcissi* are erupting from underground bulbs.

There are few truly-resident birds on Skokholm. Blackbirds eke out an existence on the few available invertebrates they can find amongst the Bracken litter, in burrows, and even on the rocky shore where they forage alongside Rock Pipits. The few Wrens present must find life even more difficult, and they are most often seen entering burrows in an incessant search for food throughout the short days. There are some species that are thought to spend the entire winter on the island, such as Robin, Song Thrush and Redwing.

On calmer days, Fulmar petrels occupy their cliff nest-sites, cackling loudly during interactions with mate and neighbours alike, between bouts of effortless soaring on the updrafts. At high water, Oystercatchers abound at their few traditional roosts of the supralittoral zone of the rocky shore, though they are gone at low water, to more-productive feeding grounds in the nearby estuaries. On moonlit nights they return to the island plateau to lay claim to their territories, but all are gone before dawn.

Frogspawn appears in many of the island's ponds and ditches, although the frogs themselves are rarely seen in daylight hours. The activities of the Minotaur Beetle are very much in evidence, mounds of earth appearing in the grasslands as the adult beetles dig holes in which to lay their eggs and where numerous Rabbit droppings will be carried to provide food for the larvae that hatch.

Towards the end of the month Lesser Black-backed Gulls begin to return to the island, many having undertaken migrations to northwest Africa for the winter. Queen bumblebees emerge, the most numerous species being

Bombus terrestris and *B. lucorum*, finding sustenance in the few gorse flowers on the handful of introduced plants at the eastern edge of Home Meadow.

March

Razorbills and Guillemots are frequently seen on the sea around the island, and occasionally they venture ashore to visit their nest-sites on the cliff-ledges and beneath large boulders. Buzzards and Peregrines display spectacularly over their chosen territories, and frequently harass each other during disputes over airspace. The resident Blackbirds, sociable through the autumn and winter, begin to fight over the few prime breeding territories that exist in the vicinity of the observatory buildings. Curlew are frequently heard at night, but rarely seen during daylight hours, when the few male Lapwings are displaying over the central Bog.

The brilliant lime-green foliage of Chickweed suddenly appears as seedlings erupt on footpaths and other areas of erosion, on heavily manured soil amongst gull colonies and on cliff-ledges. It contrasts starkly with the dull grey-green of the Sea Campion, and the result is an intricate mosaic. And the somber-looking dull purple and green leaves on prostrate stems of Ground Ivy suddenly produce delicate violet-spotted purple flowers, so attractive to the various queen bumblebees.

Towards the middle of the month the first Wheatears return from their winter in Africa, normally the splendidly-coloured males at first. They are quick to occupy their breeding territory of the previous year, and announce their intentions with quiet bursts of sub-song, not the typical bubbly and scratchy warble that they are mostly associated with later in the spring and early summer. Similarly with Meadow Pipits, although these remain in flocks and breeding is, it seems, some way from their minds. Other early migrants include Chiffchaffs, and on the few calm days they are heard uttering the familiar call that is infinitely more typical of the oak and sycamore woodlands of the nearby mainland. The first Sand Martins head north over the island and the occasional Black Redstart may be seen on rocky outcrops, boulder beaches or rooftops. The biggest surprise is the number of Goldcrests that visit the island, somehow managing to find tiny invertebrate prey on the vast expanse of sun-drenched cliff.

On south-facing cliff-slopes, encouraged by sunshine and warmth, the first flowers of Danish Scurvygrass and Sea Campion appear, at least a month before they will be seen elsewhere. In the east the leaves of Lesser Celandine and Primrose emerge from amongst the shredded Bracken litter, whilst in the Dip Pool and the small stream draining from it, the tripartite leaves of the rare Three-lobed Crowfoot emerge.

Towards the end of March the first Puffins return to the waters around the island, first just one or two, increasing over a few days until there are thousands, which form huge rafts on the sea. Then they are gone again, a tantalizing glimpse of what is to become a daily sight.

April

The Peregrine Falcons have eggs now. The Ravens meanwhile have small chicks and whilst the female broods them her mate is frantically seeking carrion, even going to the extent of robbing Great Black-backed Gulls of their kills of young Rabbits.

Puffins return in strength and the first landings are made. Clouds of dust indicate that cleaning out of burrows is underway. The yellow star-like flowers of Lesser Celandine carpet the ground in many places, particularly in the east. Solitary bees appear from holes in sandy banks, and form small swarms as part of their mating ritual. Cuckoo-bees, meanwhile, look to take advantage of them.

Bird migration is really underway, and spells of inclement weather may bring falls of Willow Warblers, with few Blackcaps and Grasshopper Warblers and the occasional rarity. On calm, sunny days the emergence of Fever Flies from the grassland turf provides much-needed sustenance for warblers and gulls alike, whilst in wet areas numerous species of midge form clouds in the air.

Late in the month Common Scurvygrass flowers in profusion as always on the north-facing slopes of Hog Bay. There also exists a patch of variable size in South Haven, and intermittently on the western slopes of Theatre Cove. The first Great Black-backed Gull eggs are laid in nests that often consist of huge mounds of dead grass situated upon a rocky outcrop or cliff-top, whilst the Lesser Black-backed Gulls are still in the process of re-establishing territorial boundaries with neighbours.

Whimbrel passage is also occurring, with flocks of various sizes seen passing over the sea daily, and some stopping off to forage on the island's grassy plains.

May

Raven fledglings take their first tentative flights, but generally spend their time loafing about on the clifftops, very approachable, much to the concern of their parents.

The next migrant birds to arrive are Spotted Flycatcher and Redstart, together with occasional Turtle Dove and Cuckoo, the latter occasionally thought to parasitise the nests of Meadow Pipits. The female Blackbirds commence incubation of their second clutch of eggs, whilst the males are still busy feeding the fledglings of the first brood.

The first Bluebell flowers appear early in the month and quickly assume dominance over large areas in the east, giving a tremendous display. But soon the first fronds of Bracken sprout between them. Common Scurvygrass sheds its translucent white petals, soon to be replaced by brilliant green spherical seed pods. The foliage on Elder, and planted Sycamore in the gardens, finally expands and affords much-appreciated cover to the island Blackbirds, amongst others. Water levels in the rain-fed ponds drop rapidly, and Amphibious Bistort suddenly achieves total dominance of North Pond.

The first Herring and Great Black-backed Gull eggs hatch, and the tiny balls of down that are the chicks illicit tender care from proud parents.

Throughout the month, Storm Petrels increase in number, reoccupying nest-sites in the island walls and under boulders, areas which then resonate with bouts of "clicking" and "purring" as the birds announce their return.

June

The brilliant white flowers of Sea Campion and Danish Scurvygrass produce a spectacular display all around the periphery of the island, in places interspersed with brick-red sorrel flowers, whilst in the rich, deep soils of the sheltered east the Bluebell flowers are starting to wither, and Bracken begins to engulf them. On the cliffs of Crab Bay, on The Stack, and also occasionally in the gardens (where seed was sown in the past), the rare Tree Mallow produces its spectacular pink blooms.

Late in the month the fledging of Razorbills and Guillemots is in full swing, a particularly moving spectacle. At two-and-a-half weeks old and just one-third the size of their parents, the youngsters are encouraged to leave the nest-ledge and reach the sea, an action that may involve a leap from a great height, or a difficult clamber across boulder beaches, or both. Then, having achieved this despite the attentions of marauding gulls, the youngster swims out to the open sea, accompanied by its father, most often towards a spectacular sunset in the west. The female remains at the cliff, to guard the nest-site from other pairs that may potentially "steal" it.

The fledging of young Wheatears, and Rock and Meadow Pipits brings about crescendos of alarm calls from frantic parents, and they are wise to do so, for there are many potential predators around in the form of gulls and corvids.

July

The chicks of Herring Gulls are now fledging, immediately exploring the sea and rocky shore that was, until now, tantalizingly close and surely most desirable to them when faced with overcrowding on tiny nest-ledges thickly coated with smelly guano.

The sorrels are at their best early in the month, casting a red haze over vast swathes of The Bog in the centre of the island. Bog Pimpernel meanwhile produces dazzling carpets of pink in the flushes and damp grassland. Greater Birds-foot Trefoil produces a spectacular display in central areas, amongst Sand Sedge, Heather and grass, coinciding with the flight period of large numbers of 5-spot Burnet Moths (the larvae of which feed on the plant). Meadow Brown and Small Copper butterflies are also widespread.

Early in the month, the number of seabirds increases dramatically as immatures of all species return to the colony of their birth, exploring potential nest-sites and perhaps seeking future mates. Traditional "loafing rocks" become covered with masses of auks, whilst after dark there is a noticeable increase in volume as thousands of Manx Shearwaters fill the night sky with their mournful cries, and Storm Petrels flutter and wheel almost silently amongst the melee. By mid-month the cliff-ledges are devoid of Guillemots and Razorbills, and an eerie quiet befalls them, save for the intermittent cackling of the few Fulmars still present with their newly-hatched young. Meanwhile, the Puffin colonies reach their peak of activity, numbers swelled dramatically by non-breeders, whilst the last of the breeding birds return frequently with beaks full of sand-eels for their rapidly-growing youngsters hidden in the cliff-top burrows.

At the month's end, passerine migration is underway again - large numbers of Willow Warblers appear and spend time foraging in the vast swathes of Bracken. The first Robins appear, usually juveniles, and take up territories, their number soon to be swelled to about 50. Hundreds of juvenile Starlings arrive, moving across the island in a few large flocks, and they are gradually seen to attain their first adult plumage. Wader passage is also observed, as Curlew roost on the island in tens, and there are frequent sightings of other species.

Lesser Black-backed Gull chicks are soon to fledge, cackling with excitement as they make short vertical flights on incomplete wings. The Bracken that previously afforded them protection from predators now proves to be a hazard to successful take-offs, and their struggles initiate waves of frenzied and often aggressive activity amongst the adult birds, particularly when the chicks stray into neighbouring territories.

August

Early in the month, the yellow flowers of Ragwort provide a splash of brightness amongst the various greens of grass and Bracken, and provide an important source of nectar for numerous insects. Goldenrod too is beginning to flower, and will continue to do so right through the month. Hoverflies of many different species appear, many presumably by migration from elsewhere, and the air hums and vibrates as they undertake short flights from flower to flower. Migrant butterflies, such as Painted Lady and Clouded Yellow, can be in abundance in some years. If there has been frequent rainfall throughout the summer, Sea Campion will have another spurt of growth and again produce carpets of white flowers around the edges of the plateau. The sea-cliff vegetation reaches its peak also, with the flowering of Sea Beet, Rock Samphire, various Oraches, Sea Mayweed and Rock Sea Spurrey.

Turnstones and Common Sandpipers are recorded frequently on the rocky shore, and second broods of Wheatears, Rock and Meadow Pipits take to the wing amidst the frantic alarm calls of the parent birds, and although there are fewer gulls at this time of year, one or two Sparrowhawks may be present and make their presence felt. This greatly upsets the remaining gulls, which panic and take to flight whenever a hawk darts low across the ground almost under their noses.

On warm, still days, the various species of ant undertake their nuptial flights. Streams of winged males and females take flight as the work of the colony reaches its conclusion. These emergences are relished by the gulls and crows, which amazingly seem to find enough of them to satisfy their appetites, picking the ants from the ground and later following them up into the sky on the thermals.

By day, there are few signs that Skokholm still houses a vast seabird colony. The cliffs are barren except for a scattering of downy Fulmar chicks, though the whitewash reveals where auks had previously nested in profusion. Gulls roost in favoured places on the plateau, their post-breeding moult well underway and resulting in masses of guano and of feathers scattered by the wind. Various Dipteran flies, and most noticeably bluebottles, take up the birds' former haunts, where the smell can be nauseating as the corpses of unfortunate youngsters rot in the warm sunshine.

Very few Puffins may still be seen bringing fish ashore to young, having to face the gauntlet of marauding gulls alone as they approach the island. The nights, however, continue to be alive until late in the month, as shearwaters continue to feed their large chicks. Then suddenly the youngsters are deserted, and the cackling is suddenly replaced by eerie, piercing whistles, cackles and screams as the young venture out onto the surface, competing with each other as they climb rocky outcrops in order to exercise their wings in preparation for their first flight, one that will result in most of them eventually reaching the South Atlantic Ocean.

September

By mid-month, the Goldenrod and Ragwort plants begin to produce fluffy seed heads, and passing seed-eating birds, particularly Goldfinches, take advantage of the vast food supply. Many of the late-to-fledge Manx Shearwaters are stricken with the mysterious disease "puffinosis", where spasticity, conjunctivitis and blistered webs on their feet, combined with incessant shivering, somehow cause the birds to venture out in the daylight where they are finally killed by the attacks of Great Black-backed Gulls. Many others simply die where they sit. Even birds seemingly not inflicted with puffinosis frequently venture out into the light, scrambling up rocks and fences, perhaps sensing the urgency of the situation – food supplies in the local waters are rapidly diminishing – and obviously keen to leave the island.

Migration is at its peak, and easterly winds often result in falls of White Wagtails, Meadow Pipits and Greenland Wheatears. There is a steady trickle of Whinchats, Stonechats and Goldcrests, and Robins continue to arrive and territories that will sustain many of them until the following spring. Swallows often pass through in their thousands, along with tens or occasionally hundreds of House Martins. Frequently there are species from the east that are way off course, such as Ortolan Bunting, Red-breasted Flycatcher and Icterine Warbler. Ripening elderberries provide sustenance for migrating Blackcaps and Garden Warblers, whilst the emergence of thousands of craneflies does likewise for insectivores such as Spotted and Pied Flycatchers.

October

Storm Petrel youngsters are departing until the middle of the month, and are occasionally seen fluttering at the windows of the Observatory buildings, still with tufts of downy feathers, and attracted by the light. Seeing them like this causes amazement in the observer that these tiny creatures can survive out on the open ocean – truly wonders of the World.

Craneflies continue to increase in number, as do bluebottle flies, providing sustenance for late migrant birds, and those lost waifs from Asia such as Yellow-browed Warbler and Red-breasted Flycatcher that frequently appear on the island. A third generation of Small Copper butterflies consists of very few individuals.

Although few in number, the pups of Grey Seals bring a new flush of life at a time when all else is withering. Born on the few boulder beaches or in shallow caves, they are lucky if rough seas do not drag them out into the maelstrom, assuming that is, that the tremendous efforts of the protective cow seals do not suffice in keeping them ashore against all the odds.

The island is generally quiet apart from the incessant "ticking" calls of Robins, which can at this time number about 50 individuals, each in a territory which may be in Bracken, garden or bay. The first gales of the autumn quickly strip the Elder bushes and Sycamore trees of their leaves. Suddenly the mosaic of green and yellow in the dying Bracken fronds is reduced to an expanse of brown as a result of the salt-laden winds. But subsequently, on the many wet days, the withered fronds take on a glowing auburn colour, before finally falling in a heap to form a dense matt of leaf-litter. Robin numbers begin to fall, as the loss of habitat causes many to move on to pastures new. There can be spectacular finch migration, with Linnets, Siskins and Chaffinches occasionally in numbers that are difficult to ascertain with any degree of certainty, they are so plentiful. Thrushes – particularly Blackbirds – have been recorded in large numbers in the past, but are generally few.

As periods of rain become more frequent and prolonged, the ponds rapidly refill, encouraging numerous species of dabbling duck to explore the seed-laden shallows. Many Mallards are seen arriving at dusk and are heard through the night, along with Shoveler and Teal. Diving ducks are rare, though there have been records of Tufted Duck and even Goldeneye.

Spectacular fungi suddenly appear, the most noticeable being the Parasol, growing up to 35 centimetres in height, and a favourite food of various fly larvae, slugs, and island Wardens. Volcanoes of earth erupt from the grassland soil right across the island as Minotaur Beetles recommence excavation.

November and December

Spring tides reveal that the autumn gales have already had an impact on the kelp forests, the frondless stipes being all that remains on those situated towards the top of the lower shore, whilst those thrown up above the high water line are bejeweled with tens of the beautiful Blue-rayed Limpet, giving a clue to just some of the wonders that are to be found beneath the depths.

At the dawn of each day, Rabbits sit quietly in the open, awaiting the first rays of sunlight that will warm their cold, damp fur after a night out exposed to the elements, grazing the very last of the year's plant growth and seemingly aware – or quickly becoming aware – of the rigours that are to follow with the arrival of winter. The grassy plains suddenly erupt with colourful displays of waxcap fungi, in various shades of red, yellow and green, a rare site in this day of artificial "improvements" to pasture that is rife on mainland Britain.

Redwings and Fieldfares are frequently heard overhead at night and a small number present on the island during the day. Manx Shearwaters are occasionally heard overhead on the darkest nights. And so the island year turns full circle with their visit, a Warden's heart is once again filled with joy to hear the cries of the bird that makes the "dream island" so special, and makes him and her long for the springtime, when these tremendous birds will once more return in force.

Appendix VIII: Birds

Recording on Skokholm commenced with R.M. Lockley in 1927. This list is accurate up to the end of 2004. All rare or scarce birds listed have been accepted by the appropriate assessing committee.

Categories of status are positioned immediately at the commencement of the text for each species, following Betts (1992) and are as follows:

Vagrant:	1 – 10 records, all listed.
Rare:	11 – 31 records (may all be listed).
Scarce:	1 – 5 birds or records per year on average.
Uncommon:	6 – 50 birds per year on average.
Fairly common:	51 – 250 birds per year on average.
Common:	251 – 1000 birds per year on average.
Abundant:	1001 – 2,500 birds per year on average.
Very abundant:	More than 2,500 per year on average.

NON-PASSERIFORMES

GAVIIDAE (Divers)

Black-throated Diver *Gavia arctica*
Vagrant. One on 8th March and two on 9th October 1988, three on 29th November 1990, one on 21st November 1991 and one on 20th February 2003.

Red-throated Diver *Gavia stellata*
Scarce. The most frequently recorded diver, seen offshore February - May and August - December. Rarely more than a handful of sightings in any one year, although there were 5 daily in late-November 1990. Referred to in 1936 by Lockley as being "less numerous than Great Northern Diver".

Great Northern Diver *Gavia immer*
Scarce. Occasionally offshore March - May and September - November, with seldom more than one or two sightings each year, often none at all, but described in 1936 as being "common offshore September to March".

PODICIPEDIDAE (Grebes)

Great Crested Grebe *Podiceps cristatus*
Vagrant. Surprisingly, there are just two records: one offshore on 13th November 1996, and two on 23rd September 1997.

Dabchick *Tachybaptus ruficollis*
Vagrant. Singles on 21st October 1929, 28th September - 4th October 1948, on 8th April and 31st October 1968, 8th - 9th September 1971, an adult on 10th April 1996, a juvenile on 28th August 2001 and another on 7th September 2003.

Red-necked Grebe *Podiceps grisegena*
Vagrant. Singles offshore on 30th October 1993 and on 21st May 1997.

DIOMEDEIDAE (Albatrosses)

Black-browed Albatross *Diomedea melanophris*
Vagrant. An adult on 19th August 1990 that flew south and then turned back towards the north was the first accepted record for Wales.

PROCELLARIIDAE (Fulmars, Petrels, Shearwaters)

Fulmar *Fulmarus glacialis*
Breeds. Common. First recorded in 1931, when an occasional light-phase adult was seen cruising near the island in May and June. There was subsequently a great increase in sightings. A pair first bred on Skokholm in 1967, and numbers have increased dramatically, virtually annually, since then. See pages 150 - 152.

Cory's Shearwater *Calonectris diomeda*
Vagrant. Singles offshore on 17th August 1979, 6th and 15th August 1989, 17th and 25th September 1995, and one on 10th July 2001.

Great Shearwater *Puffinus gravis*
Vagrant. Two on 9th September 1993, and one on 9th August 2000.

Sooty Shearwater *Puffinus griseus*
Scarce to uncommon. Seen in most autumns, although sightings each year are undoubtedly reflected in the amount of sea-watching effort, and regular watches would surely result in more of this species being seen. The highest annual total is of 19 birds in 1987.

Manx Shearwater *Puffinus puffinus*
Breeds. Very abundant. Present late February - early October, with occasional sightings offshore until November. However, in recent years birds have regularly been heard at night in late October (2002) and even mid-November as they flew over the island during the period around the new moon. See pages 105 - 116.

Balearic Shearwater *Puffinus mauretanicus*
Uncommon. First recorded in 1960. Seen regularly offshore, particularly in the period late July - October, numbers depending a great deal on sea-watching effort, the highest annual total being 14 in 1987 and 1990.

HYDROBATIDAE (Storm-petrels)

Storm Petrel *Hydrobates pelagicus*
Breeds. Present late April - October or early November. See pages 117 - 123.

Leach's Storm-petrel *Oceanodroma leucorhoa*
Vagrant. Birds have been found in the storm petrel colony at night, occasionally singing, on the following dates: 15th July 1966, 22nd - 23rd June 1976, 1st June 1978, 21st May, 9th (two birds) and 12th June 1980, and 22nd June 1989. In addition, two birds were seen and heard regularly between 1st June and 2nd July 1977, and one was seen over the sea off the lighthouse on 8th September 2003.

SULIDAE (Boobies, Gannets)

Gannet *Morus bassanus*
Very abundant. Offshore throughout due to the proximity of the island of Grassholm (breeding population of about 30,000 pairs). Scarce in the period November to March.

PHALACROCORACIDAE (Cormorants, Shags)

Cormorant *Phalacrocorax carbo*
Fairly common. Small numbers offshore throughout, though large parties pass northwards in March - April and particularly late August - September when up to 107 (12th September 2003) have been recorded flying south. An individual with head and neck as white as the continental race *P. c. sinensis* was recorded on 26th March 1963.

Shag *Phalacrocorax aristotelis*
Has bred. Fairly common. Up to 6 on the water around the island daily throughout the year, occasionally more (maximum 20 in August - September), and often roosting on The Anticline during spells of rough weather (e.g. 14 on 23rd October 2004). One pair bred in 1932 - 35, two pairs 1936 - 37 and one pair in 1987.

ARDEIDAE (Bitterns, Herons)

Little Egret *Egretta garzetta*
Vagrant. A fully-plumed adult spent the night of 18th May 1983 in the Lesser Black-backed Gull colony by Bread Rock; three birds foraged in The Dip on 10th October 1993. Of the 8 subsequent records, all but one have been of "flyover" birds: two on 1st May 1997, one on 2nd and 18th August 1998, one on 4th August 1999, one (on South Pond) on 8th June 2000, one on 3rd July 2000, one on 6th May 2002 and two on 25th April 2003. The species is now a regular winter visitor to mainland Pembrokeshire, and passage migrant.

Grey Heron *Ardea cinerea*
Scarce. Flyover birds are recorded annually, with occasional singles February - June and becoming more regular July - November. Small parties (maximum 10 birds) have been annual in this latter period since the late 1970's. They are invariably attacked by gulls, which give away their presence. In 2004, there was an unprecedented roost on the island cliff top, with 5 seen in the early morning of 5th September, and 7 birds in exactly the same spot at dawn the following day.

CICONIIDAE (Storks)

Black Stork *Ciconia nigra*
Vagrant. An adult roosted in Peter's Bay on the night of 27th April 1991, before flying north the next day. The first record for Pembrokeshire.

THRESKIORNITHIDAE (Ibises, Spoonbills)

Glossy Ibis *Plegadis falcinellus*
Vagrant. An immature was on North Pond in the early morning of 19th June 1996, and was the fourth record for Pembrokeshire (assumed to be the same individual that was present on the nearby mainland on 15th and 16th June).

Spoonbill *Platalea leucorodia*
Vagrant. A first-winter bird flew in from the south-east on 20th October 1957 and spent the day on the island. In 1988, two first-winter birds (one ringed in the Netherlands) wintered on the Cleddau estuary, and it was presumed to be those that flew west over the island on 12th October. There are 5 other records: an adult on 22nd August 1993; another on 24th June 1994 and on 1st May 1996; an immature that spent the whole day on Northern Plain on 21st September 1996; and an adult on 21st June 2001, briefly on the cliff edge at Crab Bay.

ANATIDAE (Swans, Geese, Ducks)

Mute Swan *Cygnus olor*
Vagrant. An immature on 18th May 1966, an adult on 14th October 1981 and a party of 5 flying north on 4th May 1993.

Whooper Swan *Cygnus cygnus*
Vagrant. A herd of 47 flew west on 19th February 1956; then two on 25th October 1967, three on 22nd and 29th October 1980, three from 17th - 19th May 1981, 8 on 5th October 1981, 5 on 24th October 1987, 18 on 9th October 1988 and three on 12th May 1995.

Canada Goose *Branta canadensis*
Breeds. A party of 4 birds on 3rd October 1952 was the first record for Pembrokeshire. Over a dozen records from 1971 - 1995, in all months March - October except July, with a maximum of 7 on 18th October 1980, reflecting the species' spread from introduced stock in Pembrokeshire. Then, in 1996, following regular visits

from a small flock in April, one pair bred unsuccessfully. This was soon followed by the arrival of further pairs, and in 2003 controls were initiated under license from the Welsh Assembly, where eggs were replaced with wooden fakes. Following breeding, birds disappear by early August, and return from late August onwards, making frequent visits from the mainland at all times of day, but most frequently at dusk or dawn. See pages 115 - 116 for further information.

Greylag Goose *Anser anser*

Vagrant. Just 10 records. Two on 1st October 1954, singles 22nd - 26th April 1963, 30th April - 1st May 1972, 7th April 1984, 3rd April 1992, two on 10th April 1993, one on 17th April 1994, one on 23rd and 24th April 1995, five briefly on North Pond on 15th March 2002, and another one on 3rd June 2002.

White-fronted Goose *Anser albifrons*

Rare. Fourteen records: all but three in the period 12th October - 3rd December, comprising between one and 13 birds, the exception being a single bird from 28th April until 1st May 1990. Both subspecies (Eurasian *A. a. albifrons* and Greenland *A. a. flavirostris*) have been recorded, and where sub-specific identification has been possible, *flavirostris* has been commonest. A flock of 40 on 23rd October 1994 was the largest.

Pink-footed Goose *Anser brachyrhynchus*

Vagrant. Just one record, of a nervous pair which spent half-an-hour on North Pond before flying off north on 27th May 1988.

Barnacle Goose *Branta leucopsis*

Rare. Lockley (1936) reports them being "seen passing at sea off Skokholm in winter". Otherwise, in spring, there has been one March and three April records of between one and 5 birds, and 9 autumn records between 8th October and 9th November of between one and 10 birds, during the 40-year period from 1966 to 2005, the last being in 2002, when one bird was present on North Pond on 8th April, and 8 were seen taking off from North Pond and fly eastwards on 19th October. Previously a small flock spent the winter months on nearby Skomer Island.

Brent Goose *Branta bernicla*

Vagrant. As with Barnacle Goose, Lockley (1936) mentions them passing in winter, including 16 on 10th April 1936. Then none until a dark-bellied bird (race *B. b. bernicla*) remained from 15th - 27th April 1984, and again 2nd - 24th May 1984. Few subsequent records, all of race *B. b. bernicla* unless stated: one 28th - 29th April 1987, one 15th April 1991, one momentarily on N. Pond on 27th March 1996, and then another, possibly the same, 26th April - 8th May 1996; two flew past the island over the sea on 5th October 1996, and 9 passed by northwards on 9th September 2003, their race not ascertained.

Shelduck *Tadorna tadorna*

Uncommon. Breeding suspected. Rare prior to the mid-1950's, since when it has occurred in most years with singles or small parties (maximum 11) in the period March to mid-July. There were no sightings in 1996 - 1998, but this was followed by four years out of 5 with 3 or 4 pairs present each spring, with courtship observed frequently and females entering Rabbit burrows, but breeding was never actually confirmed. There have been just three August records, three in October (two in 2001 and one in 2004) and two in November (2002 and 2003).

Wigeon *Anas penelope*

Uncommon. Referred to in 1936 by Lockley as being "an abundant winter resident, October to April, casual August to September." Recorded in most years in the period from late-August to late-April, occasionally into May, and especially late-February (the island being reoccupied by Wardens at this time in recent years) to April, and (September) October to early-December, often on North Pond, but they are particularly wary of people and tend to disappear if disturbed too often. About 100 were recorded in January 1951 and again (offshore) in December 1990, but counts are generally much smaller, with 35 on North Pond on 15th November 1999 being the maximum in recent years, and often far fewer. Unusually, there was only one record in 2003 (on 2nd April). Small numbers are frequently seen passing over the sea, occasionally with Common Scoter *Melanitta nigra*.

Gadwall *Anas strepera*

Rare. Sixteen records, all listed: a drake on 16th April 1966, a duck on 6th July 1970, two on 29th October 1970, a drake on 5th October 1976, a pair on 20th April 1977, on 27th April 1979, and on 14th May 1981; a drake on 10th March 1988, another on 11th May 1991, a pair on 13th November 1993 and on 3rd May 1996, also on 11th September 1999, two drakes on 11th April 2000, a duck on 3rd June 2001, a drake on North Pond on 13th April 2002, and a pair there on 23rd May 2002.

Eurasian Teal *Anas crecca*

Fairly common. Between 1927 and 1935, Lockley (1936) reported that there were "up to 50 resident mid-August to mid-April", but today there are scattered records in all months, and although there are fairly-large flocks in the late-winter/early-spring period (72 in early-February 2001), numbers in the autumn are fewer. The winter rains result in North Pond becoming particularly large, and undoubtedly more attractive to many more species of duck. Breeding was suspected in 1936. Up to 170 birds were present in January 1968.

Green-winged Teal *Anas carolinensis*

Vagrant. Just 4 records, all of drakes (which are far more easily identified than ducks), on North Pond on 15th and 17th April 1996, on Oystercatcher Rock on 17th April 1997, and one with 5 Eurasian Teal on the sea in North Haven on 22nd February 2001, then another on North Pond on 22nd March 2001.

Mallard *Anas platyrhynchos*

Breeds. Fairly common. Recorded in all months in small numbers, though scarcest June - August unless breeding has been successful. See page 156.

Pintail *Anas acuta*

Scarce. First recorded in 1940, with just 7 more records up to 1980. Then the species became a regular from 1981 - 1996, with a pair often present in March - April and breeding attempts were suspected in 1993 and 1995. Juveniles were present in 1987 - 89, presumably resulting from the small breeding population on Skomer at that time. There have been no further sightings since May 1996.

Garganey *Anas querquedula*

Vagrant. Just 8 records: a pair on 1st June 1951, a drake 20th - 21st May 1963, a pair 5th - 6th March 1969, a duck on 26th September 1972, drake on 11th and 14th May 1993, duck 9th - 10th May 1996, and a drake on 6th May 2000.

Blue-winged Teal *Anas discolor*
Vagrant. One on 17th September 1960.

Shoveler *Anas clypeata*
Has bred. Uncommon. Few sporadic records prior to 1964, but regular since in small numbers February - May and August - December (20 on 16th November 1997), with a few records in June and July. See page 156.

Pochard *Aythya ferina*
Vagrant. Just 6 records: a pair visited North Pond on 11th April 1948; three were seen on 5th November 1968; a pair on 7th April 1970 and a female/immature on 31st July 1970; a party of 4 flew north on 1st October 1989; and a party of 9 was offshore on 20th October 1991.

Ferruginous Duck *Aythya nyroca*
Vagrant. A drake was on North Pond with Mallards on 15th November 1992.

Tufted Duck *Aythya fuligula*
Vagrant. A scarce and very local breeding bird in Pembrokeshire, this reflected in the total of just 11 island records: a duck 6th - 20th May 1958, a duck or eclipse drake on 8th August 1961, two on 3rd May 1972, a pair on 8th May 1981, a duck on 10th October 1982, a drake 1st - 9th June 1991, three on 21st September 1994 and two on 29th September 1994, a duck on 28th August 1999, a drake on 3rd July 2000 and in the period 23rd - 26th June 2004.

Ring-necked Duck *Aythya collaris*
Vagrant. A duck on North Pond on 12th October 1986 was the first record of a female in Pembrokeshire.

Scaup *Aythya marila*
Vagrant. Just one record, of 4 birds on 7th September 1968.

Eider *Somateria mollissima*
Rare. Just 12 records, all listed: following the sighting of a duck on 19th July 1966, there has been a recent spate: a drake in Broad Sound on 14th June 1988; a duck offshore 2nd - 6th June 1989; 7 flew north on 1st October 1989 and a drake was offshore on 9th October 1989; a duck offshore 9th - 13th April 1990; a duck on 4th May 1991 and 3 on 20th September 1991; a drake with puffins in Broad Sound on 31st May 1992; two drakes and two ducks off East Bay on 30th November 1998; one duck off E. Bay on 24th November 2000; and one duck on 21st September 2001.

Long-tailed Duck *Clangula hyemalis*
Vagrant. A first-winter drake flew south on 16th October 1990, and there were two in Broad Sound on 30th October 1995.

Common Scoter *Melanitta nigra*
Common. Recorded offshore in all months, but particularly mid-May to November, and especially August - September when over 200 may pass southwards each day. A total of 420 on 28th May 1992 was exceptional, but records probably reflect the amount of sea-watching effort. The oil spilled as a result of the grounding of the *Sea*

Empress in February 1996 took a heavy toll on this species, with at least 3,500 birds wintering in Carmarthen Bay being killed (Sea Empress Environmental Evaluation Committee, 1998).

Velvet Scoter *Melanitta fusca*
Vagrant. A drake flew south on 26th October 1966.

Surf Scoter *Melanitta perspicillata*
Vagrant. A drake flew south on 25th October 1990.

Goldeneye *Bucephala clangula*
Vagrant. A duck was offshore on 26th and 29th October 1980; another on 9th April 1986; a party of 5 on 21st October 1991; and a duck/juvenile was on North Pond on 30th October 2002.

Goosander *Mergus merganser*
Vagrant. A drake was offshore on 23rd October 1961, and a party of 5 "redheads" flew north on 4th June 1988.

Red-breasted Merganser *Mergus serrator*
Rare. Just 13 records, all offshore, all listed: a redhead on 19th February and two drakes on 3rd November 1968; a drake on 12th September 1973; two on 28th October 1980; one on 24th May 1985; two on 28th September and one on 21st October 1991; singles on 4th October 1992; 22nd June and 26th September 1993; 21st July 1994; a drake on 13th May 1995; and a drake and two redheads on 21st September 2001.

ACCIPITRIDAE (Hawks, Vultures, Eagles)

Honey Buzzard *Pernis apivorus*
Vagrant. Just 5 records, all of single birds: on 10th August 1982, 13th July 1989, 19th May 1990, 26th July 1991 and 6th June 1996.

Marsh Harrier *Circus aeruginosus*
Rare, becoming scarce. A female or immature for two days 12th - 13th May 1954, then a period of 27 years until the second, an immature on 31st August 1981. Three records in 1987 - 88, then from 1994 - 2004 a spate of sightings, with 29 records in the 11 years, as follows: 5 in April, 6 in May, one in June, one in July, 13 in August and 3 in September. All but two have been female or immature (imm. male on 24th April 1987; adult male on 3rd May 2001).

Hen Harrier *Circus cyaneus*
Scarce. Records of one, occasionally two birds in the period September to November in most years following the first on 19th and 24th October 1966. One or two birds were seen virtually daily from 16th October until 3rd December 2003. Also seen once in January, twice in March and four times in April. Three were present on 23rd October 1993 including a wing-tagged bird that was marked in North Wales as a chick that same year.

Montague's Harrier *Circus pyargus*

Rare. First recorded on 5th August 1935, but then absent until 1951, from when the species was seen occasionally during the periods April - May and August - September until 1979. A first-winter bird wintered on Skomer Island 1988 - 89, and visited Skokholm on 9th October 1988 and 31st March 1989. Excluding this bird, extreme dates are 16th April (1977) and 28th September (1956).

Black Kite *Milvus migrans*

Vagrant. One on 20th May 1990 attempted to land on Northern Plain but was chased off by gulls. The first record for Pembrokeshire.

Red Kite *Milvus milvus*

Vagrant. One on 6th June 2000 is the only record, but with numbers increasing in mid-Wales (and elsewhere in Britain following introductions), there are sure to be more sightings soon.

Goshawk *Accipiter gentilis*

Vagrant. A male on 9th July 1990 was chased the length of Mad Bay by three Peregrine Falcons.

Sparrowhawk *Accipiter nisus*

Uncommon. An irregular visitor in all months, but mainly seen in the periods March - April and August - October when up to three birds have been present. Apart from a lean period 1961 - 66, there has been no real change in the pattern of occurrence. This species was responsible for the destruction of a flock of free-flying and breeding Border Canaries on the island 1939 - 40 (see Lockley, 1948).

Buzzard *Buteo buteo*

Breeds. See pages 156 - 157.

Rough-legged Buzzard *Buteo lagopus*

Vagrant. One on 9th November 1967.

PANDIONIDAE (Ospreys)

Osprey *Pandion haliaetus*

Vagrant. Becoming more frequent. The first was flushed from Spy Rock on 9th September 1966. The second flew west on 10th September 1988. Then single over-flying birds on 19th May 1992, 12th September 1993, 21st September 1996, 7th April and 24th May 1997, 13th September and 15th September 2002, and 7th September 2004.

FALCONIDAE (Falcons and Allies)

Red-footed Falcon *Falco vespertinus*

Vagrant. A male landed for a brief time on The Neck on 27th May 1975.

Kestrel *Falco tinnunculus*
Uncommon. Recorded in all months, but most regularly in the period from late-August to October, usually singles but occasionally up to five birds at any one time. Often seen hovering above the cliff-top slopes, presumably in search of mice.

Merlin *Falco columbarius*
Uncommon. Recorded in most years February to early-May and again from mid-August to early-December. Also a single record in June, 4 times in July, and on occasional winter visits.

Hobby *Falco subbuteo*
Rare. The relatively-recent national increase has been reflected by sightings on Skokholm. All are records of single birds: 16th September 1959; 22nd June 1975; 8th June 1982; 7th September 1987; 29th April and 13th September 1988; 14th and 28th August 1990; 29th May, 10th August and 26th September 1994; 17th and 25th May 1995; 14th August 1996; 12th May 2001; 25th June 2003; 15th May and 7th July 2004, and 5th - 6th June 2005.

Peregrine *Falco peregrinus*
Breeds. See pages 157 - 158.

PHASIANIDAE (Partridges, Quails, Pheasants and Allies)

Quail *Coturnix coturnix*
Rare to scarce. An irregular spring visitor, first recorded on 19th May 1938. This was a "good Quail year", as were the years 1964 and 1989, when more than two records were made, the latter with 7 sightings of up to 2 birds. Twenty-nine of the 45 records have come in May, 9 in June, and 4 in July, one in April (23rd April 1949); there are two autumn records, one on 24th September 1955 and on 27th October 1977.

RALLIDAE (Rails)

Water Rail *Rallus aquatilis*
Has bred. Scarce. A pair bred in 1929 and 1931, possibly in 1934, and a pair was present throughout the summer of 1995, but breeding was not proven. One bird called virtually incessantly each night in Orchid Bog from 28th May until 6th June 1997. Scarce but quite regular on passage, particularly in the period August - November, when their squealing gives them away. Over-wintering has been suspected, particularly 2002 - 03, with at least 5 birds recorded virtually daily from 23rd August until the island was vacated for the winter on 5th December 2002 (singles seen at East and Orchid Bogs, plus two individuals seen frequently at The Well Pool, and one frequenting a cement-lined pond to the north of the kitchen and the nearby bramble patch, and others frequently heard in favoured patches of Bracken around the island). Three present on 20th February 2003 had therefore surely over-wintered. An immature took up residence at The Well Pool on 28th August 2003, and was subsequently present until the end of the season (island vacated on 4th December), seen gradually moulting into its first adult plumage.

Spotted Crake *Porzana porzana*

Vagrant. Seven records of singles: the first was trapped at North Pond on 8th August 1968; a "month-old" corpse was discovered on 24th October 1971; others on 4th August 1973; 12th and 15th September and 24th October 1987; one flushed from Bracken on 6th May 1990 and then unceremoniously pulled out of its hiding place in a burrow.

Corn Crake *Crex crex*

Has bred. Rare, formerly scarce. Once annual in spring and virtually the same in autumn, with numerous birds in any one season. A pair bred in 1930, and males were heard calling for long periods in 1949 and 1951. The year 1971 was the last to produce more than two sightings until 1999, when an adult was seen on 26th May, and then an immature was present in an area of Yellow Iris at The Well Pool for four days 14th - 17th September, where it fed voraciously on craneflies. Between 1972 and 1990 there were just 6 records (one in late April, five in September), then the two in 1999, then none from 2000 to 2004.

Moorhen *Gallinula chloropus*
Breeds. See page 159.

Coot *Fulica atra*

Rare. An irregular visitor, with 16 of the 22 records coming in July or August. A group of 7 that flew south over the sea on 26th July 1939 was the first record, and on 9th - 11th August of the same year there was a pair on North Pond. Breeding was suspected in 1989, when two adults and a newly-fledged juvenile were seen on North Pond from 4th August to 11th September. The most recent record was on 8th April 1998, when one flew in from the east, calling when it was over the observatory buildings, and spent the day on North Pond.

HAEMATOPODIDAE (Oystercatchers)

Oystercatcher *Haematopus ostralegus*
Breeds. See pages 159 - 161.

RECURVIROSTRIDAE (Stilts, Avocets)

Black-winged Stilt *Himantopus himantopus*
Vagrant. One on North Pond at dawn on 7th May 1990, which remained until the following morning. It was part of an influx into SW Britain.

BURHINIDAE (Stone-curlews)

Stone Curlew *Burhinus oedicnemus*
Vagrant. Singles on 25th April 1940, 7th July 1982, 21st August 1991, and 18th July 2003.

CHARADRIIDAE (Plovers, Lapwings)

Little Ringed Plover *Charadrius dubius*
Vagrant. One on 5th May 1986, two on 11th and one on 12th April 1988, and one long-staying individual, 12th - 19th May 2001.

Ringed Plover *Charadrius hiaticula*
Uncommon. On passage (end of March) mid-April to early-June, and July to early-October, and seen only occasionally outside these periods. Records are usually of fly-over birds. One remained present from 27th November until 1st December 1990. Counts rarely exceed 5, although up to 13 have been recorded in May and September.

Kentish Plover *Charadrius alexandrinus*
Vagrant. A female was with Turnstones at North Pond on 28th May 1967, the first record for Pembrokeshire.

Dotterel *Charadrius morinellus*
Vagrant. The first record was of a party of 5 on 7th May 1960; then one from 2nd - 7th September 1964 and again 10th and 12th September 1964; 25th - 26th August 1970; 21st - 24th September and 6th - 7th October 1971; 18th September 1972; 13th - 17th September 1973; 11th - 17th September and 18th - 21st September 1974; 16th October 1981; and 8th - 13th October 1995.

American Golden Plover *Pluvialis dominica*
Vagrant. One on 26th September 1981 was the first record for Wales.

Golden Plover *Pluvialis apricaria*
Uncommon. On passage from March to early-June and August to October (particularly mid-September to October). Occasional in other months. Rarely reaching double figures: 15 on 5th September 2004, 50 on 2nd September 1950; and 150 on 4th March 1965. Individuals of both races *apricaria* and *altifrons* have been identified.

Grey Plover *Pluvialis squatarola*
Scarce. Irregular on migration from late-March to early-June, and again in September and October. Also recorded in July, August and January in parties of 1 - 5 birds.

Lapwing *Vanellus vanellus*
Formerly bred. See pages 161 - 162.

SCOLOPACIDAE (Sandpipers and Allies)

Knot *Calidris canutus*
Scarce. Irregular on passage from mid-July to October (particularly late-August to September), and occasionally late-April to mid-May, and with a few records in January and February. Usually single birds, though up to 7 have been recorded, and very occasionally more: 67 on 29th September 1958, 15 on 7th September 1962, and 30 on 25th August 1978.

Sanderling *Calidris alba*
Rare. On migration in May and late-August to September, with some records in all months March to October.
Singles, apart from 5 on 4th September 1979, 2 on 23rd May 1984, 11 on 7th August 1994 and 4 on 8th October
2001.

Semi-palmated Sandpiper *Calidris pusilla*
Vagrant. An adult seen on 20th July 1964 was trapped the next day at Winter Pond. It comprised the second
British and Irish record.

Little Stint *Calidris minuta*
Scarce. On passage August to October, sometimes in small parties and remaining for several days. There has
also been a single spring record, of one on 27th May 1990.

Temminck's Stint *Calidris temminckii*
Vagrant. One on North Pond on 1st September 1985.

Pectoral Sandpiper *Calidris melanotus*
Rare. There are 14 records, 3 in early-June, one in August and the remainder between 12th September and 11th
October. Some of the autumn birds remained for a few days, or even weeks, as did the first, present from 23rd
September until 12th October 1958, the first record for Wales.

Curlew Sandpiper *Calidris ferruginea*
Rare. There are 5 spring records and 7 in autumn, all listed, single birds unless stated: on 29th - 30th June and on
4th September 1955; two on 16th March and one 21st - 24th May 1959; 29th - 30th May 1963; 6th - 8th October
1973; two on 24th August 1975; 30th April 1990; 27th - 30th August 1993; 22nd September 1994: 26th - 27th July
1995; and 19th September 1996.

Purple Sandpiper *Calidris maritima*
Uncommon (formerly "fairly common"). Recorded in all months, most regularly March to early-May, and
particularly late-June to mid-September. However, in recent years there have been many more sightings (of
small parties) in October and November, birds roosting with Turnstones on the rocky shore. Double figure
counts were regular in the late 1960's and throughout the 1970's, but the 1980's saw a marked decline. The
largest count was of 32 birds on 20th March 1968 and also on 16th August 1978.

Dunlin *Calidris alpina*
Fairly common. Recorded in all months, but most regularly on passage April to early-June and again mid-July
to October, but particularly in late-April and May, when parties build up on North Pond. These are extremely
approachable, and in fact easily missed as one walks past them. Counts generally number between one and 19
birds, but up to 50 have been recorded. Occasionally present in winter, with about of 50 counted in January
1968.

Buff-breasted Sandpiper *Tryngites subruficollis*
Vagrant. One on 3rd June 1985; one for five days in the period 5th - 9th September 1988, on Northern Plain and
often accompanied by a Ruff.

Ruff *Philomachus pugnax*
Scarce. Infrequent and irregular on passage from March to May, plus two records in June, but more commonly July to October. Usually single birds or small groups, with the highest count being of 12 birds in April 1987.

Jack Snipe *Lymnocryptes minimus*
Scarce. Lockley (1936) said that the species was "common from 7th October to 24th March." Subsequently it has been far less common, but recorded in most years, usually single birds. Difficult to locate unless one searches in suitable-looking areas by walking across them in a zigzagging pattern. On passage and wintering from late-September to early-April. The extreme dates are 17th September (1972) and 22nd May (1995), ignoring two August records, on 20th in 1937 and 18th in 1938.

Black-tailed Godwit *Limosa limosa*
Scarce. Irregular on passage during the periods March to September, but mainly April and May and in July. Usually singles or small parties, though occasionally larger groups, e.g. 10 on 8th June 1989, 15 on 13th August 1990, and 12 on 2nd July 2003.

Bar-tailed Godwit *Limosa lapponica*
Uncommon. On migration during the period from March to June and again August to October, but particularly in May and September. Usually singles or small groups in spring, but occasionally larger flocks in autumn, e.g. 35 on 8th September 1963, 43 on 6th September 1988, and 11 on 8th September 1998.

Whimbrel *Numenius phaeopus*
Common. Regular on passage mid-April and July - October, more numerous in spring when up to 50 may pass though daily in April – May, although the maximum of 110 was recorded on 22nd August 1948. One or two birds clearly over-wintered regularly in the period 1968 to 1972 with records in January, February and March, and also up to 5 birds strongly suspected of doing so during successive winters between 1996/97 and 2001/02, and again 2003/04. Extreme dates are complicated by this, but the earliest date outside these two periods is 27th March (1947), and the latest 27th October (1973).

Curlew *Numenius arquata*
Common / abundant. Present throughout the year, although it has never bred. One or two summering birds are generally present from May to mid-June, then numbers increase, with a large nocturnal roost previously numbering up to 200 birds in autumn (maximum 600 on 14th October 1966), but around 20 to 40 at present. The roost generally persists through the winter with tens of birds still present in March.

Woodcock *Scolopax rusticola*
Scarce. Recorded on migration from March to April and October to November, most commonly in late-autumn, and also over-wintering. Over 200 corpses were found in February of the hard winter of 1963. One ringed on the island in February 1963 was recovered in Denmark in March 1964. Ignoring two July records, the extreme dates are: 18th September (2001) and 8th April (1965).

Snipe *Gallinago gallinago*
Fairly common. Recorded in all months, but mainly when on passage from late-July to early-May, also wintering. Counts in double figures are common, with the largest being of 70 in March 1971. Rarely seen in the height of summer, but breeding was suspected in 1927 and in 1965.

Upland Sandpiper *Bartramia longicauda*
Vagrant. One on 18th October 1960.

Spotted Redshank *Tringa erythropus*
Scarce. Just over 40 records, with around 80 percent of birds on autumn passage, mainly in the second half of August into early-September. These are mainly single birds, but occasionally 2 or 3. The few spring records are as follows: up to 5 birds 15th - 21st April 1983, singles on 24th and 25th May 1958, and 16th June 1967. There is also one July record. None recorded 1996 - 2004. Extreme dates: 15th April (1983) and 26th September (1989).

Redshank *Tringa totanus*
Uncommon. There are a few sightings in most years, all months March to November, most regularly July to mid-September, when up to 14 (on 17th August 2001) have been recorded.

Greenshank *Tringa nebularia*
Scarce. First recorded in 1934, remaining rare prior to 1955. Then virtually annual since, although somewhat irregular in spring. Singles or small parties on passage mid-April to mid-May, but more regularly August to mid-September when up to 10 have been recorded. Occasionally seen in July, very occasionally in June and October. Extreme dates: 6th April (1978) and 9th November (1958).

Lesser Yellowlegs *Tringa flavipes*
Vagrant. One was found on the evening of 9th October 1961, and was still present the following day.

Common Sandpiper *Actitis hypoleucos*
Uncommon. A small passage each spring, mid-April to the end of May, and again in the autumn, July to September. Mainly singles or small parties, but 10 on 2nd August 1955, 5th August 1974 and 22nd August 2000. Occasionally seen in October. Extreme dates: 21st March (1948) and 29th October (1975).

Green Sandpiper *Tringa ochropus*
Scarce. First recorded in 1946. Rare in spring with just ten April records and five in May. Return passage is larger, especially late July - August when one or 2 are seen in most years, but up to 5 present daily during the period 4th - 13th August 1997 was exceptional, following days of heavy rainfall which produced many pools. Extreme dates: 2nd April (1997) and 21st October (1967).

Wood Sandpiper *Tringa glareola*
Scarce. First recorded in 1955. Rare in spring with just five May and two June records. Apart from three records in July, all other sightings have been in August and September, with a total of 49 records of one or 2 birds which occasionally remain for a while (e.g. from 28th August until 6th September 1972). Extreme dates: 2nd May (1994) and 22nd September (1966).

Turnstone *Arenaria interpres*

Fairly common (formerly "common"). Recorded in all months, largest numbers in March - April and August - October. Counts of over 40 were regular in both of these periods (maximum 70 in August 1960) until the late 1970's, but figures have been noticeably lower since, usually less than 20.

Grey Phalarope *Phalaropus fulicarius*

Rare. All records are listed. Mainly found in September and October, one in November. Two off of South Bay on 17th September 1955, 2 in North Haven on 30th September 1957, singles on 7th and 27th September 1959, then an exceptional year in 1960 when strong north-westerly winds produced sightings of 35 phalaropes between 18th and 27th September and another on 9th October (maximum 17 on 18th). Of these, 9 were identified as grey phalaropes, but they probably all were. Then further records on 9th September and 24th - 25th October 1961, one on 26th October 1967, one on 31st August 1970, 3 on 21st September 1981, one on 20th November 1999; and on 9th October 2001. Single unidentified phalaropes were seen swimming just off The Stack on 27th September 1968 and in Peter's Bay on 16th September 1990.

STERCORARIIDAE (Skuas)

Pomarine Skua *Stercorarius pomarinus*

Rare. Of the total of 19 records to 2004, including the first on 13th September 1966, 6 occurred in 1989 (with a total of 9 flying north between 10th August and 22nd September, maximum 3 on 13th August). Apart from 5 on 28th May, one on 12th June 1993 and on 28th April 1997, 14th May and 18th June 2003, all refer to between one and three birds in the period 5th August to 16th October. Sea-watching effort and identification skills play an important part in the recording of this species.

Arctic Skua *Stercorarius parasiticus*

Scarce - uncommon. Irregular in spring, with around 30 records April to June (half of these in May) of between one and 3 birds. Virtually annual July - October, with the peak of passage in September, but numbers vary (partly with sea-watching effort) from one to over 20 in a year, with the maximum being 50 birds on 5th September 2004 (included a flock of 33 birds). Extreme dates: 6th April (1959) and 22nd October (1968).

Long-tailed Skua *Stercorarius longicaudus*

Vagrant. An adult chased Kittiwakes off The Head on 4th October 1995.

Great Skua *Stercorarius skua*

Scarce - uncommon. First recorded in 1956. Rare in spring, with seven April records, two in May and four in June, of one or two birds only. Almost annual from late-July to October since the mid 1960's, with passage peaking in early-September and occasionally outnumbering Arctic Skuas. Again, numbers fluctuate, producing annual totals varying from two to 22 in recent years. Fourteen amongst a flock of feeding Kittiwakes in Broad Sound on 28th September 1978 was exceptional. There has been another astonishing record, of one remaining on the island for three days 7th - 9th September 2004, and seen to capture and kill a 1st-winter Lesser Black-backed Gull. Extreme dates: 12th April (1977) and 26th October (1987).

LARIDAE (Gulls)

Mediterranean Gull *Larus melanocephalus*

Rare. A second-winter bird that fed in Broad Sound on 5 dates between 3rd and 17th November 1968 was the first record for Pembrokeshire. Longer periods of occupation by island Wardens in recent years have resulted in more late-autumn and early-winter sightings, of around 49 records in total, most of adults in October and November, but with occasional spring and summer sightings, e.g. one on 9th March 1994, four August sightings and one on 29th September 2001, all fly-past birds. On 9th September 2003, a young bird, moulting from juvenile to first-winter plumage, spent 15 minutes on Northern Plain, preening as it stood amongst Lesser Black-backed Gulls.

Little Gull *Larus minutus*

Scarce. An irregular visitor offshore in the period mid-August to November, but especially late October to November, and probably wintering in the area since there is also an early-February sighting. Seen almost annually since observations extended regularly into the early-winter period (from the late-1980's). There are also three July records (two in 1990; one in 2001 of a first-summer bird) and one in spring (of an immature on 2nd April 1960). Numbers have rarely exceeded one or two, but there were 6 on 31st October 1980 and 7 on 14th November 1967, 6 on 21st November 1996, three on 21st November 1997, and three on 6th February 1998, amidst the fleets of Black-headed Gulls and Kittiwakes in Broad Sound.

Sabine's Gull *Larus sabini*

Vagrant. All juveniles: one off The Head on 11th October 1968, one with Black-headed Gulls in Broad Sound on 25th and 28th October 1967; two on 30th October and one on 1st November 1980, one on 22nd September 1981, two on 8th September 2003 and one on 23rd September 2003.

Black-headed Gull *Larus ridibundus*

Common. Offshore August - April, increasing in October - November when the number feeding in Broad Sound may reach an estimated 2,500; occasional in all other months. Lockley anticipated breeding in 1935, and 2 pairs defended territory around North Pond in April 1968, but breeding didn't take place.

Common Gull *Larus canus*

Uncommon. Seen offshore September - March, foraging alongside other small gulls, occasionally reaching double figures and very occasionally (in November) over 100, with a maximum of around 150 counted in November 1968. There are very few records in each of the months in the period April to August.

Lesser Black-backed Gull *Larus fuscus*

Breeds. Very abundant. See the main text on pages 124 - 131. Individuals resembling "one of the Scandinavian races" *L. f. fuscus/intermedius* were recorded on 2nd April 1934, 14th, 16th (2) and 17th September 1951 and the N. Scandinavian race *L. f. fuscus* on 23rd March 1989.

Herring Gull *Larus argentatus*

Breeds. Abundant (formerly "very abundant"). See pages 152 - 153.

Iceland Gull *Larus glaucoides*

Vagrant. An immature on 19th March 1983. A third-summer bird in the Lesser Black-backed Gull colony on 23rd August and again on 9th September 1988 showed faint brown flight and tail feather markings and was perhaps a hybrid. A second-year bird was present on 27th April and 16th May 1993 and another on 26th March 1996.

Glaucous Gull *Larus hyperboreus*

Vagrant. An immature flew over on 6th April 1969, a sub-adult was recorded on 1st November 1981, a second-winter bird on 31st March 1991, a second-year bird on 17th April and 14th May 1995, and on 12th March 2004, this last one perched briefly on the Wheelhouse roof.

Great Black-backed Gull *Larus marinus*

Breeds. Common. See pages 154 - 155.

Kittiwake *Rissa tridactyla*

Very abundant. Large numbers breed on nearby Skomer Island. Offshore in all months, feeding flocks in autumn often numbering thousands (highest estimate of 8,000). Regularly roost on rocks off Crab and Wreck Bays in autumn, and in May 1959 a pair built a nest in Little Bay, but apparently no eggs were laid.

STERNIDAE (Terns)

Sandwich Tern *Sterna sandvicensis*

Uncommon. First recorded in 1936, and then there followed only 4 records in 20 years before a total of 13 birds were seen in August - September 1957; from then on their occurrence has been virtually annual. Still irregular in spring, although up to 11 have been seen in May; occasional records in June and July; more frequent August to early-October, especially late-August to- September when up to 32 have been recorded, although numbers are usually much lower. Extreme dates: 29th March (1984) and 25th October (1967).

Roseate Tern *Sterna dougalli*

Vagrant. Just 9 autumn records of a species which has probably been overlooked in the past. One on 1st and two on 5th September 1963, one on 28th September 1967, one on 9th August 1977, a family party of 4 feeding in the Wild Goose Race on 31st July 1989 and 2 juveniles on 27th August 1989; 4 on 24th August 1992 and two on 2nd and 4th August 1994. Sustained sea-watching effort by experienced observers would surely produce more sightings, although the species is in decline and has never been common. Mathew (1894) states that roseate terns formerly bred on the Stack.

Common Tern / Arctic Tern *Sterna hirundo / paradisaea*

Fairly common. On passage April - June in small numbers (40 on 10th May 1968 was exceptional) and in some years not recorded in spring at all. Returning birds July - October are more numerous, with peak counts usually coming in the last few days of August and the first-half of September when up to 150 may feed offshore (320 were present on 29th August 1958). Common Terns are more often identified than Arctic, but the latter seems more prone (very occasionally) to land on or fly over the island, or even visit the ponds. Mathew (1894) noted a small breeding colony of Common Terns on The Stack, believed by Lockley to have disappeared in 1916. Extreme dates: 27th March (1967) and 8th November (1967).

Little Tern *Sterna albifrons*
Rare. Described by Lockley in 1936 as being "Irregular 9th - 18th September". There was a single on 24th June 1936 and up to 4 were seen on 6 days 28th October - 6th November 1980. The remaining 23 records lie in the period 13th August - 27th September, half of them in 1992 - 94, including the maximum count of 11 on 31st August 1992.

Black Tern *Chlidonias niger*
Rare. Twenty-five autumn records of up to 12 birds between 14th August and 11th November, including three consecutive days 31st August - 2nd September 1997. Greater sea-watching effort in the last-mentioned period would undoubtedly reveal more, since this time is known for movements of this species, though the birds are generally some distance away from the island.

White-winged Black Tern *Chlidonias leucopterus*
Vagrant. One in breeding plumage flew north with 4 Black Terns on 3rd September 1990, and was just the fourth Pembrokeshire record.

ALCIDAE (Auks)

Black Guillemot *Cepphus grylle*
Vagrant. A lone adult came ashore with Puffins in South Haven on 15th June 1968.

Guillemot *Uria aalge albionis*
Breeds. Abundant. See the main text on pages 132 - 138. Occasional northern race birds *U. a. aalge* are seen late autumn/winter, and rarely during the breeding season.

Little Auk *Alle alle*
Vagrant. At least two on 17th December 1928, one on 15th January and at least three on 2nd February 1930 and an oiled bird on 12th December 1932. Fourteen corpses were found on the Neck in April 1950 following a period of gales and two more at North Pond in March 1988. A single circled the Observatory, calling, with starlings on 22nd November 1990 and further singles were offshore on 29th November and on 1st December 1990; one flew directly over the Observatory buildings on 10th November 2001 and another circled twice over The Quarry on 14th November 2001.

Razorbill *Alca torda*
Breeds. Abundant. See the main text on pages 139 - 142.

Puffin *Fratercula arctica grabae*
Breeds. Very abundant. See the main text on pages 143 - 149. White puffins were seen in 1936, 1978, and 1993, plus a partial albino in 2004, which was ashore in Crab Bay for many days in July.

COLUMBIDAE (Pigeons)

Feral Pigeon *Columba livia* (domest.)
There are regular (and sometimes prolonged) visits paid by race drop-outs over the summer period. In 1997, one of these remained on the island from 8th August until late-November. Its owner was traced through the number on its ring, and it was taken off by lighthouse staff in a helicopter to Swansea, driven from there to Bridgend, and then collected by the owner. The story made the local newspaper. A pair was seen regularly around the cliffs between 27th April and 6th May 1980.

Stock Dove *Columba oenas*
Has bred. Scarce (formerly "fairly common"). First recorded in 1939. A very occasional spring visitor until it showed signs of becoming more regular in the mid-1960's, and then, in 1967, a pair raised young in Hog Bay. The resulting colonization was swift and dramatic, with 10 pairs by 1969 and 62 pairs by 1975. An even more remarkable decline followed, from 60 pairs in 1978 to 10 in 1980, and on to extinction (as a breeding species) by 1984. This rapid sequence reflects a national expansion and subsequent decline in the 1970s, related in part to agricultural changes. The Stock Dove is once again a very occasional visitor to Skokholm, with one recorded once every other year on average.

Wood Pigeon *Columba palumbus*
Breeds. See page 162.

Collared Dove *Streptopelia decaocto*
Uncommon. The first Skokholm record was of one bird that spent the day of 7th July 1962 on The Knolls. Within a few years records covered most months, although concentrated in the period April - June, with up to 15 birds in any one day, the increase peaking in the late 1970's. Singles or parties are now regular on passage in the period mid-February - July, and in August - October, though fewer in number.

Turtle Dove *Streptopelia turtur*
Uncommon. Regular on passage April - June (especially the latter half of May) in small numbers, maximum 14 in May 1979, though there was no spring sighting in 2002. Rather scarce on return August - September, records often solely comprised of juveniles. Extreme dates: 1st April (1949) and 17th October (1974).

CUCULIDAE (Cuckoos)

Cuckoo *Cuculus canorus*
Has bred. Scarce. Generally a handful of spring singles, late-April to June, very occasionally two or three, and one or two returning birds (usually juveniles) July to August. Breeding definitely occurred in 1928. The island's breeding Meadow pipits are always particularly anxious when one does appear on Skokholm. Extreme dates: 6th April (1960) and 8th September (1956).

TYTONIDAE (Barn Owls and Allies)

Barn Owl *Tyto alba*
Vagrant. One from 7th November - 20th December 1929, one at dusk on 4th June 1962, a third seen around the Observatory on 6 dates in the period 4th - 17th March 1966, and a fourth at dusk on 28th September 2001.

STRIGIDAE (Typical Owls)

Scops Owl *Otus scops*
Vagrant. One roosting in Mad Bay was trapped on 25th April 1955, providing the second record for Wales.

Little Owl *Athene noctua*
Has bred. Scarce. In the early 1930's small influxes occurred September to November, and between 5 and 10 were actually resident in winter. One pair attempted to breed in most years until 1954, but nests were often destroyed and adults deported (to the local village of Marloes, and when this proved not far enough, to Bath and London) due to them hunting Storm Petrels. Scarce and irregular since 1962, although individuals have occasionally stayed for long periods, e.g. October 1967 - April 1968, March - July 1976 and March - June 1984. No records 1996 - 2004. Breeds on nearby Skomer Island in small numbers.

Long-eared Owl *Asio otus*
Vagrant. Just 6 records, with 4 coming in the past decade. The first was caught in the Heligoland trap on 5th May 1963 and another, also trapped, on 27th October 1975. The third spent the whole day roosting on a fallen ladder outside the Bullhouse on 16th October 1999; the fourth was around the Observatory buildings at dusk on 21st October 2002; the fifth spent the whole day roosting in the Cottage Garden sycamore tree on 9th November 2002; the sixth was present daily in the trees around the cottage for 6 days, 28th October – 2nd November 2003. All autumn records are consistent with hypothetical dispersal from Ireland.

Short-eared Owl *Asio flammeus*
Scarce. Described in 1936 as "a rare visitor", this species has since become an annual sighting, recorded in all months February to November, usually singles, but up to 9 have occurred in the period September to November (perhaps linked to the size of the House Mouse population). A breeding species on the neighbouring island of Skomer, some sightings are most probably of birds visiting from there.

CAPRIMULGIDAE (Nightjars)

Nightjar *Caprimulgus europaeus*
Vagrant, formerly scarce. Formerly an annual visitor May - June (especially in the middle part of May), much scarcer in September on return, but recorded in only 5 years since 1960. Two birds have occasionally been seen, but they suffer attacks by gulls and nightjar wings have been found more than once. There are singles records in July and August. Extreme dates: 1st May (1957) and 29th September (1946). No records 1996 - 2004.

APODIDAE (Swifts)

Little Swift *Apus affinis*
Vagrant. One on 31st May and 1st June 1981 with Swallows and House Martins was the fourth British and Irish record and the second for Wales.

Swift *Apus apus*
Common. Usually first seen in the last week of April with peak passage coming in May, when up to 150 have passed through in a day, though usually far fewer. Summer sightings presumably incorporate feeding movements by mainland birds, before the return passage in August (generally less pronounced, although up to 100 have been recorded in that month), with stragglers in September. On 6th August 2003 – a day of mist and rain – one landed on the cliff face in North Haven and was undoubtedly exhausted. A party of 32 spent the night of 4th - 5th August 1997 "roosting" in the sky above the island, facing into a stiff easterly breeze. Extreme dates: 26th March (1953) and 28th October (1976).

Alpine Swift *Apus melba*
Vagrant. One on 13th July 1972; a second on 24th March 2002, part of an influx into Britain and Ireland.

ALCEDINIDAE (Kingfishers)

Kingfisher *Alcedo atthis*
Rare. There have been 12 records, all of single birds, and 11 of them in the period 6th July - 28th August, the one outside this period being on 29th September 1975.

MEROPIDAE (Bee-eaters)

Bee-eater *Merops apiaster*
Vagrant. Just two records, one on 13th May 1997, part of an influx into Britain, and another on 8th June 2003, both seen to catch and eat numerous bumblebees.

CORACIIDAE (Rollers)

Roller *Coracias garrulus*
A first-winter bird on 26th October 2001 was the first record for Skokholm and only the second for Pembrokeshire, observed for half an hour, firstly on Home Meadow, then perched on the fence at The Well, and finally on a wall on Northern Plain before it flew off headlong into a strong north-westerly wind.

UPUPIDAE (Hoopoes)

Hoopoe *Upupa epops*
Rare. Over the years there have been around 20 spring sightings, March to early-May (especially the last two-thirds of April), with two birds on occasion. One very obliging bird was present for a week 5th - 11th May 1996. Much scarcer in autumn, just half a dozen late August to early-October, with both spring and autumn birds inclined to linger for several days. In early April 1989, Hoopoe remains were found in a Peregrine's pellet, and one in 2000 was chased relentlessly by a female Merlin before presumably succumbing. There are two records in July and one in June. Extreme dates: 12th March (1940) and 10th October (1980).

PICIDAE (Wrynecks and Woodpeckers)

Wryneck *Jynx torquila*
Scarce. First recorded on 6th May 1938, with no autumn record until 1956. They have since become more regular in autumn (over 30 records) than in spring (8 records). All but three of the spring records sit within the first 3 weeks of May; those in autumn, when birds may remain for up to a fortnight, in the period late-August to mid-October. Extreme dates: 3rd April (1995) and 19th October (2003).

Order: PASSERIFORMES

ALAUDIDAE (Larks)

Short-toed Lark *Calandrella brachydactyla*
Vagrant. One from 9th - 13th April 1952 was the first record for Wales. There have been 4 more spring sightings, of single birds: 10th - 20th April 1956, 27th - 28th June, 10th - 14th May 1976 and 17th - 18th May 1986; and in autumn on 10th, 13th and 16th October 1995 involving at least two different birds.

Woodlark *Lullula arborea*
Vagrant. Two from 12th - 13th October 1961, a single between 4th and 11th February 1963, other singles on 19th November 1967 and 7th September 1968, two from 3rd to 5th April 1978 and two on 23rd October 1993.

Skylark *Alauda arvensis*
Breeds. Common. See page 162.

Shore Lark *Eremophila alpestris*
Vagrant. Just three records, all of single birds: on 23rd - 24th April 1957, 23rd - 25th April 1961 and on 4th June 1990.

HIRUNDINIDAE (Swallows)

Sand Martin *Riparia riparia*
Common. Usually arriving late-March to early-April with peak passage mid-April to early May, when up to 400 have passed through in a day. Few seen in June and July. Return passage in August - September has produced counts of up to 500, but numbers are usually much smaller. Extreme dates: 8th March (2000) and 25th October (1971).

Swallow *Hirundo rustica*
Breeds. Very abundant. See page 162. Extreme dates: 11th March (2000) and 14th November (2001).

Red-rumped Swallow *Hirundo daurica*
Vagrant. One that flew north on 30th April 1990 was the first Pembrokeshire record. Another (a juvenile/first-winter plumaged bird) flew east over Home Meadow on 21st October 2003 was just the 12th record for Wales.

House Martin *Delichon urbica*
Common. On passage, usually first seen mid- to late-April, occasionally up to 300 in May. Return is later than for Sand Martin, with records of up to 250 in a day in September to early October (usually far fewer), but with mid-October sightings also common. Extreme dates: 20th March (1988) and 29th October (1975).

MOTACILLIDAE (Pipits, Wagtails)

Richard's Pipit *Anthus novaeseelandiae*
Rare. Recorded every year during the period 1967 - 1971 and subsequently in 9 of the 28 years 1976 - 2004. The one on 13th September 1967 was the first record of this species in Pembrokeshire. All sit within the period 12th September - 10th November, most often single birds, rarely 2, but with 4 on 26th October 1968 and 29th September 1970.

Tawny Pipit *Anthus campestris*
Vagrant. Singles on 19th September 1961, 18th and 26th - 28th September 1968, 13th September 1970, 30th September 1975 and 11th and 12th October 1991.

Olive-backed Pipit *Anthus hodgsoni*
Vagrant. One trapped on 14th April 1948 could not be certainly identified using the limited literature available at the time, but was photographed and the description subsequently re-submitted to the British Birds Rarities Committee and accepted as Britain and Ireland's first Olive-backed Pipit some 30 years later.

Tree Pipit *Anthus trivialis*
Uncommon. Typically a handful of records of between one and 4 birds from mid-April to May (sometimes there is no spring passage recorded), occasionally in June, then with singles or small parties (maximum 12) more frequent mid-August to early October. Extreme dates: 16th March (1966) and 23rd October (1994).

Meadow Pipit *Anthus pratensis*

Breeds. Abundant to very abundant. See page 163.

Red-throated Pipit *Anthus cervinus*

Vagrant. One on 13th October 1970 was the first recorded in Pembrokeshire; since then there have been three other records: singles from 10th to 23rd September 1989, and on 17th and 27th September 1992.

Rock Pipit *Anthus petrosus*

Breeds. Common. See the main text on page 163. A leucistic bird was present in September 1987 and at least 2 similar juveniles, presumably Skokholm birds, in 1989 and again in 1990, with another, distinctively marked partially leucistic bird present 2001 - 03, and another on 14th May 2004. Birds resembling the Scandinavian race *A. p. littoralis* were noted on 25th and 28th April and 4th - 5th May 1988, 2nd and 21st April 1991, 28th and 29th April 1992, 9th April 1993 and on several dates during the period 9th - 30th May 1995.

Water Pipit *Anthus spinoletta*

Vagrant. Two on 8th October 1933, one on 30th and 31st October 1988, and one on 1st May 1994.

Yellow Wagtail *Motacilla flava flavissima*

Uncommon. Spring passage normally results in a few singles or small parties present in mid-April to June (up to 10 have been recorded in May), with more on return from late-July to early-October. Fifty have been recorded on occasion in August and September (with up to 150 in August 1952), but numbers are usually much smaller. Extreme dates: 10th March (1956) and 18th November (1967).

The following races have been identified:

Blue-headed wagtail *M. f. flava*: over 35 records, all between 20th April and 29th June apart from those on 8th and 10th September 1965, 23rd August 1988 and 21st September 1991, 4th September 2000, and 9th, 11th and 12th September 2003, 1st October 2001 and 17th April 2004; all records refer to single birds except for two on 18th May 1961 and two on 24th September 2000.

Grey-headed wagtail *M. f. thunbergi*: single males on 31st May 1978, 10th - 12th May 1987, 3rd - 5th May 1989 and 31st May - 5th June 1990 and 25 June 1992.

Spanish Blue-headed Wagtail *M. f. iberiae*: a male at The Dip on 19th April 1989.

Grey Wagtail *Motacilla cinerea*

Uncommon. Noted as "a curiously-rare visitor" in 1938. Very occasionally on passage February to April, rare from May to late-August, then typically a handful of autumn records each year until November, though in some years recently this species has become far more frequent (e.g. in 2003, there were up to three on thirteen dates during the period 3rd - 27th September; singles on six dates in the period 1st - 28th October, plus three on 16th October; one on 6th November and finally one on 4th December). The large majority are singles, flying over or visiting streams, but up to 25 have been recorded in late-August and September.

Pied Wagtail *Motacilla alba*
Breeds. Fairly common. See page 163.

White wagtail *M. a. alba*: on passage late-March to May and August to early-October, with up to 30 on occasion in April and up to 500 in late August to mid-September. Extreme dates: 18th March (1990) and 29th October (1988).

TROGLODYTIDAE (Wrens)

Wren *Troglodytes troglodytes*
Breeds. Common. See page 164.

PRUNELLIDAE (Accentors)

Dunnock *Prunella modularis*
Has bred. Fairly common. See page 164.

TURDIDAE (Chats, Thrushes)

Robin *Erithacus rubecula*
Has bred. Common. Generally there has been a very small springtime passage recorded in the period March to May (seldom reaching double figures), and a larger return late-August to October when up to 150 have been recorded; the first to arrive is often in juvenile plumage. Varying numbers of these (up to about 50) stay on through at least the early part of the winter, in territories in the Bracken, amongst the few planted shrubs around the buildings, or in rocky coves, habitats undoubtedly of varying suitability. Perhaps the wintering birds are confused with spring migrants. Ringing has shown that individual Robins will return to Skokholm in successive winters. Surprisingly, there are just 3 breeding records: these occurred in the years 1939, 1940 and 1980.

White-throated Robin *Irania gutteralis*
Vagrant. A female was present, mainly around the Observatory buildings and The Well, from 27th to 30th May 1990. It comprised the second British and Irish record.

Nightingale *Luscinia megarhynchos*
Rare. Just 8 spring records, between 16th April and 2nd June, the first one on 4th May 1951 being only the second record for Pembrokeshire. On 2nd June 2002, one sang in short bursts from within a courtyard Sycamore tree, this being contrary to Saint David having reputedly banned them from doing so in the region, because they disturbed his "heavenlie cogitacions" (sic). More regular in autumn, with about 15 sightings between 14th August and 25th September.

Bluethroat *Luscinia svecica*
Rare. A total of 12 records. The seven in the period 1955 - 1968 were all in autumn, and 4 of the 5 records since were in spring: a first-winter male red-spotted subspecies *svecica* on 10th October 1955, a first-winter bird from

12th to 15th September 1956; first-winter males on 15th and on 29th September 1964 (the latter assigned to the subspecies *svecica*) with a female on 24th September 1964; one from 16th September to 1st October 1967 and on 20th October 1968 (white-spotted subspecies *cyanecula*), then single red-spotted males on 21st May 1975, 15th May 1982, and 14th May 1985; a male (the race of which was not mentioned in the annual reports) on 27th September 1992 and a first-summer male *svecica* on 29th June 1995.

Black Redstart *Phoenicurus ochruros*

Uncommon. Irregular on passage from March to early-June (particularly the second half of March) and from late-September to November (the peak occurring from late-October to early-November). Sightings in December and February suggest occasional over-wintering. There are a few July and August records, e.g. an adult male was present in The Quarry on 4th and 20th August (perhaps the same bird throughout that period). Numbers are very variable, with larger influxes generally coming in the autumn (up to 40 in October 1968; 28 on 23rd October 1997, many of these roosted in the island's privy), although 50 were recorded in March 1948 and 30 in March 1949; in general, counts are much smaller.

Redstart *Phoenicurus phoenicurus*

Uncommon. On passage mid-April to June and August to October, with peaks in early-May and late-September and with very occasional sightings in July. Numbers are small, generally only 1 - 3 birds, but up to 10 have been counted in May and up to 20 in the period from late-August and through September. Extreme dates: 1st April (1991) and 2nd November (1968).

Whinchat *Saxicola rubetra*

Fairly common. On passage from mid-April to the end of May and August to October, with occasional June and July sightings. Numbers are small, with a spring maximum of just 7 in a day; autumn passage is more prolonged and counts have reached double figures, but 40 in September 1968 was exceptional. Extreme dates: 9th April (1966) and 26th October (1968).

Stonechat *Saxicola torquata*

Fairly common. One pair bred in 1928 and in 1932. On passage February to May and July to November, with occasional June sightings (a juvenile 25th - 29th June 1998, and on 20th June 2001). Birds tend to remain present for many days. As many as 10 have been present in March and up to 25 in October. One ringed on Skokholm in September 1960 was found in Spain in the following November.

Siberian Stonechat *S. t. maura / stejnegeri*: singles on 11th - 15th October 1991, and 30th September - 2nd October 1992, were the second and third records for Pembrokeshire.

Wheatear *Oenanthe oenanthe*

Breeds. Common - abundant. See the main text on page 164. On passage from mid-March to May and again from August to mid-October with up to 150 birds occasionally in late-April and early-May (but see below) and up to 240 recorded in September. The breeding population is generally installed by the end of April and has departed by the end of August. Extreme dates: 2nd March (2003) and 13th November (1999).

Birds of the Greenland/Iceland race *O. o. leucorhoa* pass through in late-April and May and again in September and October (providing the majority of October records). An exceptionally-heavy passage in the spring of 1938 brought an estimated 1,500 birds to the island on 28th April, with 500 still present on 8th May.

Isabelline Wheatear *Oenanthe isabellina*

A bird was present from 24th - 26th September 1997, inhabiting the thrift-land of The Dip. It was the first record for Pembrokeshire and the second for Wales (following one on Bardsey Island, north Wales, the previous week).

Pied Wheatear *Oenanthe pleschanka*

Vagrant. A female trapped on 27th October 1968 stayed until the 29th, the first Welsh and fourth British and Irish record.

Desert Wheatear *Oenanthe deserti*

A female at The Dip on 12th December 1997 was the first record for Pembrokeshire and the third for Wales. Another on 13th November 2003 was the second Pembrokeshire record and the fourth for Wales.

Swainson's Thrush *Catharus ustulatus*

Vagrant. One trapped on 14th October 1967 remained until the 19th, providing the first live British and Irish record (one was previously found dead at Black Rock lighthouse, County Mayo, on 26th May 1956).

Ring Ouzel *Turdus torquatus*

Uncommon. On passage from late-March to early-May and late-August to November. There are usually only a handful of records in both seasons, more regularly in spring, with highest daily counts of 10 in April and 8 in October. A male present for 4 days 26th - 29th May 2004 frequently sang from a small Sycamore tree in the observatory yard. A group of four birds on 28th October 2001 consisted of an adult male and female, and a first winter male and female – a family party? Extreme dates: 15th March (1955) and 21st November (1989).

Blackbird *Turdus merula*

Breeds. Common. See pages 165 - 166. Occasionally noted on passage, but it is difficult to distinguish from the resident population unless the arrival consists of a large number of birds. Large movements have previously been evident in October when up to 1,000 have been recorded, but there have been very few in recent years.

Fieldfare *Turdus pilaris*

Fairly common. On passage from early-October (but occasionally in September) to May (most frequently in March) and also a winter visitor, usually in small numbers, but hard weather has brought 300 birds in October (105 on 9th October 2004) and 250 in March. In 1980 a single Fieldfare was seen on 10th and 13th June, but otherwise the extreme dates are: 31st May (1982) and 14th September (1977).

Song Thrush *Turdus philomelos*

Common. On passage September to April, occasionally in other months, up to 25 (2002 - 2003) often over-wintering from early-October, most leaving by mid-March. Ringing has shown that a bird from Oxfordshire returned in successive winters, and a distinctively-marked partial-albino was seen in successive autumns, 1996 and 1997. One bird ringed on the island in February 1956 was recovered in Oxfordshire the following June. October movements have involved up to 200 birds, and 350 have been present during cold weather in March. Between 1927 and 1935, it was noted that thousands were occasionally present in "hard east winds" (Lockley, 1936), though not present at all in some years.

Redwing *Turdus iliacus*

Common. On passage or over-wintering from October to April (occasionally early-May). Up to 400 have been present as part of October movements. Singles were seen on 13th June 1929 and 18th June 1979, but excluding these two the extreme dates are: 6th May (1984) and 20th September (2001).

Mistle Thrush *Turdus viscivorus*

Scarce. An irregular visitor (for example, just 6 records in the period 1996 - 2004), but has been recorded in all months February to November, most often March to April and October, almost always single birds and never more than four.

SYLVIIDAE (Old World Warblers and Allies)

Cetti's Warbler *Cettia cetti*

Vagrant. Singles in Wall's End Bay on 9th September 1986 and at The Cutting on 30th September 1987.

Grasshopper Warbler *Locustella naevia*

Uncommon. Annual on passage mid-April to May (very few records in June), especially late-April to early-May when up to 40 have been recorded although counts very rarely reach double figures. Birds have often sung in recent years, which makes locating them easier than would otherwise be the case, and the planting of shrubs and trees around the observatory buildings has undoubtedly encouraged this behaviour. Scarcer on return late-July to October (it is not unusual for there to be no visible autumn passage) when the combination of a skulking habit and the extensive Bracken cover makes it much harder to find this species. Exceptionally, up to 40 were recorded in September 1970. Extreme dates: 7th April (1961) and 7th November (1968).

Savi's Warbler *Locustella luscinioides*

Vagrant. One on 31st October 1968 was the first record for Wales.

Aquatic Warbler *Acrocephalus paludicola*

Vagrant. One seen at North Pond on 5th September 1949 and caught in a net the following day was the first record for Wales. Further singles were trapped on 20th September 1961 (remained until 21st) and 24th August 1970, and seen on 19th September 1971 and 13th October 1980.

Sedge Warbler *Acrocephalus schoenobaenus*

Breeds. Fairly common. See page 167. On passage late-April to June and late-July to October. Extreme dates: 6th April (1961) and 17th October (1957).

Reed Warbler *Acrocephalus scirpaceus*

Scarce. First recorded on 1st June 1947, then there were only 5 records in the next 20 years. Practically annual since 1968, on passage late-April to mid-June and August to October, especially in late-May and late-September to early-October, though August 2003 was exceptional, when up to 3 birds were frequently found over a period of 5 weeks in a stand of Common Reed *Phragmites communis* that had been allowed to establish in the Well Pool. There is one July record. Generally fewer than 5 sightings each year on average. Extreme dates: 19th April (1996) and 30th October (1997).

Marsh Warbler *Acrocephalus palustris*

Vagrant. One at the Well Pool, then Garden Rocks on 21st and 22nd September 1995, the first record for Pembrokeshire.

Great Reed Warbler *Acrocephalus arundinaceus*

Vagrant. Two singles, the first on 13th and 14th May 1967 (the first record for Wales) and the second on 11th May 1970. Both were trapped and ringed.

Booted Warbler *Hippolais caligata*

Vagrant. One during the period 25th - 28th September 1993 was the first record for Wales.

Icterine Warbler *Hippolais icterina*

Rare. A first-winter bird on 31st August 1955 was the first for Wales. There have been 26 records, with 20 of them in autumn between 21st August and 1st November, with late-August the favoured period; just 5 spring records (3 of them in 1982) between 14th May and 28th June; and one summer record, of an adult on 20th July 1996. Two birds were seen on 3rd September 1962. Extreme dates: 14th May (1982) and 1st November (1995).

Melodious Warbler *Hippolais polyglotta*

Scarce. Also first seen in 1955, but subsequently a far more regular visitor than Icterine Warbler with over twice as many records, seen in all years 1955 - 71, and most years in the autumn up to and including 1996. Most frequent in the period between 3rd August and 12th October, with the middle half of August and September to early-October the most productive times. There has been just one sighting between 1997 and the end of 2004, on 30th and 31st May 2002. Rare in spring, just 7 records, in the period 23rd May to 30th June. Up to 3 have been present in the autumn, mainly first-year birds which may linger for up to a fortnight.

Dartford Warbler *Sylvia undata*

Vagrant. A female was present around The Well for two days 1st - 2nd June 1981, following SE winds and fog.

Subalpine Warbler *Sylvia cantillans*

Rare. One on 1st October 1953 was the first for Wales. Ten subsequent records, all but one in spring: a first-year male on 3rd May 1970, an adult male on 7th June 1976, a female on 11th May 1990, a male on 15th May 1992, a female on 29th May 1994, a female on 7th and 29th May 1995, a long-staying female 2nd - 8th April 2001, another on 3rd November 2001, and one for two days 4th - 5th May 2003.

Sardinian Warbler *Sylvia melanocephala*

Vagrant. A first-year male trapped on 28th October 1968 was the first Welsh and third British and Irish record.

Barred Warbler *Sylvia nisoria*

Rare. A total of 17 records of first-winter birds, all in the period September to October except one, and all singles apart from one; 12th September 1956 (second for Wales), 20th September 1960, 18th September 1963, 16th September 1965, 25th September 1967, 18th September 1969, 23rd - 24th October 1971, 22nd September 1988, 8th and 26th October 1990, two on 30th September 1992, one on 4th October 1992, 12th, 13th and 15th October 1993, 2nd and 6th October 1995, 1st - 2nd September 2001, and 27th August 2004.

Lesser Whitethroat *Sylvia curruca*

Scarce. Irregular on passage late-April to early-June and late-August to November, with early-May and late-September to early-October being the best times. Not recorded every year and then seldom more than 2 or 3 sightings (rarely of 2 birds); 1990 was exceptional, with 4 in May and 4 in September - October, and also in 1996, when there were three, possibly four, in May. Extreme dates: 23rd April (1984) and 3rd November (1927). There was also one on 2nd November in 2001.

Whitethroat *Sylvia communis*

Breeds. Fairly common (formerly "common"). Regular on passage mid-April to June, and July to October, with peaks in May and August to September. Formerly the most-abundant migrant warbler, especially in spring, producing counts of up to 500 birds. The well-documented crash due to drought in the Sahel region of Africa brought counts down to single figures in 1969, and even today influxes of more than 20 birds are still unusual. Single pairs bred in 1931, 1932, 1965, 1988, 1989, 1997 and 1998, and 2 pairs in 1990. Extreme dates: 5th April (1966) and 30th October (1968).

Garden Warbler *Sylvia borin*

Uncommon. On passage late-April to June and August to October, particularly in May and late-September to early-October. Most records are of singles, with highest counts of 30 the spring and 5 in the autumn. Spring birds are occasional heard singing. Extreme dates: 6th April (1966) and 2nd November (1968).

Blackcap *Sylvia atricapilla*

Uncommon. Passage migrant mid- (occasionally early-) April to June and September to November, peaking in early-May and late-October. Formerly known only as a scarce and irregular spring visitor, it became more frequent during the 1950's and similarly in autumn during the late-1950's and early-1960's. Now annual at both seasons, but an influx of 20 in October 1989 and 10 on 24th April 2005 are the only double figure counts so far. Extreme dates: 9th March (1997) and 5th December (1996), the latter a long-staying bird (it relished eating discarded apple cores) and was last seen on the day the island was vacated for the winter period. These extreme dates are progressively becoming earlier/later, undoubtedly linked with the species' habit of over-wintering in Britain.

Greenish Warbler *Phylloscopus trochiloides*

Vagrant. Five records. The first three were all trapped, a female on 31st August 1960, and first-year birds on 30th - 31st August 1961 and 31st August 1976 (obviously the prime date for this species on Skokholm); then one on 23rd June 1997, and 4th - 5th June 2003.

Yellow-browed Warbler *Phylloscopus inornatus*

Rare. One on 2nd and 3rd October 1959 was the first record for Wales. There have been sixteen further records, all between 30th September and 27th October, all of single birds apart from two on 8th October 1994.

Radde's Warbler *Phylloscopus schwarzi*

Vagrant. One trapped on 22nd October 1968 was the first for Wales.

Bonelli's Warbler *Phylloscopus bonelli*

Vagrant. One trapped on 31st August 1948 (killed and sent to the Yorkshire Museum for identification) was the first for Britain and Ireland. A second, miraculously on the same date, 31st August, in 1991. Following Eastern

Bonelli's Warbler being awarded specific status in 1997, the British Birds Rarities Committee reassessed all records. The criteria employed were wing formulae in the case of trapped birds, and call-note, if heard, on untrapped birds. As a result, the 1948 record was accepted as Western Bonelli's Warbler *P. bonelli*, but the 1991 record was deemed "indeterminate" because it did not call, i.e. listed as Eastern / Western Bonelli's Warbler.

Wood Warbler *Phylloscopus sibilatrix*

Rare. Irregular passage migrant early-April to mid-May (just 10 records, 7 of them in the period 1988 - 94) and early-August to mid-September (24 records, including singles in 4 successive autumns 1999 - 2003). Extreme dates: 7th April (1977) and 20th September (1991).

Chiffchaff *Phylloscopus collybita*

Common. On passage mid- (occasionally early-) March to May and August to December, with peaks in April, early-August and September to early-October; June and July records are not unusual, occasionally with birds singing throughout. Generally (along with the Wheatear) the first spring arrival, and up to 75 have been present March - April, but larger influxes (maximum 500 in 1970) have occurred in the autumn. November sightings have become more frequent in recent years. Chiffchaffs ringed on Skokholm have been recovered in North and West Africa. Birds presumed to be of the N. Eurasian races *P.c. tristis* and *P.c. abietinus* have been noted in March, May and September - November. The race *tristis* is a spectacularly pale subspecies, buff-grey in colour. The island was graced with one on 29th October 2001, then two virtually inseparable birds for twelve days 1st – 12th November 2001. They were particularly lively when compared to the nominate race, rarely sitting still, constantly fly-catching and wing-flicking in addition to tail-dipping.

Extreme dates: 19th February (1998) and 14th December (2000). These extremes are progressively becoming earlier/later, undoubtedly linked with the species' habit of over-wintering in Britain. Birds are possibly present on occasion throughout the winter months, but there is usually no Warden present to record them.

Willow Warbler *Phylloscopus trochilus*

Common or abundant. On passage late-March or early-April to June and July to October with peaks in mid-April and early-August. Several hundred have been present on occasion in autumn, and July and August 1948 saw an estimated 3,000 on the island. It may be significant that, since the termination of ringing in 1976, counts have seldom exceeded 100 and then usually only in spring. Individuals resembling the Eastern European race *P.t. acredula* have been seen in May and August - October. Extreme dates: 23rd March (1972 and 1997), and 31st October (1954). Unspecified *Phylloscopus* records are common (certainly in the past before identification knowledge improved), presumed to be Willow Warbler or Chiffchaff, but these records are not elaborated upon here (see Betts, 1992 for more information).

Goldcrest *Regulus regulus*

Fairly common or common. Just 3 records prior to the autumn of 1950, but since then this species has become a regular visitor on passage March to early-May and late-August to November, although numbers vary considerably, perhaps in relation to the severity of winters. An estimated 250 - 300 forced down by rain in October 1959 was exceptional. Birds are extremely difficult to locate in the autumn, hidden by the mass of Bracken, unless they begin to utter their contact call, but even then numbers are very difficult to ascertain.

Firecrest *Regulus ignicapillus*
Scarce. One for two days 17th - 18th April 1949 was the first for Pembrokeshire and is one of only two April records. There are also five March records, three in May and 4 in June. More frequent on autumn passage (around 60 records) late-September to mid-November (but especially in the latter half of October when up to 7 have been seen), but irregular, e.g. recorded annually 1966 - 76, absent entirely 1981 - 87 then annual again 1988 - 1997, and 1999 - 2004. A male was present around the observatory buildings for twelve days in the period 24th September - 3rd October 2003.

MUSCICAPIDAE (Old World Flycatchers)

Red-breasted Flycatcher *Ficedula parva*
Rare. A first-winter bird in Purple Cove on 26th September 1949 was the first for Pembrokeshire and the second for Wales. The are just three spring records: first of a male in the Observatory garden on 20th May 1988, second a female or first-summer male on 18th - 19th May 2001 and again on 27th and 29th May 2002. The 20 or more autumn records have come in the period 20th August - 3rd November, over half of them in October (first-winter birds), with three in the autumn of 2001 being exceptional (with one remaining for 6 days, 21st - 26th October 2001).

Spotted Flycatcher *Muscicapa striata*
Fairly common. Main passage late-April to June and July to early-October, with peaks in May and late-August, and again in mid-September. Usually 12 birds or less in a day, but up to 40 have been recorded in May and August to September (e.g. 21 on 10th September 2004). On 23rd May 1997 an influx of 18 birds resulted in two singing and disputing territory and in the days that followed, but this was short-lived and by early-June all had departed. Extreme dates: 19th April (1966) and 23rd October (1968 and 2001).

Pied Flycatcher *Ficedula hypoleuca*
Uncommon. Spring passage in late-April to May usually involves few birds and occasionally none at all, while the return in August to early-October is more regular, with peaks in late-August and mid-September which may feature up to 20 birds. There are very few June records, e.g. one on 4th June 1998. Extreme dates: 10th April (1993) and 17th October (1982 and 1988).

TIMALIIDAE (Babblers)

Bearded Tit *Panurus biarmicus*
Vagrant. Two on 24th October 1993 comprised the second Pembrokeshire record.

AEGITHALIDAE (Long-tailed Tits and Allies)

Long-tailed Tit *Aegithalos caudatus*
Vagrant. Just 8 records: two on 11th October 1957, three on 22nd August 1969, 8 on 28th October 1973, three on 7th and one on 24th - 25th October 1975, one on 9th November 1980, three on 24th October 1993 and one on 12th October 2004.

PARIDAE (Tits)

Marsh Tit *Parus palustris*
Vagrant. One near the lighthouse in company with various other tits on 12th October 1988.

Coal Tit *Parus ater*
Rare. A very occasional visitor in late-September to October, with records for only 14 widely scattered years. Most often singles or small parties, exceptions being in 1957 when groups of up to 10 were seen throughout October, in 1988 when 20 were recorded on 10th October, and in October 1992 with 15 birds. One over-wintered 8th November 1930 to 6th March 1931 and one was present 17th - 28th March 1992.

Blue Tit *Parus caeruleus*
Scarce. An infrequent visitor, singles or small parties, seen on average about one year in three, almost always in October, very occasionally in September or March to early-April. Larger influxes, e.g. up to 50 throughout October 1957 and in October 1964 have resulted in individuals over-wintering, but in addition the provision of peanuts in November has resulted in small numbers presumably remaining on the island (i.e. still present in mid-February of the following year), e.g. winters of 1996 - 97, 1997 - 98, 1999 - 2000 and 2000 - 01, 2001 - 02, and 2002 - 03.

Great Tit *Parus major*
Rare. About 19 arrivals (excluding 1957 – see below) of between one and 10 birds, two of them in March and the remainder in October - November, except for one. In 1957, up to 25 were present throughout October and one remained to over-winter in the company of a Blue Tit, both birds finally leaving on 8th April 1958. More recently, one wintered in 1992 - 93, and another 1997 - 98 (the island was vacated on 13th December 1997, and reoccupied 23rd January 1998. The Great Tit was present until 1st March 1998).

CERTHIIDAE (Treecreepers)

Treecreeper *Certhia familiaris*
Rare. Just 18 records, 11 of them in the period mid-June to early-August (July is the commonest month), the remainder late-September to early-November when there is some association with wandering tit flocks. Two were present on 8th July 1989; all other records were of single birds. The bird present for one day in June 2001 chose to give observers a real close view as it proceeded to enter the Wheelhouse and perch for a while on the head of the figurehead of the wrecked ship *Alice Williams*. It then spent a few hours plucking spiders from the roof-space, and various Dipteran flies from the window, before finally heading back outside.

ORIOLIDAE (Old World Orioles and Allies)

Golden Oriole *Oriolus oriolus*
Vagrant. Just 5 records, though very many more have appeared on neighbouring Skomer island and the nearby mainland. An almost-complete set of feathers belonging to a first-summer male was discovered on 28th May 1966 in North Haven. Live birds were: an immature male on 25th May 1982, an adult male on 27th May 1990, and single females on 5th June 1994 and 13th May 2001.

LANIIDAE (Typical Shrikes)

Red-backed Shrike *Lanius collurio*

Rare. First recorded 1938. Irregular on spring passage with just 10 records mid-May to late-June, 8 of them in the fortnight bridging the two months, plus an exceptionally-early male in April 1966 following persistent SE winds. There have been a further 18 autumn sightings in the period from late-August to early-October, 12 of them in September. Interestingly, this species was scarcer than Woodchat Shrike prior to 1968 but has occurred three times as often since. Extreme dates: 9th April (1966) and 20th October (2004).

Woodchat Shrike *Lanius senator*

Rare. The first for Skokholm, a male from 12th - 17th June 1948, was the second record for Pembrokeshire. Nine spring records late-April to late-June, with 6 of them in the first half of June (slightly later than Red-backed Shrike). Fourteen more in autumn, in the period late-July to mid-September, 8 of them in August (earlier than Red-backed Shrike). There have only been 6 records since 1968. The first British recovery of a Woodchat Shrike was of a bird that had been ringed on Skokholm on 3rd June and recaptured in Suffolk 17 days later. Extreme dates: 30th April (1966) and 12th September (1951).

CORVIDAE (Crows and Allies)

Magpie *Pica pica*

Vagrant. Surprisingly, in view of breeding birds on Skomer and on the mainland, there are just 10 records in all: single birds on 2nd June 1964, 16th May 1966, 27th May 1974, 15th March 1975, 8th - 10th March and 12th October 1984, 17th May 1989, 11th August and 22nd October 1991, and 12th - 17th November 1996.

Chough *Pyrrhocorax pyrrhocorax*

Breeds. See the main text on pages 167 - 169. Prior to 1992 (first recent breeding record), in most years there were a few spring records March - May, then regular visits by family parties from July onwards. Larger flocks have been seen in September - November, the largest of 32 birds in September 1965.

Jackdaw *Corvus monedula*

Breeds. Common. See the main text, pages 169 - 170.

Rook *Corvus frugilegus*

Scarce. An irregular visitor March - May and August - October (with April the best month), records generally involving up to 4 birds, although up to 35 have been seen in spring; on 6th October 2002 a flock of 21 flew over the island in a westerly direction, promptly turned around upon reaching the lighthouse and headed straight back to the mainland. Many of the autumn records are of immature birds. There are occasional June records.

Carrion Crow *Corvus corone corone*

Breeds. See page 170. Flocks of up to 30 were not unusual in the past before and after the breeding season (prior to a decline), but more recent counts only occasionally reach double figures.

Hooded crow *C. c. cornix*. Ten records: 11th April 1939, 11th May 1951, 14th April 1959, 21st May 1970, 26th - 27th April 1978, 15th June 1981 and 30th March, 18th and 23rd April (two birds) 1982, and 31st May 1994.

Raven *Corvus corax*
Breeds. See the main text, pages 171 - 172.

STURNIDAE (Starlings)

Rose-coloured Starling *Sturnus roseus*
Vagrant. An adult from 8th - 10th June 2000; an dull-coloured sub-adult 3rd - 4th June 2002, then a more-colourful bird on three occasions, 7th, 9th and 17th June; a juvenile 19th - 20th September and 30th September 2002, and another 1st - 3rd October 2002; and a juvenile on 6th and 9th September 2004.

Starling *Sturnus vulgaris*
Breeds. Very abundant. See page 173.

PASSERIDAE (Sparrows)

House Sparrow *Passer domesticus*
Scarce. An irregular visitor April to June and late-September to early-November, with 6 records in March and 4 in July. Never more than 4 birds have been involved. There were only 7 records prior to 1957, has subsequently been annual until 1978, then recorded in just under half of the last 25 years.

Tree Sparrow *Passer montanus*
Scarce. There were just 6 records prior to 1959 (one on 15th May 1934 was only the second for Pembrokeshire), then recorded on average in 2 years out of 3 in the period up to 1994, and none since. It was an irregular visitor April - June, especially in May, with one or two records in all other months March - October, mainly of single birds or small parties. Larger flocks have occurred in May, highest count of 30 in 1975.

VIREONIDAE (Vireos)

Red-eyed Vireo *Vireo olivaceous*
Vagrant. An immature trapped on 14th October 1967 was the fifth record for Britain and Ireland and the first for Wales.

FRINGILLIDAE (Finches)

Chaffinch *Fringilla coelebs*
Common to very abundant. On passage, and previously over-wintering in small numbers, October - April, although recorded in all months. Up to 430 have been counted in March but the larger movements have occurred in October - November, e.g. 3,200 passed through on 22nd October 1966 and over 2,000 were grounded by fog (with large numbers of Siskins) on 26th October 1988. Such high numbers occur during a period when a cyclonic weather system is situated over Scandinavia and results in fresh or strong east to south-easterly winds over Britain.

Brambling *Fringilla montifringilla*

Uncommon. Spring passage is rare, with around 20 records of between one and 3 birds during the period February - April. Recorded almost annually October - December, usually singles or small parties, but a series of larger movements in the period 1964 - 75 brought up to 90 in October 1971 and a quite exceptional 800+ on 22nd October 1966. Extreme dates: 3rd October (1964) and 17th April (1997).

Serin *Serinus serinus*

Vagrant. Males were present on 10th June 1967 (trapped) and 11th May 1978, and a female on 23rd November 2003.

Greenfinch *Carduelis chloris*

Fairly common to common. Recorded in all months but mainly on passage March - May when numbers are small (generally single figures) but appearances regular, and in the months of October and November when up to 270 have been counted.

Goldfinch *Carduelis carduelis*

Fairly common. Recorded in all months but mainly on passage April - May and October - November. Autumn movements involve larger numbers, with 130 on 24th October 1966 the only three-figure count.

Siskin *Carduelis spinus*

Uncommon. First recorded on 29th September 1949, then almost annual since 1957. Just 7 spring records, between 19th March and 9th July. Fairly regular from mid-September to November with up to 180 on occasion (usually far fewer) and an estimated 1,200 brought down by fog on 26th October 1988.

Linnet *Carduelis cannabina*

Has bred. Common. One pair bred in 1929, breeding was suspected in 1994, and confirmed in 1997 when two broods were raised by a pair nesting in planted gorse within The Well rabbit-exclosure. There was a third breeding record in 1998, with one brood of young also raised in a nest in the same gorse bush as the previous year. Recorded in all months but mainly on passage March - May and September - October. Counts rarely exceed double figures but up to 220 have been noted in October. Small numbers have been seen on winter visits.

Twite *Carduelis flavirostris*

Vagrant. A total of 10 records: a male on 8th April 1933, two on 20th April and 6 on 6th October 1958, two for 4 days 26th - 29th March 1962, a male on 17th June 1967, two on 23rd October 1977, one on 13th October 1988, three on 3rd November 1990, three on 21st September 1991, one on 28th October 1995, two on 6th October 1996 and one on 3rd May 2000.

Redpoll *Carduelis* spp.

Recent taxonomic changes have decreed that the "Redpoll group" actually consists of three species, namely *Carduelis flammea* or Common Redpoll, *C. cabaret* or Lesser Redpoll, and *C. hornemanni* or Arctic Redpoll. The Lesser Redpoll is the common breeding species in the British Isles, and most Skokholm records probably refer to these. Most birds seen on the island are "fly-overs", and thus have not been identified to species level given the new classification. However, a summary of all records follows:

Scarce. Small numbers are seen almost annually on passage March to July and late-September to early-November, and Lockley used to see Redpolls occasionally in winter. Recorded slightly more consistently in spring although larger parties (maximum of 17) occur in October. A bird resembling *C. flammea* was present 4th - 11th October 1985 and two "very pale" birds, on 24th October 1964 may possibly have been *hornemanni* (Arctic Redpoll). Since the reclassification, a flock of 5 Lesser Redpolls was present on 25 April 2004. Other certain Lesser Redpolls (from good views of perched birds) are as follows: a female on 18th - 19th June 1996; single males on 8th and 28th May 1998.

Common Crossbill *Loxia curvirostra*
Rare. One on 5th July 1929; five on 2nd and 4 on 4th July 1953 and 4 on 13th and 14th September 1953; 4 on 27th July and 3 on 1st September 1959; up to 11 birds between 5th and 25th July 1966, three on 30th August (one until 1st September) 1993; an immature on 13th July 1997, and on 12th and 29th August 2002 (eating seeds of Ragwort plants).

Common Rosefinch *Carpodacus erythrinus*
Rare. A first-winter male trapped on 26th June 1949 was the second for Wales. Nineteen further records, all listed: 21st and 29th May 1969, a female on 3rd May 1970, one on 17th September 1974, an immature on 3rd June 1984 and a first-summer male in song on 24th July 1989, singles on 29th - 30th June 1991, 21st - 27th September 1991, 16th June 1992, 13th and 16th September 1994, 6th - 9th June 1995, and 6th - 8th and 11th - 12th October 1995, 16th - 17th September 1997, one on 11th September 1999, one female 7th - 8th October 2000 (captured by a Merlin), three females/juveniles on 11th October 2001, and a female on 25th May 2003.

Bullfinch *Pyrrhula pyrrhula*
Vagrant. Just three records, the first of a pair trapped on 25th July 1972, the second of a female/immature on 30th October 1997, and then again on 30th November 1997.

Hawfinch *Coccothraustes coccothraustes*
Vagrant. Just 3 records, of single birds: on 4th June 1949, 15th October 1957 and 7th May 1989.

EMBERIZIDAE (Buntings)

Reed Bunting *Emberiza schoeniclus*
Has bred. Scarce. First recorded in 1929; just 4 records prior to 1955, then subsequently a few sightings annually March to early-May and September to November, usually of ones and twos, but up to 12 have been recorded in October; there are also records for February. A pair bred in The Bog in 1960, raising 2 broods, and again in 1967. Numbers increased to 5 pairs by 1977, then 3 in 1978, none in 1979 and 2 in 1980, where the "colonization attempt" finally ended.

Little Bunting *Emberiza pusilla*
Vagrant. One on 19th November 1967 was the first for Pembrokeshire. The second, on 11th October 2001, was only the fifth Pembrokeshire record.

Lapland Bunting *Calcarius lapponicus*

Scarce. Single immatures in the period 5th - 11th September 1936 and another the following day were the first records for Wales. Became almost annual from 1952, almost entirely during the period mid-September to November, with typically a handful of sightings of between one and 5 birds (a maximum of 11 on one date in October 1993), and in the autumns of 1956 and 1993 when over 30 and 40 different Lapland Buntings passed through respectively. Sighted in 3 years out of nine in the period 1996 - 2004 (totalling 5 birds). There have been three early arrivals, in late-July to August of 1957 - 58, and just 4 spring records: single males in breeding plumage on 10th May 1948 and 8th June 1963, a pair on 14th May 1981 and another spectacular male on 18th May 1995.

Snow Bunting *Plectrophenax nivalis*

Scarce. Irregular on passage late-September to November (the earliest being on 22nd September 1981), with lone birds or small flocks (the largest being of 17 in October 1961). Singles were also recorded on 31st January 1998 and 2nd February 1998, during a rare period of winter occupancy by the island Wardens. There are 5 other spring records: 3rd March 1932, 10th - 11th March 1958, 22nd - 25th April 1959, 22nd March 1969 and 29th March 1981.

Pine Bunting *Emberiza leucocephalos*

One stunning male at breakfast time on 28th April 2000 was perched all too briefly in leafless trees in the Wall Garden before flying off towards Gateholm Island. The first record for Skokholm and for Wales.

Yellowhammer *Emberiza citrinella*

Rare (formerly "scarce"). Recorded annually until 1971, in all months March - October, but typically a handful of sightings March - May and September - October of not more than 3 birds. Since then, however, Yellowhammers have been seen on Skokholm only rarely, that is in only 6 of the 33 years to 2004. In the most recent year, 1996, there were 4 records: one male sang on and off from 13th - 27th April, with a second present on 20th April, another (perhaps the same?) on 5th - 6th May, and a female/immature was present on 25th September.

Ortolan Bunting *Emberiza hortulana*

Scarce. About 50 records, almost all of them in the period 25th August - 14th October, especially the first three weeks of September when up to 4 birds have been present. There are 5 spring records: on 2nd June 1931 (first record for Pembrokeshire), 19th May 1938, 3rd June 1962, 29th April - 2nd May 1987 and 11th May 1995.

Rustic Bunting *Emberiza rustica*

Vagrant. A female trapped on 8th June 1953 was the first for Wales. A male was present 6th - 7th June 1975, also trapped. Then a male on 20th May 1993 and a female or first-year male on 23rd May 1994.

Black-headed Bunting *Emberiza melanocephala*

Vagrant. Spring males were found at North Pond on 11th May 1965, in South Haven on 3rd June 1965, at the lighthouse on 26th May 1987, and one remained in the vicinity of the Observatory buildings from 29th May until 6th June 1996, singing frequently from the Sycamore trees in the cottage garden.

Corn Bunting *Miliaria calandra*

Vagrant. Presence described as "casual, March to June" by Lockley (1936) when referring to the years 1927 - 1935, but there have been just 5 records since, four of which were within a 6-year period during which Corn Buntings were increasing in Britain: on 3rd October 1960, 2nd April 1961, 31st May 1963 and 6th June 1965, and finally on 31st May 1992.

Rose-breasted Grosbeak *Pheucticus ludovicianus*

Vagrant. A female trapped on 5th October 1967 was the fourth for Britain and Ireland and first for Wales.

ICTERIDAE (New World Blackbirds, Orioles and Allies)

Northern Oriole *Icterus galbula*

Vagrant. An adult female trapped on 5th October 1967 (and remaining until 10th October) was the fifth for Britain and Ireland and the first for Wales.

Bobolink *Dolichonyx oryzivorus*

A juvenile on two days 12th - 13th October 1999 was the first record for Wales and 22nd for Britain. It fed voraciously on craneflies *Tipula* spp. in the Bracken near Garden Rocks.

CATEGORY D: Species which may have escaped:

PHOENICOPTERIDAE (Flamingoes)

Greater Flamingo *Phoenicopterus ruber*

One on 13th September 1965.

ANATIDAE (Wildfowl)

Snow Goose *Anser caerulescens*

Three immatures on North Pond on 13th June 1971. One on 9th May 1975 had been ringed at Slimbridge in 1974. Five white-phase adults flew north with 4 Barnacle Geese on 15th April 1991.

In June 2000, three pinioned Snow Geese somehow reached the island. Extremely emaciated, they made their way up to the island plateau, and eventually met up. They were given food, and survived. A fourth bird was seen at the base of a sheer cliff, and was not seen subsequently. They were left to their own devices, survived the winter months, and two formed a pair in 2001 and raised 4 young. One of these subsequently disappeared, as did the unpaired adult.

In 2002, the three fully-winged immatures (the survivors of the brood of 2001) and one flightless adult were still present on the island upon reoccupation by the Wardens. The adult mated with one of the offspring, but the nest was destroyed by the author under instruction. One of the youngsters disappeared on 20th November, and at the same time one was reported from Hook on the nearby mainland in association with a large flock of Canada Geese.

Two winged immatures and one flightless adult parent were still present on the island in the spring of 2003. The third surviving youngster of that same brood was associating with a large flock of Canada Geese, and returned to the island intermittently. The adult then disappeared in mid-summer, presumed to have gone to the sea with families of Canada Geese. The young, all fully-winged birds, subsequently made frequent excursions away from the island, and were reported from Skomer and the mainland throughout the year. In 2004, all three youngsters were part of the large Canada Goose flock, and were often seen leading them in flight.

Greylag Goose *Anser anser*
A leucistic bird was around the Observatory 7th - 27th October 1987; five flew over the island *en route* for North Pond on 15th March 2002, and another one on 3rd June 2002, also alighting on North Pond amongst the Snow Geese (see above).

COLUMBIDAE (Pigeons)

Barbary Dove *Streptopelia risoria*
One on 31st May 1972.

EMBERIZIDAE (Buntings)

Red-headed Bunting *Emberiza bruniceps*
A singing male on 2nd August 1953, a female on 14th August 1954, a male 16th - 23rd May 1959, a male 19th - 25th September 1961, singles on 18th July 1962 and 15th September 1963, at least 2 males and 2 females between 1st June and 16th July 1967, a male 10th - 11th August 1979 and a singing male 30th May - 4th June 1989. Those in 1959, 1979 and 1989 were described as "shy", and thus most likely truly wild.

Painted Bunting *Passerina ciris*
A male from 18th - 20th August 1971.

Appendix IX: Complete list of invertebrates

Introduction

Of Skokholm's invertebrates, very few of the insect and arachnid groups have been studied or enumerated in detail. In particular, Collembola (springtails), Coleoptera (beetles), Trichoptera (caddis flies), Lepidoptera (butterflies and moths) and some arachnids (spiders and harvestmen) have had work published about them. An extensive list of aquatic invertebrates was published in 1956 by Angela Davis.

The majority of the records below are either transcribed from these published studies or are extracted from the island card-index system which was started in the early 1950's. The card-index records are generally unchecked and are not backed up by reference collections so records of some of the rarer species should be interpreted with caution. Nearly all of the invertebrate records for the island (excepting Lepidoptera) date from the 1950's and some (e.g. some of the spider records) are older than this. There are numerous marine species listed in the record cards, but not all of these are included here.

English names, where known, follow the binomial (genus and species) and the name of the author, and are in bold type. Status according to rarity is listed, all those with no qualifying feature are considered to be "common".

THE PROTOZOA

Skokholm's protozoan fauna has not been studied, though Davis (1956a) lists 5 freshwater species. Two marine species and one (Lophocephalus insignis) found in the gut of a Tenebrionid insect are recorded in the island card index.

Phylum: MASTIGOPHORA (Flagellata)
Noctiluca scintillans (Macartney) Kofoid & Swezy
Colacium vesiculosum Ehrenberg

Phylum: SARCODINA
Haliphysema tumanowiczii Bowerbank
Arcella vulgaris Ehrenberg (Sarcodina)

Phylum: SPOROZOA
Lophocephalus insignis (Schneider) Labbé

Phylum: CILIOPHORA
Oxytricha sp. Bory de St. Vincent
Spirostomum sp. Ehrenberg
Vorticella sp. L.

Phylum: COELENTERATA

The only non-marine coelenterate recorded from Skokholm is: Hydra vulgaris L.

Phylum: PLATYHELMINTHES

Class: TURBELLARIA

Tricladida: Flatworms

A. Davis (1956a) collected and critically reviewed the card-index to produce the following list of freshwater flatworms:

Dalyellidae
Dalyellia sp. Fleming

Typhloplanidae
Rhynchomesostoma rostratum (Müller)

Planariidae
Phagocata sp. Leidy
Crenobia alpina (Dana). Local.
Polycelis cornuta Johnston
P. nigra (Müller)

Phylum: ANNELIDA

Class: OLIGOCHAETA

Of the following terrestrial species, those listed in the card-index are marked *; a recent survey (November 2002 and March 2003) by the author revealed those species marked +.

Lumbricidae (earthworms)
Aporrectodea caliginosa (Savigny) Grey Worm *
A. chlorotica (Savigny) Green Worm *+
A. longa (Ude) +
Lumbricus castaneus (Savigny) Chestnut Worm *
L. festivus (Savigny) Ruddy Worm *
L. rubellus Hoff. Red Worm * +
L. terrestris L. Common Earthworm or Night Crawler *
Octolasion tyrtaeum tyrtaeum (Savigny) +
Eiseniella tetrahedra Sav. *

A. Davis (1956a) recorded Eiseniella sp. Michaelsen, and numerous other unidentified oligochaetes from several freshwater habitats.

Class: HIRUDINEA (leeches)

A. Davis (1956a) lists the following 4 species of leech from freshwater on Skokholm.

Glossiphonidae

Theromyzon tessulatum (Müller).

Helobdella stagnalis (L.).

Hirudinidae

Haemopsis sanguisuga (L.) Horse Leech. Local.

Erpobdellidae

Dina lineata (Müller). Local.

Phylum: MOLLUSCA (slugs and snails)

Helicidae

Helix aspersa Müller

Cepaea nemoralis (L.) Brown Lipped Snail

C. hortensis (Müller)

Pupillidae

Lauria cylindracea (da Costa)

Limacidae

Limax maximus L. Great Grey Slug

Deroceras laeve (Müller)

D. agreste (L.) Field Slug. Nationally scarce

D. reticulatum (Müller) Netted Slug

Zonitidae

Oxychilus alliarius (Müller) Garlic Snail

Milacidae

Milax gagates (Draparnaud). Smooth Jet Slug. Local.

Endodontidae (discus snails)

Discus rotundatus (Müller) Marsh Slug

Arionidae

Arion ater (L.) Great Black Slug

Clausiliidae

Clausilia rugosa (Draparnaud)

Clausilia bidentata (Strom)

Cryptomphalus aspersa (OF Müller)

Cochlicopodidae

Cochlicopa lubrica (Müller)

Davis (1956a) lists the following gastropods:

Hydrobiidae

Hydrobia jenkinsi Smith

Limnaeidea

Limnaea truncatula (Müller)

L. peregra (Müller) Wandering Snail

Ancylidae

Ancylus fluviatilis Müller River Limpet

Planorbidae (ramshorn snails)

Planorbis spirorbis (L.)

Anisus leucostoma (Millet) Button Ramshorn

Succineidae

Succinea sp. Draparnaud

Pisidiidae (pea mussels)

Pisidium nitidium Jenyns

Phylum: ARTHROPODA

Subphylum: CRUSTACEA

Class: BRANCHIOPODA

Order: CLADOCERA

Simocephalus vetulus (Müller)
Ceriodaphnia laticaudata (Müller). Local.
Moina rectirostris (Leydig)
Ilyocryptus sordidus (Lieven). Nationally scarce.
Alona affinis (Lilljeborg)

A. tenuicaudis Sars
A. guttata Sars
Graptoleberis testudinaria (Fischer)
Chydorus sphaericus (Müller)

Class: OSTRACODA

Order: PODOCOPA

Cypridae
Herpetocypris chevreuxi (Sars). Local.
Bradleystrandesia reticulata (Zaddach 1844).
Strandesia obliqua (Brady)

Class: COPEPODA

Order: CALANOIDA

Diaptomidae
Diaptomus castor (Jurine). Local.

Order: CYCLOPOIDA

Cyclopidae
Cyclops strenuus Fischer
Megacyclops viridis (Jurine)
Diacyclops bicuspidatus (Claus)
Paracyclops fimbriatus (Fischer)
Eucyclops agilis (Koch)

Order: HARPACTICOIDA

Canthocamptus pygmaeus (Sars)
C. staphylinus (Jurine)

Order: CALANOIDA

Diaptomus castoe (Jurine)

Class: MALACOSTRACA

Order: ISOPODA

Suborder: Oniscoidea

Ligiidae
Ligia oceanica (L.) Sea-slater

Oniscidae
Oniscus asellus L.

Philoscidae
Philoscia muscorum (Scop.)

Armadillidiidae
Armadillidium vulgare (Latr.) Pill-bug

Porcellionidae
Porcellio scaber Latr.

Suborder: Asellota

Asellidae
Asellus meridianus Racovitza

Order: AMPHIPODA

Gammaridae
Echinogammarus stoerensis (Reid)
Gammarus duebeni Lillj.
G. finmarchicus Dahl
G. locusta L.
G. marinus Leach
G. obtusatus Dahl

Melitidae
Melita hergensis Reid
M. palmata Montagu

Talitridae (sand-hoppers)
Orchestia gammarellus (Pallas)

SUBPHYLUM: URINAMIA

"MYRIAPODS"

Class: CHILOPODA (centipedes)

Lithobius fortificatus (L.)
Lithobius lapidicola Meinert. **Red Data Book:** Insufficiently known.
Necrophloephagus longicornis (Leach)
N. flavus (De Geer)
Geophilus insculptus Attems
Geophilus proximus C.L. Koch

Class: INSECTA (Hexapoda)

Subclass: Apterygota

Order: THYSANURA (Bristle-tails)

Petrobius brevistylis (Carp)
P. maritimus (Leach)
Lepisma saccharina L. Silver-fish

Order: DIPLURA (Two-pronged Bristle-tails)

Campodea sp. Westwood

Order: COLLEMBOLA (Springtails)

Gough (1971) lists 36 species of springtail, and provides an identification key for them. Three of these (marked *) are first British records. A 37th species (marked **) recorded by Green (1956) is uncommon and was not found by Gough.

Hypogastruridae
Hypogastrura denticulata (**Bagna**)

Xenylla acauda Gisin

X. maritima Tullberg

Neanuridae
Friesea truncata Cassagnau

Pseudachorutes boerneri Schött

Anurida maritima (Guerin)

Micranusida pygmaea Borner

Neanura muscorum (Templeton)

Anuridella marina Willem *

Onychiuridae
Onychiurus meridiatus Gisin *

Tullbergiidae
Paratullbergia callipygos (Borner)

Mesaphorura krausbaueri Borner

Stenaphorura quadrispina (Borner)

Isotomidae
Folsomia bisetosa Gisin * UK status unclear

F. quadrioculata (Tullberg)

Isotomiella minor (Schaffer)

Cryptopygus scapelliferus (Gisin)

Pseudisotoma sensibilis (Tullberg)

Isotoma viridis Bourlet

Cyphoderidae
Cyphoderus albinus Nicolet

Entomobryidae
Entomobrya albocincta (Templeton)

E. multifasciata (Tullberg)

E. nicoleti (Lubbock)

Willowsia nigromaculata (Lubbock)

Lepidocyrtus cyaneus Tullberg

L. lignorum (Fabricius)

Pseudosinella alba (Packard)

Tomoceridae
Tomocerus longicornis (Müller)

Neelidae
Megalothorax minimus Willem

Sminthuridae
Sminthurus sp. Latreille

Bourletiellidae
Bourletiella arvalis (Fitch)

Deuterosminthurus repandus (Ågren)

Dicyrtomina saundersi (Lubbock). Status unclear

Sminthurididae
Sminthurides malmgreni (Tullberg)

Sphaeridia pumilis (Krausbauer)

Order: ORTHOPTERA (Grasshoppers and allies)

Omocestus viridulus (Linn.). Common Green Grasshopper
Chorthippus bicolor (Charp.). Common Field Grasshopper
Stenobothrus lineatus (Panzer). Stripe-winged Grasshopper

ORDER: DERMAPTERA (Earwigs)

Forficula auricularia (L.)

ORDER: MALLOPHAGA (Bird Lice)

The following species are listed in Skokholm Bird Observatory Reports for 1937 - 39.

Menoponidae
Actornithophilus sp. Ferris
(on dunlin *Calidris alpina*)

Austromenopon crocatum Nitzch
(from oystercatcher *Haematopus ostralegus*)

Myrsidea rustica Nitzs.
(from swallow *Hirundo rustica*)

Philopteridae
Bruelia gracilis Burmeister
(on swallow *Hirundo rustica*)

B. merulensis (Denny)
(from blackbird *Turdus merula* and cuckoo
Cuculus canorus)

Philopterus exisus Burmeister
(from swallow *Hirundo rustica*)

Degeeriella sp. Neumann
(from dunlin *Calidris alpina*)

Philoteridae (continued)

Degeriella sp. Neumann
(from puffin *Fratercula arctica*)

Halipeurus diversus (Kellog)
(on Manx shearwater *Puffinus puffinus*)

Saemundsonnia gonothorax (Giebel)
(on great black-backed gull *Larus marinus*)

Saemundsonnia sp. Timmermann
(from snipe *Gallinago gallinago*)

Saemundsonnia sp. Timmermann
(from herring gull *Larus argentatus*)

S. alpina Giebel
(from dunlin *Calidris alpina*)

S. gonothorax Giebel
(from *Larus* gulls)

Sub-class: PTERYGOTA

Order: EPHEMEROPTERA (Mayflies)

Baetidae
Chloeon diptrum (L.)

Order: ODONATA (Dragonflies and Damsel Flies)

Sub-order: Zygoptera

Calopterygidae
Calopteryx virgo (L.). Beautiful Demoiselle.

Lestidae
Lestes sponsa (Hausemann). Emerald Damselfly.

Platycnemididae
Platycnemis pennipes (Pallas) White-legged Damselfly.

Coenagrionidae
Ischnura elegans (van der Linden). Blue-tailed Damselfly.
Coenagrion puella (L.). Azure Damselfly.
Enallagma cyathigerum (Charpentier). Common Blue Damselfly.
Pyrrhosoma nymphula (Sulzer). Large Red Damselfly

Sub-order: Anisoptera

Aeshnidae
Brachytron pratense (Müller). Hairy Dragonfly. Nationally scarce.
Aeshna juncea (L.). Common Hawker.
A. cyanea (Müller). Southern Hawker.
A. mixta Latreille. Migrant Hawker.
Anax imperator Leach. Emperor.

Cordulegasteridae
Cordulegaster boltonii (Donovan). Golden-ringed Dragonfly.

Libellulidae
Libellula quadrimaculata L. Four-spot Chaser.
Libellula depressa L. Broad-bodied Chaser.
Sympetrum striolatum (Charpentier). Common Darter.
S. flaveolum (L.). Yellow-winged Darter

ORDER: Hemiptera (Bugs)

Only aquatic heteroptera (suborder Prosorrhyncha) and aphids and leafhoppers of the "homoptera" (Sternorrhyncha and Auchenorrhyncha) have received detailed attention. The taxonomy of the Hemiptera is currently in dispute.

Sub-order: PROSORRHYNCHA

Gerridae (Pond Skaters)
Gerris thoracicus Scummel.

Pleidae (Pygmy Backswimmers)
Plea minutissima (Linn).

Notonectidae
Notonecta glauca Linn.
Notonecta viridis Delcourt
Notonecta marmorea Fabricius

Aepophilidae
Aepophilus bonnairei Signoret

Corixidae
Corixa punctata (Illg). The Punctate Corixa
C. affinis Leach . Local
Hesperocorixa moesta (Fieb). Local
H. linnei (Fieb)
Sigara lateralis (Leach)
S. nigrolineata (Fieber)
S. stagnalis (Leach)
S. dorsalis (Leach)
S. distincta (Fieb)
S. limitata (Fieb)
S. concinna (Fieb)
Callicorixa praeusta (Fieb)

Miridae (plant bugs)
Calocoris norvegicus (Gmelin).
Lygus rugulipennis Poppius. European
Tarnished Plant Bug

Tingidae (lace bugs)
Kalama tricornis (Schrank). Local.
Tingis cardui (Linn.).

Lygaeidae (seed bugs)
Stygnocoris fuligineus (Geoff.).

Sub-order: STERNORRHYNCHA

Aphididae
Macrosiphum euphorbiae (Thomas)
M. fragriae (Walker)
Dorlais fabae Scop.
D. urticaria (Kalt)
Brachycaudus cardui (Linn.)
B. halichrysi (Kalt)
B. lychnidis (Linn.)
Rhopalosiphum nymphaeae (Linn.)

Sub-order: AUCHENORRHYNCHA

Cercopidae (spittle bugs)
Philaenus spumarius (L.)

Cicadellidae
Evacanthus interruptus (L.)
Cicadella viridis (L.)

Order: NEUROPTERA (Lacewings)

Sisyra fuscata (Fabr.). Local.

Chrysopa carnea Steph.

Order: COLEOPTERA (Beetles)

Carabidae (Ground beetles)

Carabus violaceus L. var. asperipennis Lapou.

Calathus fuscipes (Goeze)

C. melanocephalus sens. lat. (L.)

Notiophilus biguttatus (Fab.)

N.quadripunctatus Dej. Nationally scarce.

N. aquaticus (L.). Local.

N. palustris (Duft.). Local.

N. substriatus Waterhouse. Local.

Clivina fossor (Linnaeus)

Bembidion harpaloides (Serv.)

Trechus fulvus Dej. Nationally scarce.

Chlaenius nigricornis (F.). Nationally scarce.

Badister bullatus (Fab.)

Harpalus affinis (Schrank)

H. brevicollis Serville

H. latus (L.)

H. rufibarbis Fabr.

Stenolophus mixtus (Hbst.). Local.

Acupalpus dorsalis (F.). Local.

A. dubius Schilsky. Local.

Amara aenea (Degeer)

A. aulica (Panzer)

A. ovata (F.)

A. communis (Pz.). Local.

A. aenea (Deg.) Common Sun Beetle.

A. familiaris (Dft.).

A. lumicollis Schioedte. Local.

A. vulgaris Duftsihm.

Asaphidion curtum (Heyden)

Pterostichus versicolor Sturm. Local.

P. vernalis (Pz.). Local.

P. nigra (Schaller).

P. nigrita agg. (Paykull)

P. minor (Gy.). Local.

P. diligens (Stm.).

P. madidus (F.). Black Clock.

Abax parallelepipedus (Pill. and Mitt.).

Calathus fuscipes (Gz.).

C. melanocephalus agg. (L.).

Laemosteunus terricola (Hbst.). Local.

Synuchus nivalis (Pz.). Local.

Olisthopus rotundatus (Pk.)

Agonum marginatum (L.). Local.

A. albipes (Fab.)

Metabletus foveatus (Fourcroy.)

Harpalus rufipes (Deg.). Strawberry Seed Beetle.

Nebria salina Fairmaire & Laboulbene

Dyschirius globosus (Hbst.). Local.

Agonum viduum (Pz.)

A. dorsale (Pont.)

Loricera pilicornis (F.)

Aepopsis robinii (Laboulbene)

Haliplidae (Haliplid Water Beetles)

Haliplus lineatocollis (Marsh.)

H. ruficollis (Deg.)

H. immaculatus Gerh. Local.

H. fulvus (F.). Local.

Hygrobiidae (screech beetles)

Hygrobia hermanni (F.). Screech Beetle.

Dytiscidae (carnivorous water beetles)

Hygrotus inaequalis (F.)

H. confluens (Fabr.). Local

Hydroporus palustris (L.)

Hydroporus discretus Fair. Local

H. erythrocephalus (L.)

H. longulus Muls. Nationally scarce

H. memnonius Nicolai

H. pubescens (Gyll.)

Agabus nebulosus (Forst.)

Ilybius chalconatus (Panzer)

A. bipustulatus (L.)

Ilybius ater (Deg.)

I. quadriguttatus (Lac. & Bois)

Copelatus haemorrhoidialis (Fabr.)

Colymbetes fuscus (L.)

Noteridae (burrowing water beetles)

Noterus clavicornis (Deg.)

Hydrophilidae (vegetarian water beetles)

Helophorus brevipalis Bed.

H. minutus ssp affinis F.

H. griseus (Hbst.). Nationally scarce.

H. flavipes (F.).

Coelostoma orbiculare (F.).

Sphaeridium bipustulatum F.

S. scarabaeoides (L.).

Cercyon haemorrhoidalis (F.).

C. melanocephalus (L.).

C. marinus Thomson. Local.

Paracymus scutellaris (Rosen.). Nat. scarce.

Anacaena limbata (F.), sens. lat.

Hydrobius fuscipes (L.)

Laccobius bipunctatus Thomson.

Enochrus ochropterus (F.). Nationally scarce.

Chaetarthria seminulum (Hbst.). Nat. scarce.

Megasternum obscurum (Marsh.).

Silphidae (sexton or burying beetles)

Nicrophorus humator (Gleditsch).

N. investigator Zett.

N. interruptus (S.). Nationally scarce.

Thanatophilis rugosus (L.).

T. sinuatus (F.).

Leioidae

Catops fuliginosus (Erichson).

Sciodrepoides watsoni (Spence.).

Ptilidae

Ptenidium pusillum (Gy.).

P. nitidum (Heer).

Staphylinidae (rove beetles)

Anolytus rugosus (F.).

A. sculpturatus (Gr.).

A. inustus (Grav.).

Stenus brunnipes Stephens

S. picipennis Erich. Local.

Astenus longelytratus Palm.

Sunius propinquus (Bris.). Local.

Xantholinus glabratus (Gr.).

Staphylinidae (continued).

X. jarrigei (coiffati). Local.

X. longiventris Heer.

X. linearis (Ol.).

Philonthus succicola Thomson. Local.

P. addendus Sharp. Local.

P. cognatus (Stephens).

P. laminatus (Creutzer)

P. varius (Gy.).

P. micans (Gr.).

P. marginatus (F.).

Gabrius nigritulus(Gr.).

G. keysanius Sharp. Nationally scarce.

Platydracus stercorarius (Olivier). Local.

Staphylinus dimidiaticornis Gemm. Local.

Ocypus olens (Mueller).

O. aenocephalus (Deg.).

O. ater Gr.

O. globulifer Fourc.

O. compressus (Marsh.). Local.

Creophilus maxillosus (L.).

Quedius tristis (Gr.).

Mycetoporus splendidus (Gr.).

M. lepidus (Gr.)

Tachyporus obtusus (L.).

Tachyporus nitidulus (F.).

T. pusillus (Gr.).

T. chrysomelinus agg. (L).

Tachinus marginellus (F.).

Cordalia obscura (Gr.).

Amischa analis (Gr.).

Atheta melanocera Thoms.

A. atramentaria (Gy.).

A. longicornis (Gr)

A. parvula (Mannerheim).

Zyras limbatus (Pk.). Local.

Aleochara curtula (Gz.).

A. brevipennis Gr. Nationally scarce.

A. lanuginosa Gr.

A. bipustulata (L.).

Calodera aethiops (Grav.).

Histeridae

Saprinus semistriatus (Scriba)

Hister impressus F.

Paralister purpurascens (Herbst.). Local.

Cantharidae (soldier beetles)

Rhagonycha fulva (Scop.). Soldier Beetle.

Elateridae (click beetles)

Agrypnus murinus (L.). Local.

Hemicrepidius hirtus (Hbst)

Athous haemorrhoidalis (F.)

Agriotes sputator (L.)

A. sordidus (Ill.). Rare.

A. lineatus (L.)

A. obscurus (L.)

Dryopidae

Dryops luridus (Erichson)

Dermestidae

Dermestes murinus L. Local.

Byrrhidae

Simplocaria semistriata (F.)

Nitidulidae

Kateretes rufilabris (Lat.)

Brachypterus glaber (S.)

Meligethes aeneus (F.). Common Pollen Beetle.

Nitidula bipunctata (L.). Two-spotted Carrion Beetle.

Omosita discoidea (F.). Local.

O. colon (L.)

Cryptophagiadae

Cryptophagus umbratus Er

C. ruficornis S. Nationally scarce.

Atomaria pusilla (Paykull)

Ephistemus globulus (Paykull)

Lathridiidae

Corticarina fuscula (Gy.)

Coccinellidae (Ladybirds)

Subcoccinella viginiquattuorpunctata (L.). 24-spot Ladybird.

Hippodamia tredicimpunctata (L.). 13-spot.

Scymnus haemorrhoidalis Hbst.

Coccinella septempunctata L. 7-spot.

Coccidula rufa (Hbst.).

Coccinella undecimpunctata L. 11-spot.

Anatis ocellata (L.). Eyed Ladybird.

Anobiidae

Anobium punctatum (Deg.)

Tenebrionidae (darkling beetles)

Crypticus quisquillius (L.). Nat. scarce.

Cylindrinotus laevioctostriatus (Gz.)

Isomira murina (L.).

Scarabaeidae (scarabs and chafers)

Typhaeus typhoeus (L.). Local.

Aphodius ater (Deg.).

A. rufipes (L.).

A. nitidulus (Fab.)

Serica brunnea (L.). Brown Chafer. Local.

Trogidae

Trox scaber (L.).

Chrysomelidae (leaf beetles)

Cryptocephalus fulvus Gz.. Local.

Phaedon tumidulus (Germ.). Celery Leaf Beetle.

P. armoraciae (L.). Mustard Beetle.

Chrysomela populi L. Local.

Longitarsus succineus (Foud.) Chrysanthemum Flea Beetle.

L. jacobaeae (Wat.)

L. membranaceus (Foud.)

L. gracilis Kuts.

L. aeruginosus (Foud.). Endangered.

L. atricillus (L.)

L. luridus (Scop.)

Crepidodera transversa (Marsham)

Chaetocnema hortensis (Fourcroy)

Sphaeroderma rubidum (Graells)

Altica oleracea (L.)

Cassida vittata de Vill. Tortoise Beetle. Local.

Gastrophysa viridula (Deg). Green Dock Beetle.

Apionidae (seed weevils)

Perapion violaceum (Kby.)

P. marchicum (Hbst.). Local.

P. curtirostre (Germ.)

Apion frumentarium (L.)

A. haematodes Kby.

A. cruentatum Walton. Local.

Diplapion confluens (Kirby). Local.

Curculionidae (weevils)

Ceratapion carduorum (Kirby). Local.

Otiorhynchus arcticus (Fab.). Local.

O. ligneus (Ol.)

O. sulcatus (F.). Vine Weevil.

O. rugifrons (Gy.). Local.

Trachyphloeus scabriculus (L.). Local.

T. bifoveolatus (Beck.)

Phyllobius argentatus (L.). Silver-green Leaf Weevil.

Strophosomus faber (Hbst.). Nationally scarce.

Strophosoma capitatus Deg.

Barynotus obscurus (F.). Ground Weevil.

Sibinia arenariae S. Nationally scarce.

Hypera (Phytonomus) rumicis (L.)

H. arator (L.)

Gronops lunatus (F.). Nationally scarce.

Sibinia primita (Hbst.). Nationally scarce.

Sitona hispidulus (F.). Clover Weevil.

Rhinoncus perpendicularis (Reich)

Pelenomus canaliculatus (Fahr.). Nationally scarce.

Order: SIPHONAPTERA (Fleas)

Pulicidae

Ornithopsylla laetitiae Roths.

Echidnophaga gallinacea (Westwood)

Ceratophyllidae

Ceratophyllus borealis Roths. (especially on Wheatear)

C. vagabundus insularis Roths. (on several bird spp)

C. garei Roths. (on Rock Pipit and Wheatear)

C. gallinae Schrank (various migrant birds)

Ctenophthalmus nobilis nobilis (Roths.)

Ctenophthalmus nobilis vulgaris Smit (House Mouse)

Nosopsyllus fasciatus (Bosc). The European Rat Flea

Dasypsyllus gallinulae gallinulae (Dale)

Hystrichopsyllidae

Hystrichopsylla talpae talpae (Curtis)

Order: DIPTERA (True flies)

F.W. Edwards collected free-living Diptera on Skokholm in August 1934 and identified about 60 species (Edwards, 1934). In 1949, P. Driver identified numerous species. In June 1950, Smith collected a similar number of species and only recorded 8 of those found by Edwards, bringing the total to 99 species in 33 families. To this list are added three species of parasitic Hippoboscid that were collected by Stansfield (1954) and one earlier flat-fly record (Skokholm Bird Observatory Report 1938). A few others have been added recently, as a result of collecting by the author.

Conopidae
Sicus ferrugineus (L.). Local.

Tipulidae (crane flies)

Tipuliinae
Tipula (Acutipula) maxima Poda
Tipula (T.) oleracea L.
T. (T.) paludosa Meigen
T. (Yamatipula) lateralis Mg.
T. (Savtshenkia) rufina Mg.
T. (Vestiplex) scripta Mg.
Limnophila (Euphlidorea) fulvonervosa (Schu.)
Nephrotoma flavescens (L.)
Limonia (Geranomyia) unicolor (Haliday)

Limoniinae
Dicranomyia (Limonia) autumnalis (Steiger)
Phylidorea ferruginea (Meigen)
Dicranomyia chorea (Meig.)

Bibionidae
Bibio marci (L.) St. Mark's Fly
Dilophus febrilis (L.) Fever Fly

Cedidomyidae (gall midges)
Dasyneura glechomae (Kieffer)

Ptychopteridae
Ptychoptera albimana (Fab.)

Psychodidae (owl midges, moth flies)
Pericoma avicularia Tonn.

Culicidae
Culex pipiens L.

Thaumaleidae
Thaumalea verralli Edw.

Ceratopogonidae (biting midges)
Culicoides pulicaris L.
Palpomyia flavipes (Mg.)

Chironomidae (non-biting midges)
Anatopynia notata Mg.
Cricotopus vitripennis Mg.
Cricotopus fucicola Edw.
Thalassosmittia thalassophila (Goet.)
Chironomus plumosus L. Buzzer Midge
C. riparius Mg.

Anisopodidae
Anisopus fenestralis Scop.

Mycetophilidae
Sciara sp.
Macrocera vittata Mg.

Scatopsidae
Scatopse notata (L.)

Rhagionidae (snipe flies)
Chrysopilus cristatus (Fab.)

Tabanidae
Haematopota pluvialis (L.). Common Clegg

Empididae (dance flies)
Rhamphomyia variabilis (Fallen)
Empis (Xanthempis) punctata Mg.
Empis (Kritempis) livida L.

Dolichopodidae (long-headed flies)

Dolichopus ungulatus (L.)

D. vitripennis Mg.   Local.

D. plumipes (Scop.)

Aphrosylus celtiber Haliday.   Local.

A. ferox Hal.   Local.

Liancalus virens (Scop.)   Local.

Medetera dendrobaena Kow.   Local.

Hercostomus germanus (Wiedemann)

Campsicnemus loripes (Hal.)

Sympycnus desoutteri Parent

Family: Syrphidae

Sub-family: Syrphinae

Tribe: Bacchini

Melanostoma mellinum (L.)

Platycheirus albimanus (Fabr.)

P. clypeatus (Meigen)

P. manicatus (Meigen)

P. scutatus (Meigen)

Tribe: Syrphini

Chrysotoxum cautum (Harris)

Epistrophe eligans (Harris)

Episyrphus balteatus De Geer

Meliscaeva auricollis (Meigen)

Eupeodes corollae (Fabr.)

Metasyrphus latifasciatus (Macquart)

M. luniger (Meigen)

Scaeva pyrastri (L.)

Sphaerophoria scripta (L.)

Syrphus ribesii (L.)

S. vitripennis Meigen

Sub-family: Milesiinae

Tribe: Cheilosiini

Rhingia campestris Meigen

Sub-family: Milesiinae (continued)

Tribe: Chrysogastrini

Lejogasta metallina (Fabr.)

Neoascia podagrica (Fabr.)

Tribe: Eristalini

Eristalis tenax (L.)

E. pertinax (Scopoli)

E. intricarius (L.)

E. nemorum (L.)

E. arbustorum (L.)

Eristalinus aeneus (Scopoli)

E. sepulchralis (L.)

Helophilus pendulus (L.)

Helophilus trivittatus (Fabricius)

Tribe: Volucellini

Volucella bombylans (L.): var. plumata.

Tribe: Xylotini

Syritta pipiens (L.)

Tephritidae (gall flies)

Trupanea stellata (Fuess.).   Local.

Acanthiophilus helianthi (Rossi).   Nationally scarce.

Sphenella marginata (Fallen).   Local.

Terellia tussilaginis (Fabricius)

Xyphosia miliaria (Schrank)

Psilidae

Chamaepsila (Psila) pallida Fallen.

Chamaemyiidae

Chamaemyia polystigma (Mg.)

Sapromyzidae (=Lauxaniidae)

Sapromyza consobrina Ztt.

Coelopidae

Coelopa frigida (Fabr.)

Heleomyzidae

Tephrochlamys rufiventris Mg.

Sepsidae (lesser dung flies)

Sepsis cynipsea (L.)

Themira minor (Haliday)

Sciomyzidae (snail-killing flies)

Ilione albiseta Scop. 1763

Colobaea punctata (Ldbk.) (Ctenulus punctata Ldbk.). Nationally scarce.

Sphaeroceridae (lesser dung flies)

Leptocera caenosa Rond. (?)

Copromyza equine Fall.

Ephydridae

Notiphila cinerea (Fall.)

Scatella tenuicosta Collin

S. silacea Loew

Hydrellia griseola (Fall.)

H. maura Mg.

Diastatidae

Diastata unipunctata Ztt. Local.

Drosophilidae

Scaptomyza pallida (Zetterstedt)

Canacidae

Canace nasica Hal.

Chloropidae

Thaumatomyia notata (Mg.)

T. glabra Mg.

Chlorops troglodytes (Ztt.). Nationally scarce.

Tachinidae

Thelaira nigripes (F.)

Eriothrix rufomaculata (De G.)

Siphona geniculata (De G.)

Sarcophagidae (grey flesh flies)

Helicophagella melanura Meigen. Local.

Pierretia nigriventis (Mg.)

Sarcotachinella sinuata Mg. Local.

Calliphoridae

Calliphora vicina Robineau-Desvoidyi

Lucilia sericata (Mg.)

L. illustris (Mg.)

Melinda gentilis Robineau-Desvoidyi.

Rhinophoridae

Frauenfeldia rubricosa Mg.

Scathophagidae

Scathophaga stercoraria L. Yellow Dung-fly

Ceratinostoma ostiorum (Curtis). Local.

Anthomyiidae

Hylemya variata (Fall.)

Anthomyia procellaris Rond.

Fucellia maritima Hal.

Muscidae

Myospila meditabunda (Fabr.)

Phaonia perdita (Mg.)

P. incana (Weid.)

Limnophora olympiae Lyneborg. Local.

Hydrotaea armipes (Fallen)

Caenosia tigrina (F.).

Helina obscurata (Mg.). Local

Coenosia pumila (Fallen)

Chirosia crassiseta Stein

Fanniidae

Fannia canicularis (L.). Lesser House Fly

Hippoboscidae

Ornithomyia fringillina Curtis

O. avicularia (L.)

O. chloropus Bergroth

O. lagopodis Sharp

Order: TRICHOPTERA (Caddis Flies)

Limnephilidae
Limnephilus hirsutus (Pict.)
L. extrictatus McLach.
L. vittatus (F.)

Lepidostomatidae
Lepidostoma hirtum (F.)

Beraeidae
Beraea maurus (Curt.)

Polycentropidae
Plectrocnemia conspersa (Curt.)
P. geniculata McLach.

Philopotamidae
Philopotomus montanus (Don.)
Wormaldia occipitalis (Pict.)

Order : LEPIDOPTERA (butterflies and moths)

Suborder: MACROLEPIDOPTERA

Hepialidae
Hepialus humili L. Ghost Moth
Hepialus sylvina L. Orange Swift
Hepialus lupulinus L. Common Swift
Hepialus fusconebulosa De Geer Map-winged Swift

Zygaenidae
Zygaena filipendulae Six-spot Burnet
Zygaena trifolii decreta Verity Five-spot Burnet

Sesiidae
Bembecia muscaeformis Esper Thrift Clearwing

Pieridae
Colias hyale L./C. alfacariensis Ribbe
Pale/Berger's Clouded Yellow
Colias crocerus Fourcroy Clouded Yellow
Gonepteryx rhamni L. Brimstone
Pieris brassicae L. Large White
Pieris rapae L. Small White
Pieris napi L. Green-veined White
Anthocharis cardamines L. Orange Tip

Lycaenidae
Lycaena phlaeas L. Small Copper
Cupido minimus Fuellsy Small Blue
Celastrina argiolus L. Holly Blue
Plebejus argus L. Silver-studded Blue
Aricia agestis Denis & Schiffer. Brown Argus
Polyommatus icarus Rottem. Common Blue

Nymphalidae
Danaus plexippus L. Monarch
Inachis io L. Peacock
Vanessa atalanta L. Red Admiral
V. cardui L. Painted Lady
Aglais urticae L. Small Tortoiseshell
Polygonia c-album L. Comma
Clossiana selene D & S. Small Pearl-bordered Fritillary
C. euphrosyne L. Pearl-bordered Fritillary
Fabriciana adippe D & S. High Brown Frit.
Speyeria aglaja (L.) Dark Green Fritillary
Argynnis paphia L. Silver-washed Fritillary

Satyridae
Pararge aegeria L. Speckled Wood
Lasiommata megera L. Wall
Pyronia tithonus L. Gatekeeper

Satyridae (continued)

Melanargia galathea L. Marbled White
Hipparchia semele L. Grayling
Maniola jurtina L. Meadow Brown
Aphantopus hyperantus L. Ringlet
Coenonympha pamphilus L. Small Heath

Hesperiidae

Pyrgus malvae L. Grizzled Skipper
Ochlodes faunus Turati Large Skipper

Lasiocampidae

Malacosoma neustria L. The Lackey
Lasiocampa quercus quercus L. Oak Eggar
Macrothylacia rubi L. Fox Moth
Philudoria potatoria L. The Drinker

Geometridae

Archiearis parthenias L. Orange Underwing
Timandra griseata Peters. Blood-vein
Scopula marginepunctata Goeze. Mullein Wave
Idaea biselata Hufn. Small Fan-footed Wave
I. aversata L. Riband Wave
I. emarginata L. Small Scallop
Xanthoroe designata Hufn. Flame Carpet
X. ferrugata Haw. Dark-barred Twin-spot Carpet
X. fluctuata L. Garden Carpet
Scotopteryx mucronata umbrifera Heyd. Lead Belle
Epirrhoe galiata D. & S. Galium Carpet
Camptogramma bilineata Steph. Yellow Shell
Hydriomena furcata Thunb. July Highflyer
Eupithecia venosata venosata Fabr. Netted Pug
E. centaureata Denis & Schiff. Lime-speck Pug
E. absinthiata Clerck Wormwood Pug
E. goossensiata Mabil. Ling Pug
E. nanata angusta Prout Narrow-winged Pug
Gymnoscelis rufifasciata Haw. Double-striped Pug
Abraxas grossulariata L. The Magpie
Semiothisa clathrata clathrata L. Latticed Heath
Petrophora chlorosata Scop. Brown Silver-line
Opisthograptis luteolata L. Brimstone Moth

Geometridae (continued)

Selenia dentaria Fabr. Early Thorn
S. tetralunaria Hufn. Purple Thorn
Crocallis elinguaria L. Scalloped Oak
Biston betularia L. Peppered Moth Erannis defoliaria Clerck Mottled Umber
Peribatodes rhomboidaria D. & S. Willow Beauty
Lomographa temerata D. & S. Clouded Silver
Gnophos obscuratus D. & S.. The Annulet
Aspitates ochrearia Rossi Yellow Belle

Sphingidae

Agrius convolvuli L. Convolvulus Hawk-moth
Macroglossum stellatarum L. Humming-bird Hawk-moth
Hyles lineate livornica Esper Striped Hawk-moth
Laothoe populi L. Poplar Hawk-moth
Deilephila elpenor L. Elephant Hawk-moth

Notodontidae

Phalera bucephala L. Buff-tip
Cerura vinula L. Puss Moth

Lymantriidae

Orgyia antique L. The Vapourer
Calliteara pudibunda L. Pale Tussock
Euproctis similes Fuessly Yellow-tail

Arctiidae

Eilema lurideola Zincken Common Footman
Lithosia quadra L. Four-spotted Footman
Utetheisa bella L. Beautiful Utetheisa
Arctia caja L. Garden Tiger
Diacrisia sannio L. Clouded Buff
Spilosoma lubricipeda L. White Ermine
S. luteum Hufn. Buff Ermine
Diaphora mendica Clerck Muslin Moth
Phragmatobia fuliginosa L. Ruby Tiger
Callimorpha dominula L. Scarlet Tiger
Tyria jacobaeae L. The Cinnabar

Noctuidae

Euxoa obelisca grisea Tutt Square-spot Dart

E. tritici L. White-line Dart

E. cursoria Hufn. Coast Dart

Agrotis segetum Den. & Schiff. Turnip Moth

A. clavis Hufn. Heart and Club

A. exclamationis L. Heart and Dart

A. trux lungera Stephens Crescent Dart

A. ipsilon Hufn. Dark Sword-grass

Axylia putris L. The Flame

Ochropleura plecta L. Flame Shoulder

Standfussiana lucernea L. Northern Rustic

Noctua pronuba L. Large Yellow Underwing

N. comes Hübner Lesser Yellow Underwing

N. interjecta caliginosa Schaw. Least Yellow Underwing

N. janthina D. & S. Lesser Broad-bordered Yellow Underwing

Paradiarsia glareosa glareosa Esp. Autumnal Rustic

Lycophotia porphyrea D.& S. True Lover's Knot

Peridroma saucia Hübner Pearly Underwing

Diarsia mendica mendica Fabr. Ingrailed Clay

D. rubi Vieweg Small Square-spot

Xestia c-nigrum L. Setaceous Hebrew Character

X. xanthographa D. & Sch. Square-spot Rustic

X. agathina agathina Duponchel Heath Rustic

Cerastis rubricosa Den. & Schiff. Red Chestnut

Discestra trifolii Hufn. The Nutmeg

Hada nana Hufn. The Shears

Sideridis albicolon Hübner White Colon

Mamestra brassicae L. Cabbage Moth

Lacanobia oleracea L. Bright-line Brown-eye

Ceramica pisi L. Broom Moth

Hadena rivularis Fabr. The Campion

H. perplexa perplexa Dn. & Sch. Tawny Shears

H. luteago barrettii Doubleday Barrett's Marbled Coronet

H. confuse Hufn. Marbled Coronet

H. albimacula Borkhausen White Spot

H. bicruris Hufn. The Lychnis

Cerapteryx graminis L. Antler Moth

Tholera cespitis D. & Schiff. Hedge Rustic

T. decimalis Poda Feathered Gothic

Orthosia stabilis D. & S. Common Quaker

O. incerta Hufn. Clouded Drab

O. gothica L. Hebrew Character

Mythimna farrago Fabr. The Clay

M. albipunctata D. & S. White-point

M. vitellina Hübner The Delicate

M. impura impura Hübner Smoky Wainscot

M. pallens L. Common Wainscot

M. comma Hüb. Shoulder-striped Wainscot

M. loreyi Duponchel The Cosmopolitan

Cucullia chamomillae D. & S. Chamomile Shark

C. verbasci L. The Mullein

Aporophyla lutulenta Haworth Black Rustic

Xylena exsoleta L. Sword-grass

Lithophane ornitopus lactipennis Dadd. Grey Shoulder-knot

Blepharita adusta Esper Dark Brocade

Polymixis flavicincta D. & Sch. Large Ranunculus

P. xanthomista statices Gregson Black-banded

Eumichtis lichenea Hübner Feathered Ranunculus

Agrochola circellaris Hufn. The Brick

A. lychnidis Denis & Schiff. Beaded Chestnut

Omphaloscelis lunosa Haw. Lunar Underwing

Acronicta psi L. Grey Dagger

A. euphorbiae myricae Guenée Sweet Gale

A. rumicis L. Knot Grass

Cryphia domestica Hufn. Marbled Beauty

C. muralis muralis Forster Marbled Green

Amphipyra tragopoginis Clerc. Mouse Moth

Rusina ferruginea Esper Brown Rustic

Euplexia lucipara L. Small Angle Shades

Phologophora meticulosa L. Angle Shades

Ipimorpha subtusa Denis & Shiff. The Olive

Apamea monoglypha Hufn. Dark Arches

A. lithoxylaea Denis & Schiff. Light Arches

Noctuidae (continued)

Oligia versicolor Bork. Rufous Minor
O. fasciuncula Haw. Middle-barred Minor
Mesoligia furuncula D. & S. Cloaked Minor
M. literosa Haworth Rosy Minor
Mesapamea secalis L. Common Rustic
Photedes minima Haw. Small Dotted Buff
P. pygmina Haworth Small Wainscot
Luperina testacea D. & S. Flounced Rustic
Amphipoea crinanensis Burrows Crinan Ear
Hydraecia micacea Esper Rosy Rustic
Gortyna flavago D. & Schiff. Frosted Orange
Celaena leucostigma Hübner The Crescent
Hoplodrina alsines Brahm The Uncertain
H. blanda Denis & Schiff. The Rustic
Caradrina morpheus Hufn. Mottled Rustic
Caradrina clavipalpis Scop. Pale Mottled Willow
Heliothis peltigera D. & Schiff. Bordered Straw
Eublemma ostrina Hübner Purple Marbled
Diachrysia chrysitis L. Burnished Brass
Plusia festucae L. Gold Spot
Autographa gamma L. Silver Y
Abrostola triplasia L. The Spectacle
Callistege mi Clerck Mother Shipton
Scoliopteryx libatrix L. The Herald
Rivula sericealis Scopoli Straw Dot

Suborder: MICROLEPIDOPTERA

Sessiidae (clear-winged moths)
Aegeria philanthiformis (Lasp.)

Phaloniidae (webworms)
Euthanthis zoëgana (L.)

Eucosmidae
Endothenia sellana (Froel.)
Argyroploce lacunana (Schniff.)

Plutellidae (diamondback moths)
Plutella maculipennis (Curt.)

Oecophoridae (concealer moths)
Endrosis sarcitrella L. White-shouldered House Moth

Pyralidae

Crambinae
Agriphila genculea (Haworth)

Crambinae (continued)
A. straminella (Denis & Schiffer.)
A. tristella (Denis & Schiffer.)
Crambus pratellus (L.)
C. hortuellus (Hübn.)
Euchromius ocellea (Haworth)

Scopariinae
Eudonia angustea (Curtis)

Pyraustinae
Eurrhypara hortulana (L.) Small Magpie
Nomophila noctuella (D. & S.) Rush Veneer
Nymphula nympheata L. Brown China-mark
Scoparia dubitalis (Hübn.)
Udea ferrugalis (Hübn.)

Phycitinae
Myelois cribrella (Hübner)

Order: HYMENOPTERA (Ants, bees and wasps and their relatives)

No systematic survey has been carried out, although the author made some effort recently in collecting specimens of both hymenoptera aculeata and parasitica. Approximately half of the following ichneumonids are from the card-index, but those marked with an asterix (*) were collected in 2003 by the author and identified by M. Shaw, and also the sawfly *Pristiphora denudata*.

Sub-order Symphyta (sawflies):

Tenthredinidae
Pristiphora denudata Konow * Status unknown.

Sub-order Apocrita (ants, bees and wasps):

Ichneumonidae (ichneumon flies).
Ophion luteus (L.)

Barichneumon (Zaplethocornia) procurator Grav.

Coelichneumon consimilis (Wes.)

Virgichneumon albosignatus (Gravenhorst)

Diplazon laetatorius (Fabr.)

Horogenes (=Angitia) sp.

Ichneumon albicollis Wes.

I. sarcitorius L.

Meloboris sp.

Dorylaimus (Meloboris) stagnalis Dujardin

Scambus (Pimpla) rufator Aubert

Stilpnus sp.

Homotropus pictus (Gravenhorst)

Campoletis viennensis (Grav.)

Campoplex sp.

Aptesis sp.

Pimpla rufipes (Miller) (= instigator = hypochondriaca) * Status unknown.

Diplazon laetatorius (Fabr.) * Status unknown.

Gelis proximus (Foerster) *

Trychosis legator (Thunberg) *

Exetastes illusor (Gravenhorst) *

Virgichneumon maculicauda (Perkins) *

Enicospilus ramidulus (L.). * Status unknown.

Glypta sp. *

Braconidae
Macrocentrus nidulator (Nees) *

Chrysidae (ruby-tailed wasps)
Chrysis ignita agg. (L.)

Formicidae (ants)
Lasius flavus (F.). Yellow Meadow Ant

L. alienus sensuo lato (s.s.)

L niger (s.s.).

L. mixtus (Nylander). Local.

Tetramorium caespitum (L.) Turf Ant. Local.

Myrmica scabrinodis Nyl.

Anthophoridae
Nomada goodeniana (Kirby). Gooden's Nomad Bee

Epeolus cruciger Panzer. Notable A.

Eumenidae (Potter and Mason Wasps)
Ancistrocerus trifasciatus (Müller)

A. gazella (Panzer)

A. scoticus (Curtis). Local.

Vespidae (Social Wasps)
Dolichovespa sylvestris (Scop.) Tree Wasp

Vespula vulgaris (L.) Common Wasp

Sphecidae (Digger Wasps)
Crossocerus dimidiatus (Fabricius) Blunt-tailed Digger Wasp. Local.

Apidae
Bombus terrestris (L.) Buff-tailed Bumblebee

B. lucorum L. White-tailed Bumblebee

B. lapidarius (L.) Large Red-tailed Bumblebee

B. pratorum (L.) Early Bumblebee

B. monticola Smith (B. lapponicus (F.)) Local.

B. soroeensis (F.). Local.

B. pascuorum (Scop.). Common Carder Bee

B. hortorum (L.). Small Garden Bumblebee

B. muscorum (L.). Local.

B. humilis Il1. Brown-banded Carder. Local.

Psithyrus bohemicus (Seidl). Gipsy Cuckoo-bee

P. rupestris (Fabr.) Hill Cuckoo-bee. Nat. Scarce.

Apis mellifera L. Honey Bee

Halictidae

Sphecodes monilicornis (Kirby). Local.

Sphecodes geoffrellus (Kirby).

Halictus rubicundus (Christ).

Lasioglossum albipes (Fabricius)

Lasioglossum morio (Fabr.) Brassy Mining Bee

Lasioglossum smeathmanellum (Kirby). Status unknown.

Colletidae

Colletes succinctus (L.). Local.

Colletes similis Schenck. Locally common.

Andrenidae

Andrena cineraria (L.) Grey Mining Bee. Local.

A. angustior (Kirby). Local.

A. nigroaenea (Kirby)

A. fulva (Müller). Tawny Mining Bee.

Sub-phylum: CHELICERATA

Class: ARACHNIDA
Order: PSEUDOSCORPIONES

Neobisiidae
Neobisium (Neobisium) maritimum (Leach)
Nationally Scarce.

Order: ARANEA (spiders)

Atypidae
Atypus affinis Eichwald. Purse-web Spider

Amaurobiidae
Amaurobius ferox (Walckanaer)
A. fenestralis (Stroem)
A. similis (Blackwall)

Oonopidae
Oonops pulcher Templeton

Dysderidae
Dysdera crocata C.L.Koch. Woodlouse-eating Spider
Harpactea hombergi (Scopoli)

Segestriidae
Segestria senoculata (Linnaeus)

Pholcidae
Pholcus phalangiodes (Fuesslin)

Gnaphosidae
Drassodes lapidosus (Walckenaer)
Haplodrassus signifer (C.L.Koch)
Zelotes latreillei (Simon)
Micaria pulicaria (Sundevall)

Clubionidae
Clubiona reclusa O.P.-Camb.
C. terrestris Westring
C. genevensis L. Koch

Liocranidae
Agroeca proxima (O.P.-Camb.)
Phrurolithus festivus (C.L. Koch)

Thomisidae
Xysticus erraticus (Blackwall)
X. cristatus (Clerck)
Ozyptila sanctuaria (O.P. -Camb.)

Salticidae
Salticus scenicus (Clerck)
Heliophanus cupreus (Walckenaer)

Lycosidae
Pardosa pullata (Clerck)
P. monticola (Clerck)
P. nigriceps (Thorell)
P. proxima (C.L. Koch)
P. agrestis (Westring)
Trochosa terricola Thorell
Alopecosa pulverulenta (Clerck)
Pirata piraticus (Clerck)

Pisauridae
Pisaura mirabilis (Clerck). Nursery Web Spider

Agelenidae
Tegenaria duellica Simon
T. domestica (Clerck)

Hahniidae
Antistea elegans (Blackwall)
Hahnia montana (Blackwall)
H. nava (Blackwall)

Theridiidae
Enoplognatha ovata (Clerck)
E. thoracica (Hahn)
Robertus lividus (Blackwall)
Steatoda grossa (C.L. Koch)

Tetragnathidae

Tetragnatha extensa (Linnaeus)

Pachygnatha clercki Sundevall

P. degeeri Sundevall

Metellina segmentata (Clerck)

Meta merianae (Scopoli)

M. menardi (Latreille)

Araneidae

Araneus diadematus Clerck. Cross Spider

Larinioides cornutus (Clerck)

Zygiella x-notata (Clerck)

Linyphiidae

Ceratinella sp.

Walckenaera antica (Wider)

W. acuminata Blackwall

W. vigilax (Blackwall)

Dicymbium nigrum (Blackwall)

Dismodicus bifrons (Blackwall)

Oedothorax fuscus (Blackwall)

Tiso vagans (Blackwall)

Monocephalus fuscipes (Blackwall)

Lophomma punctatum (Blackwall)

Gongylidiellum vivum (O.P.-Camb.)

Erigone dentipalpis (Wider)

E. atra Blackwall

Halorates reprobus (O.P.-Camb.)

Porrhomma pygmaeum (Blackwall)

Centromerita bicolor (Blackwall)

Bathyphantes gracilis (Blackwall)

Diplostyla concolor (Wider)

Stemonyphantes lineatus (L.)

Lepthyphantes tenuis (Blackwall)

L. zimmermannii Bertkau

Order: OPILIONES (harvestmen)

Phalangiidae

Phalangium opilio L.

Paroligolophus agrestis (Meade)

Mitopus morio (Fabr.)

Opiliones (continued)

Leiobunidae

Leiobunum blackwalli Meade

Nelima gothica Lohmander. Local.

ACARINA (mites)

Order: Trombidiformes

Eylaidae

Eylais extendens (Mull.)

E. hamata Koenike

Sperchontidae

Sperchon squamosus Kramer

S. glandulosus Koenike

Pionidae

Laminipes ornatus (Koch)

Piona nodata (Müller)

Halacaridae

Porohalacarus alpinus Sig. Thor.

Soldanellonyx sp. Walter

Bdellidae

Neomolgus littoralis (L.)

Hoplomolgus berlesei (Trag.) var. pallipes (L. Koch)

Ixodidae

Acarus reduvius L.

Ixodes (Ceratixodes) uriae White

I. (Multidentatus) rothschildi Nutt & Warb.

Parasitidae

Poecilochirus carabi G. Can. & R. Canestrini

Appendix X: Butterfly transect totals and estimates, 1977 – 2001

-1 indicates that the species was not recorded but might have been if the flight period had been recorded or adequately recorded.

-2 indicates that the species was recorded, but too many weeks were missed during the flight period for a reliable estimate to be made.

	Brood	'77	'78	'79	'80	'81	'82	'83	'84	85	'86	'87	'88	'89	'90	'91	'92	'93	'94	'95	'96	'97	'98	'99	2000	'01
Small/Essex Skipper	1	0	-1	-1	-1	-1	-1	0	0	0	0	0	0	0	0	-1	-1	-1	-1	-2	-1	-1	0	0	0	0
Clouded Yellow	1	0	-1	-1	-1	-1	-1	0	0	0	0	0	0	0	3	0	0	0	0	-2	-2	-2	13	11	4	0
Large White	1	0	-2	-1	-1	-1	-1	3	1	3	1	2	8	1	3	6	5	3	-2	-1	-1	-1	6	-1	0	5
Small White	2	0	-2	0	-1	-1	-1	15	0	0	0	0	0	0	0	0	0	0	-2	-1	-1	-2	-1	-1	16	0
Green-veined White	2	0	-2	-1	-1	-1	-1	31	0	0	0	2	1	-2	-1	6	4	3	-2	-1	-2	-2	-1	2	0	1
Small Copper	1	43	3	-2	-1	-1	-1	1	14	9	24	83	28	12	6	-1	-2	3	-2	-2	-2	-2	24	28	43	109
Common Blue	2	0	0	-2	-1	-1	-1	64	488	9	128	686	28	242	53	141	-2	-1	-1	-2	-1	-2	22	21	13	0
Red Admiral	1	3	0	-1	-1	-1	-1	11	1	3	4	6	0	12	27	0	-1	-1	-2	-2	-2	-2	0	0	42	25
Painted Lady	1	1	-1	-1	-1	-1	-1	8	4	3	0	6	0	5	7	-2	-1	-1	-1	-2	-2	-2	-2	9	0	0
Small Tortoiseshell	1	4	-2	-1	-1	-1	-1	0	1	0	0	36	8	2	10	-2	0	-2	-1	-1	-1	-1	8	7	99	8
Peacock	2	0	4	-2	-1	-1	-1	4	12	3	0	0	0	0	0	31	0	0	-2	-1	-1	-1	-2	-2	18	10
Dark Green Fritillary	2	0	3	-2	-1	-1	-1	6	2	1	2	5	0	0	0	-1	-1	0	-2	-1	-1	0	0	0	3	1
Grayling	1	0	-1	-1	-1	-1	-1	0	0	0	0	0	0	0	0	0	2	-1	-1	-2	-1	-1	-1	-1	-1	0
Gatekeeper	1	0	80	-1	-1	-1	-1	291	472	39	103	238	273	346	391	375	398	-2	-2	133	-2	195	309	309	368	318
Meadow Brown	1	80	0	-1	-1	-1	-1	0	0	0	0	0	0	0	0	0	-2	-2	-2	-1	-1	-1	0	0	0	0
Small Heath	1	0	0	-1	-1	-1	-1	0	0	0	2	0	0	0	0	0	-1	-1	-2	-1	-1	-1	0	0	0	0

List of References

Opposite: Figure 33. The author coaxing a young Manx shearwater back down into its burrow, after it had been forced onto the surface by flooding. A temporary wooden shelter had prevented it from being predated, but subsequently it seemed to prefer the dry carpet of thrift to its muddy hole.

Akeroyd, J.R & Preston, C.D. (1984). *Halimione portulacoides* (L.) Aellen on coastal rocks and cliffs. *Watsonia* 15, 95 - 103.

Anon., 1996 a. Selectivity of fishing gears in Irish waters. Final report on EU Contract BIO/ECO 1993/11 to DG XIV of the Commission of the European Communities.

Anon., 1996 b. Report of the Scientific Committee: review of harbour porpoises in the North Atlantic region. Reports of the International Whaling Commission, 46: 84 - 90.

Ashcroft, R.E. (1976). Breeding biology and survival of puffins. Unpublished D. Phil thesis, Oxford.

Ashcroft, R.E. (1979). Breeding biology and survival of puffins on Skomer Island, Wales. *Ornis scandinavica* 10: 100 - 110.

Baines, M.E. (1993). West Wales Grey Seal Census: Report on 1992 Season. Unpublished report to West Wales Naturalists' Trust.

Baines, M.E., Earl, S.J., Pierpoint, C.J.L. and Poole, J. (1995). The West Wales Grey Seal Census. Report by The Dyfed Wildlife Trust to the Countryside Council for Wales. CCW Contract Science Report no. 131.

Baines, M.E, Pierpoint, C.J.L. and Earl, S.E. (1997). A Cetacean Sightings Database for Wales and an evaluation of impacts on cetaceans from the Sea Empress oil spill. Report to the Sea Empress Environmental Evaluation Committee. The Countryside Council for Wales. 70pp.

Ballantine, W.J. (1961) A biologically defined exposure scale for the comparative description of rocky shores. Field Studies 1 (3): 1 - 19.

Barham, K. (1959). Warden's Report for 1959. Skokholm Bird Observatory Report (SBOR) for 1959: pp 2 - 4.

Barrett, J.H. (1959). The birds of the parish of Dale, including Skokholm. *Field Studies* Volume 1, no. 1: pp 1 - 16.

Batten, L.A., Bibby, C.J., Clement, P., Elliot, G.D, & Porter, R. (1990). Red Data Birds in Britain. Poyser, London.

Bellamy, D. (1975). The monitoring of ecosystem stability using quantifiable polymorphic characters of common invertebrate populations. Fieldwork Report, University College Cardiff. Unpublished.

Bendelow, V. & Hartnup, R. (1980). Climatic classification of England & Wales. Soil Survey. Technical Monograph No. 15. Rothamsted Experimental Research Station.

Burger, J., and Gochfeld, M. (1994). Predation and effects of humans on island-nesting seabirds. BirdLife Cons. Ser. 1: 39 - 67.

Berrow, S.D., Tregenza, N.J.C. & Hammond, P.S. (1994). Marine Mammal by-catch on the Celtic Shelf. Report to the Commission of the European Communities, DG XIV/C/1. Study Contract 92/3503.

Berry, R.J. (1964). The Evolution of an Island Population of the House Mouse. Evolution 18: 469 - 483.

Berry, R.J. (1968). The Ecology of an Island population of the House Mouse. Journal of An. Ecol. 37: 445 - 470.

Berry, R.J. (1977). Inheritance and Natural History. Collins (New Naturalist series), London.

Berry, R.J. (1996). Small mammal differentiation on islands. *Phil. Trans. R. Soc. Lond.* 351: 753 - 764.

Berry R.J. & Jakobson M.E. (1971). Life & Death in an Island Population of the House Mouse. Exp. Geront. 6: 187 – 197.

Betts, M. (1992). Birds of Skokholm. Bioline. University of Wales, College of Cardiff.

Betts, M (1995). Skokholm Warden's Annual Report to the Dyfed Wildlife Trust. Unpublished.

Betts, M. & Price, S. (1993). The Lepidoptera of Skokholm Island. Report to Dyfed Wildlife Trust.

BIM (Irish Sea Fisheries Board), 1998. The Physical Interaction between Grey Seals and Fishing Gear. Report to the European Commission. Reference PEM/93/06. 74 pp.

Blacker, N.C. & Collingwood, C.A. (2002). Some significant new records of ants (Hymenoptera: Formicidae) from the Salisbury area, South Wiltshire, England, with a key to the British species of *Lasius*. British Journal of Entomology & Natural History, 15: 25 - 46.

Bolton, M. (1996). Energy expenditure, bodyweight and foraging performance of Storm Petrels *Hydrobates pelagicus* breeding in artificial nesting chambers. Ibis 138: 405 - 409.

Botham (1999). Evidence for selective predation of limpets *Patella vulgata* by Oystercatchers *Haematopus ostralegus* on Skokholm, S. Wales. Unpublished thesis in part fulfillment of the BSc hons. biology degree.

Bowen, D.R. (1975). Leaf Hopper project - Skokholm, September 1975. Fieldwork Report, University College, Cardiff. Unpublished.

Bristowe, W.S. (1935). The Spiders of Skokholm (S.Wales) with notes on a Phalangid new to Britain. Proceedings of the Zoological Society of London, 2: 233 - 239.

Brooke, M. de L. (1977). The breeding biology of the Manx shearwater. D. Phil. Thesis, Oxford.

Brooke, M. de L. (1978). The dispersal of female Manx shearwaters *Puffinus puffinus*. Ibis, 120: 545 - 551.

Brooke, M. de L. (1983). "Memories that linger". Bulletin of the Friends of Skokholm and Skomer 5: 15 - 16.

Brooke, M. de L. (1990). The Manx Shearwater. Poyser.

Brooke, M., Lees, D.R. & Lawman, J. Spot distribution in the Meadow Brown butterfly. Biological Journal of the Linnaean Society, 24: 337 - 348.

Brown, D.G. & Sankey, J.H.P., 1949. The Harvest Spider *Nelima sylvatica* in Great Britain. Proc. Zool. Soc., Vol. 119, Part IV, pp. 867 - 871.

Brun, E. (1958). Notes on the fledging-period of the Razorbill. SBOR 1958: 23 – 26.

Cantos, F.J. (1993). Evolucion de la invernada y fenologia de la Gaviota Sombria *Larus fuscus* in Madrid. *Giam (Grupo Iberico de Aves Marinas) Boletin* 16: 4.

Caswell, H., Brault, S., Read, A., Smith, T. and Barlow, J. (1995). Uncertainty analysis of harbour porpoise population growth rate and by-catch mortality. Paper SC/47/SM28 submitted to the Scientific Committee of the International Whaling Commission, May 1995.

Chambers, B. (1971a). The birds of Skokholm. Skokholm Bird Observatory Report 1971: 22 – 34.

Chambers, B. (1971b). Manx Shearwaters in North America. SBOR 1971: 18 – 21.

Chatty Logs, Skokholm Island, 1946 - present.

Conder, P.J. (1949a). Individual Distance. Ibis, 91: 649 - 655.

Conder, P.J. (1949b). Observations on a migration of *Pieris brassicae* L. at Skokholm Island, Pembrokeshire, in August 1947. Proceedings of the Royal Entomological Society of London, 24, parts 4 - 6, 15th June 1949.

Conder, P.J. (1952). Some individual feeding habits of gulls breeding on Skokholm. SBOR 1952: 30 - 34.

Conder, P.J. (1953). A list of the birds of Skokholm, Pembrokeshire. Northwestern Naturalist XXIV: 211 - 219.

Conder, P.J. (1980). The need to control Lesser Black-backed Gulls on Skokholm. Unpublished report to Dyfed Wildlife Trust, unpublished.

Conder, P.J. (1990). The Wheatear. Helm Books.

Conder, P.J. and Keighley, J. (1950). The leg colouration of the Willow Warbler and Chiffchaff. British Birds XLIII: 238 - 240.

Connor, .W., Allen, J.H., Golding, N., Howell, K.L., Lieberknecht, L.M., Northen, .O. & Reker, J.B. (2004). The Marine Habitat Classification for Britain & Ireland, Version 04.05. JNCC, Peterborough.

Corbet, G.B. (1956). The phoresy of Mallophaga on a population of *Ornithomyia fringillina* Curtis (Dipt., Hippoboscidae). Entomologists' Monthly Magazine 198: 207 - 211.

Corkhill, P. (1969). Notes from Skomer NNR. Nature in Wales, Vol. 12: No. 1, p. 89 - 95).

Corkhill, P. (1970). Factors affecting auk attendance during the pre-egg stage. Nature in Wales 12: 258 - 262.

Corkhill, P. (1973). Food and feeding ecology of Puffins. Bird Study 20: 207 - 220.

Coulson, J. C. and Butterfield, J. (1986). Studies on a colony of colour-ringed Herring Gulls *Larus argentatus*, 2.: Colony occupation and feeding outside the breeding season. Bird Study 33: 55 - 59.

Craik, J.C.A. (2000). A simple and rapid method of estimating gull productivity. Bird Study 47: 113 - 116.

Cremer, G.A., Farrer, M.E. and Staches, B.W. (1965) The distribution of dominant animals in relation to exposure on Skokholm shores. SBOR 1965: 25 - 31.

Czechowski, W., Radchenko, A & Checkowska, W. (2002). The ants (Hymenoptera, Formicidae) of Poland. Studio 1, Warszawa. 200pp.

Dane, D.S. (1948). A disease of Manx Shearwaters. Journal of Animal Ecology 17: 158 - 164.

Dane, D.S., Miles, J.A.R. & Stoker, M.G.P. (1953). A disease of Manx Shearwaters: further observations in the field. Journal of Animal Ecology 22: 123 - 133.

Davidson, F. (1994). The ecology of the Puffin *Fratercula arctica*. Unpubl. Ph.D. thesis, University of Oxford.

Davis, A (1955). The habitats of two amphipods on Skokholm. Skok. Bird Observatory Report 1955: 23 - 25.

Davis, A. (1956a). The freshwater fauna of Skokholm. Skokholm Bird Observatory Report 1956: 25 - 33.

Davis, A. (1956b) The Corixid fauna of North Pond, Skokholm. Ent. Mon. Mag. xcii: 297 - 299.

Davis, A. (1960) Breeding cycles of *Gammarus duebeni* on Skokholm. Skokholm Bird Observatory Report 1960: 23 - 28.

Davis, J.W.F. (1970). Topographic memory in limpets (*Patella*). Rev. Comp. Animal 4: 42 - 45.

Davis, J.W.F. (1973). Aspects of the breeding ecology and feeding of certain gulls. D. Phil. thesis, Oxford.

Davis, J.W.F. (1974). Herring Gull populations and Man. Nature in Wales vol. 14, no. 2, 85 - 90.

Davis, JE & Anderson, SS, (1976). Marine Pollution Bulletin, Vol. 7, no. 6.

Davis, J.E. & Davis, H.M. (1975). A study of the breeding biology and pup mortality in Grey Seals (Halichoerus grypus) at Skomer Island, Dyfed, 1975; obtained for comparison with data collected after an oiling incident in 1974. Unpublished report to The West Wales Naturalists' Trust.

Davis, J.W.F. & Dunn, E.K. (1976). Intraspecific predation and colonial breeding in Lesser Black-backed Gulls *Larus fuscus*. Ibis 118: 65 - 77.

Davis, P. (1956). The Storm petrel study in 1956. Skokholm Bird Observatory Report 1956: 18 - 19.

Davis, P. (1957). The breeding of the Storm Petrel. British Birds L: 85 - 101.

Davis, P. (1966). Puffinosis amongst Manx shearwaters. British Birds 59: 84 - 85.

Davis, R. A. 1956. Fleas from Skokholm House Mice. Skokholm Bird Obs. Report 1956: 24.

Davis, R.A. (1957a). Mammal fleas on Skokholm. Ent. Mon. Mag. XC111: 25 - 26.

Davis, R.A. (1957b). House Mice on Skokholm Island. Skokholm Bird Observatory Report 1957: 26.

Davis, T.A.W. & Saunders, D.R. (1965). The diet of Buzzards *Buteo buteo* on Skomer Island. Nature in Wales 9: 116 - 124.

Diamond, A.W. (1963). Measurements of eggs of Razorbills and Oystercatchers. SBOR 1963: 14 - 16.

Dickinson, H. (1958). Puffins and burrows. SBOR 1958: 27 - 34.

Donovan, J.W. and Rees, G.H. (1994). Birds of Pembrokeshire: status and atlas of Pembrokeshire birds. Dyfed Wildlife Trust.

Dowdeswell, W.H., Fisher, R.A. & Ford, E.B. The quantitative study of populations in the Lepidoptera. 2. *Maniola jurtina* L. Heredity, Vol. 3: 67 - 84.

Downhill, I.R. (1961). A list of Skokholm macro-lepidoptera. Skokholm Bird Observatory Report 1961, 17 - 25.

Duncan, C.J. (1960). The grasshoppers of Skokholm Island. Entomologist 93: 25 - 26.

Dunn, E. (1973). Incubation in the Lesser Black-backed Gull. Skok. Bird Obs. Report 1973.

Edwards, F.W. (1934). Diptera found on Skokholm Island 25th - 27th August 1934. Unpublished list.

Evans, P.G.H. (1998). *Sightings in Wales*, issue 1, April 1998. Nekton, Newport, Wales.

Evans, P.R. (1966). Some results from the ringing of Rock Pipits on Skokholm 1952 - 1965. Skokholm Bird Observatory Report 1966.

Evans, S.B. (1997). The Divided Sedge *Carex divisa* - a Nationally Scarce plant on Skokholm. The Island Naturalist 34 : 34 - 35.

Evans & Lansdown (2000). A review of available information on the management history of *Ranunculus tripartitus* populations. For BSBI, UK biodiversity Action Plan.

Fenton, R. (1903). An historical tour through Pembrokeshire. London.

Fletcher, A. (editor) (1997). Lichen Habitat Management. Proceedings of a Workshop held at Bangor, 3rd - 6th September 1997. British Lichen Society.

Fowles, A. (1986). Dyfed Invertebrate Group, newsletter 3, September 1986.

Fursdon, G.H.John. (1983). *Some Pembrokeshire Impressions.* West Wales Naturalists' Trust, 1983.

Gaston, A. J., & Hipfner, J. M. (2000). Thick-billed Murre (Uria lomvia). In *The Birds of North America*, no. 497 (A. Poole and F. Gill, Eds.). Birds of North America, Inc., Philadelphia.

Gibbons, D.W., Avery, M.I., Baillie, S.R., Gregory, R.D., Kirby, J.S., Porter, R.F., Tucker, G.M. & Williams, G. (1996). Bird Species of Conservation Concern in the United Kingdom, Channel Islands and Isle of Man: revising the Red Data List. RSPB Conservation Review 10: 7 - 18.

Gillham, M.E. (1952). The distribution of seeds by gulls. Skokholm Bird Observatory Report 1952: 34 - 35. The West Wales Field Society.

Gillham, M.E. (1953a). An ecological account of the vegetation of Grassholm Island. Journal of Ecology, 41: 84 - 99.

Gillham, M.E. (1953b). An annotated list of the flowering plants and ferns of Skokholm Island, Pembrokeshire. North Western Naturalist, December 1953: 539 - 557.

Gillham, M.E. (1954a). The marine algae of Skokholm and Grassholm Islands, Pembrokeshire. Northwestern Naturalist. June: 204 - 225.

Gillham, M.E. (1954b). An annotated list of the Bryophytes and Lichens of Skokholm Island, Pembrokeshire. Northwestern Naturalist, March 1954 : 37 - 38.

Gillham, M.E. (1955). Some Possible consequences if Rabbits should be exterminated by *Myxomatosis* on Skokholm Island, Pembrokeshire. *North Western Naturalist* March 1955, pp. 30 - 34.

Gillham, M.E.(1956a). Plant notes 1954 - 56. New species not recorded in the 1953 plant list. Skokholm Bird Observatory Report 1956: 23 - 24.

Gillham, M.E. (1956b). Ecology of the Pembrokeshire Islands, IV. Effects of treading and burrowing by birds and mammals. Journal of Ecology 44: 51 - 82.

Gillham, M.E. (1956c). Ecology of the Pembrokeshire Islands, V. Manuring by the colonial seabirds and mammals, with a note on seed distribution by gulls. Journal of Ecology 44: 429 - 454.

Goodman, G.T. & Gillham, M.E. (1954). Ecology of the Pembrokeshire Islands, III. Skokholm, the environment and vegetation. Journal of Ecology 42: 296 - 337.

Gynn, E. (1984). Dead shearwaters on Skokholm. Bulletin of the Friends of Skomer & Skokholm 7: 10 - 11.

Gynn, E. (1985). Flora of Skokholm. West Wales Trust for Nature Conservation.

Gynn, E. & Gynn. G. (1982). Effects of goat removal. Bulletin of the Friends of Skomer & Skokholm 4: 5 - 6.

Gynn, E. & Gynn. G. (1985). Birds of Skokholm. West Wales Trust for Nature Conservation.

Hammond, P.S., Benke, H., Berggren, P., Borchers, D.L., Buckland, S.T., Collet, A., Heide-Jorgensen, M.P., Heimlich-Boran, S., Hiby, A.R , Leopold, M.F. and Øien, N. (1995). Distribution and abundance of the harbour porpoise and other small cetaceans in the North Sea and adjacent waters. Report of EC Life project 92-2/UK/027. 240pp.

Harris, M.P. (1962). Migration of the British Lesser Black-Backed Gull as shown by ringing data. Bird Study 9: 174 - 182.

Harris, M.P. (1963). Bird ringing on Skokholm. Skokholm Bird Observatory Report 1963: 25 - 34.

Harris, M.P. (1964a). Ring loss and wear of rings on marked Manx shearwaters. *Bird Study* 11: 39 - 46.

Harris, M.P. (1964b). Recoveries of ringed Herring Gulls. Bird Study 11: 183 - 191.

Harris, M.P. (1964c). Measurements and weights of Great Black-Backed Gulls. British Birds 57: 71 - 75.

Harris, M.P. (1965). The food of some *Larus* gulls. Ibis 107: 43 - 53.

Harris, M.P. (1966a). Age of return to the colony, age of breeding and adult survival of Manx Shearwaters. Bird Study l3: 84 - 95.

Harris, M.P. (1966b). Breeding biology of the Manx Shearwater *Puffinus puffinus*. Ibis 108: 17 - 33.

Harris, M.P. (1967a). Food of some *Larus* gulls. Ibis, 107: 43 - 53.

Harris, M.P. (1967b). Biology of Oystercatchers. Ibis, 109: 180 - 193.

Harris, M.P. (1970a). Rates and causes of increase of some British gull populations. Bird Study 17: 325 - 335.

Harris, M.P. (1970b). Abnormal migration and hybridization of *Larus argentatus* and *L. fuscus* after interspecies fostering experiments. Ibis 112: 488 - 497.

Harris, M.P.(1970c). Territory limiting the size of the breeding population of the Oystercatcher (Haematopus ostralegus): a removal experiment. J. Anim.Ecol. 39: 707 - 713.

Harris, M.P. (1972). Inter-Island movements of Manx Shearwaters. Bird Study 19: 167 - 171.

Harris, M.P. (1984). The Puffin. Poyser.

Harris, M.P. & Brooke, M.de.L. (1974). Skokholm Oystercatchers and the Burry Estuary. SBOR 1974: 17 - 19.

Harris, M.P. & Wanless, S. (1996). Survival and non-breeding of adult Common Guillemots *Uria aalge.* Ibis 137: 192 - 197.

Harris, M.P., Wanless, S. & Barton, T.R. (1996). Site use and fidelity in the Common Guillemot *Uria aalge.* *Ibis* 138: 399 - 404.

Harris, M.P. and Wanless, S. (2003). Postfledging occupancy of breeding sites by female common murres (*Uria aalge*). The Auk 120: 75 - 81.

Harris, M.P., Wanless, S., Barton, T.R. & Elston, A. (1997). Nest-site characteristics, duration of use and breeding success in the Guillemot *Uria aalge.* Ibis 139: 468 - 476.

Hart, J.S. & Heroux, O. (1953). A comparison of some seasonal and temperature-induced changes in *Peromyscus*: cold resistance, metabolism and pelage insulation. Canadian journal of Zoology 31: 112 - 116.

Hensley, R. T.. (1996). A preliminary survey of benthos from the *Nephrops norvegicus* mud grounds in the north-western Irish Sea. Est., Cstl Shelf sci., 42: 457 - 466.

Hodges, J. (1994). *A Chough Conservation Strategy for Pembrokeshire.* Pembrokeshire Coast National Park Authority.

Horwood, J.W. & Goss-Custard, J.D. (1977). Predation by the oystercatcher, *Haematopus ostralegus* (L.) in relation to the cockle *Cerastoderma edule* (L.) fishery in the Burry Inlet, South Wales. Journal of Applied Ecology, 14: 139 - 158.

Howells, R. (1968). The Sounds Between. Llandysul books.

Howgate, M.E. (1986). Kleptoparasitism by the Lesser Black-backed Gull (*Larus fuscus*) on Skokholm Island, Pembrokeshire. Nature in Wales.

Hudson, P. J. (1979). The parent-chick feeding relationship of the puffin *Fratercula arctica.* Journal of Animal Ecology, 48, 889 - 898.

ICES (1992). Report of the working group on ecosystem effects of fishing activities. ICES CM 1992/G:11, Ref: Session T, 144pp.

IWC (International Whaling Commission) (1994). Report of the workshop on mortality of cetaceans in passive fishing nets and traps. In: Gillnets and Cetaceans, Report of the International Whaling Commission Special Issue 15. W.F. Perrin, G.P. Donovan, and J. Barlow, eds. IWC, Cambridge.

Jakobson, M.E. (1971). Acclimatization to cold in House Mice living on an Island. Int. J. Blometr. 15: 330 - 336.

Jakobsen, M.E. (1973). A search for physiological adaptation in a natural mouse population. Ph.D thesis, London.

James, P.C & Robertson, H.A. (1985). The use of playback recordings to detect and census nocturnal burrowing seabirds. Seabird 8: 18 - 20.

James, P.W. & Rose, F. (1978). A list of sites of national/international importance for lichens. Report to NCC (unpublished).

Johnson, W.L. (2002). Bryophytes found on Skokholm in June 2002. Unpublished list.

Jones, D., Gresham, G.A., Lloyd, H.G. & Howard, A.N. (1965). Yellow Fat in the Wild Rabbit. Nature 207: 205.

Jones, E. (1949). An extract from "a report on the geology of Skokholm Island. SBOR 1949: 27 - 30.

Keighley, J. & Buxton, E.M.J. (1948). The incubation period of the Oystercatcher. British Birds XLI: 261 - 265.

Kuiken, T., Simpson, V.R., Allchin, C.R., Bennett, P.M., Codd, G.A., Harris, E.A., Howes, G.J., Kennedy, S., Kirkwood, J.K., Law, R.J., Merrett, N.R., & Phillips, S. (1994). Mass mortality of common dolphins (*Delphinus delphis*) in south west England due to incidental capture in fishing gear. Vet. Record, 134: 81 - 89.

Lack, D. (1962). Radar evidence on migratory orientation. British Birds 55: 139 - 158.

Lawman, J. (1974). Jackdaws on Skokholm. SBOR for 1974: 14 - 16.

Lawman, J. (1975). Observations on the fledging of Razorbill chicks. Nature in Wales 14: 250 - 254.

Lawman, J. (2000). Skokholm – an island remembered. Halsgrove, Devon.

Lees, D.R., Chater. J. & Dewar, K. (1986). A map showing the locations of *Cepaea nemoralis*. Unpublished.

Lindeboom, H.J. and de Groot, S.J., (1998). IMPACT-II: The effects of different types of fisheries on the North Sea and Irish Sea benthic ecosystems. NIOZ-Rapport 1998-1/RIVO-DLO Report C003/98. 404pp.

Linley-Adams, G. (1999). The accumulation and impact of organotins on marine mammals, seabirds and fish for human consumption. Report to WWF.

Lloyd, C.S. (1972). Attendance at auk colonies during the breeding season. SBOR 1972: 15 - 23.

Lloyd, C.S. (1974). Movement and survival of British Razorbills. Bird Study 21: 102 - 116.

Lloyd, C.S. (1976). The breeding biology and survival of the razorbill *Alca torda*. D. Phil. thesis, Oxford.

Lloyd, C.S. (1977). The ability of the Razorbill *Alca torda* to raise an additional chick to fledging. *Ornis Scand.* 8: 155 - 159.

Lloyd,C.S. (1979). Factors affecting breeding of Razorbills on Skokholm. Ibis 121: 165 - 176.

Lloyd, C.S. and Perrins, C.M. (1977). Survival and age at first breeding in the Razorbill. Bird Banding 48: 239 - 252.

Lloyd, C., Tasker, M.L. & Partridge, K. (1991). The Status of Seabirds in Britain & Ireland. Poyser.

Lloyd, H.G. (1964). Influences of environmental factors of some aspects of breeding in the wild rabbit *Oryctolagus cuniculus*. Thesis for MSc, University of Wales.

Lloyd, H.G. (1970a). Variation and adaptation in reproductive performance. Symposium of the Zoological Society of London, 26: 165 - 188.

Lloyd, H.G. & McCowan, D. (1968). Some observations of the breeding burrows of the wild rabbit *Oryctolagus cuniculus* on the island of Skokholm. Journal of the Zoological Society of London, 156: 540 - 549.

Lockley, R.M. (1930). On the breeding habits of the Manx Shearwater. British Birds XX111: 202 - 218.

Lockley, R.M. (1932a). The status of shearwaters on the West Coast. The Northwestern Naturalist, 1932. pp. 298 - 301.

Lockley, R.M. (1932b). On the breeding habits of the Storm Petrel. British Birds XXV: 206 - 211.

Lockley, R.M. (1935). Movements of Manx Shearwaters. British Birds, no. 4, vol. XXIX, pp. 105 - 107.

Lockley, R.M. (1934). On the breeding habits of the puffin: with special reference to its incubation and fledging periods. *British Birds*, 27, 214 - 223.

Lockley, R.M. (1936). Skokholm Bird Observatory. British Birds No. 8, Volume XXIX, pp. 222 - 235.

Lockley, R.M. (1938). I Know an Island. Harrap.

Lockley, R.M. (1940a). Rabbits on an island, I: Trapping, and Chinchillas. *The Field*, 1st June 1940, p. 854.

Lockley, R.M. (1940b). Rabbits on an island, II: A trial of disease as a method of control. *The Field*, 8th June 1940, p. 884.

Lockley, R.M. (1940c). Rabbits on an island, III: the results of fumigation with cyanogas. *The Field*, 15th June 1940, pp. 922 - 923.

Lockley, R.M. (1942). *Shearwaters*. Dent, London.

Lockley, R.M. (1947). *Letters from Skokholm*. Dent, London.

Lockley, R.M. (1948). *The Cinnamon Bird*. Staples Press Limited, London.

Lockley, R.M. (1953). *Puffins*. Dent, London.

Lockley, R.M. (1955). Failure of myxomatosis on Skokholm Island. *Nature* 175: 906.

Lockley, R.M. (1969). *The Island*. Deutsch.

Lockley, R.M. (1973). Bird Observatories and Field Study Centres. The Emu 73; 222 - 229.

Lockley, R.M. (1983). *Flight of the Storm Petrel*. David & Charles, London.

Loxton, R.G. (1995). Welsh Islands: ecology, conservation and land use. Pages 70 - 78. CCW, Bangor.

Loxton, R.G. & Jones, P.H. (1995). The Breeding Birds of Bardsey, Skomer, Skokholm and the Calf of Man, part 1: Introduction and species accounts. *Bardsey Bird and Field Observatory Report*, 38: 84 - 159.

Loxton, R.G. & Silcocks, A. (1997). The rise and fall of Bardsey Blackbirds. Bardsey Bird Observatory Report no 40: 1996: pp. 76 - 99.

Loxton, R.G. & Sparks, T.H. (1999). Arrival of spring migrants at Portland, Skokholm, Bardsey and Calf of Man. A report in the Bardsey Observatory Report 42, 1998.

Loxton, R.G. (2002). Daily census data held by the observatories for Corn Crake, European Turtle Dove, Eurasian Wryneck and Spotted Flycatcher, 1946 - 2000. Report to the BOU compiled by RG Loxton for the Bird Observatories Council.

Marine Accident Investigation Branch. Report of the Chief Inspector of Marine Accidents into the grounding and subsequent salvage of the tanker *Sea Empress* at Milford Haven between 15 and 21 February 1996. The Department of Transport. The Stationary Office.

Macdonald, J.W., McMartin, D.A., Walker, K.G., Carins, M. and Dennis, R.H. (1967). Puffinosis in Fulmars in Orkney and Shetland. *British Birds*, Vol. 60, No. 9: 356 - 360.

Mathew, M.A. (1894). The Birds of Pembrokeshire. London.

Matthews, G.V.T. (1950). Homing experiments with Lesser Black-Backed Gulls from Skokholm. Skok. Bird Obs. Report 1950: 20 - 21.

Matthews, G.V.T. (1953). Navigation in the Manx Shearwater. Journal of Experimental Biology 30 (3): 370 - 396.

Matthews, G.V.T. (1954). An experiment in bird navigation. The Marine Observer, January 1954, 38 - 41.

Matthews, G.V.T. (1964). Individual experience as a factor in the navigation of Manx shearwaters. The Auk, volume 8, no. 2, 132 - 146.

Meyer, R.M, Buckland, P.C., & Monaghan, P. (1994). The diet of the Chough *Pyrrhocorax pyrrhocorax* as indicated by analysis of digested prey remains. *Avocetta* 18: 95 - 106.

Molloy, C. (2000). A study into the change in flight direction and flight activity of Lesser Black-backed Gulls *Larus fuscus* and Herring Gulls *L. argentatus* on Skokholm since 1982. Unpublished report presented in part fulfillment of the BSc Honours Zoology degree, Cardiff University.

Morizur, Y., Tregenza, N., Heessen, H., Berrow, S. and Pouvreau, S. (1997). Incidental mammal catches in pelagic trawl fisheries of the North east Atlantic. ICES-CM-1997/Q:05.

Myrberget, S. (1962). (Contributions to the breeding biology of the puffin *Fratercula arctica*). *Meddelesler fra statens viltundrsokeleser*, 2, 11.

Nedderman, R.M. (1953). Notes on the nesting of Oystercatchers on Skokholm in 1953. SBOR 1953: 27 - 29.

Nelson, B. (2001). The Gannet. Poyser.

Northridge, S.P. (1991). World review of interactions between marine mammals and fisheries. Food and Agricultural Organisation of the United Nations. Fisheries Technical Paper 251: Supplement 1.

Olden, B., Peterz, M. and Kollberg, B. (1985). Seabird mortality in the gill net fishery, southeast Kattegat, south Sweden. Anser, 24: 159 - 180.

Parker-Rhodes, A.F. (1954). The Basidiomycetes of Skokholm Island, part I: annotated species list. Trans. Brit. Mycol. Soc. 37: 324 - 339.

Parr, S.J., Haycock, R.J. & Smith, M.E. (1997). The impact of the *Sea Empress* oil spill on birds of the Pembrokeshire coast and islands. Proceedings of the 1997 International Oil Spill Conference, Fort Lauderdale, April 1997.

Perrins, C.M. (1967). The number of Manx Shearwaters on Skokholm. Skok Bird Obs. Report 1967.

Perrins, C.M. (1972). Edward Grey Institute of Field Ornithology's studies on Skokholm. Skok. Bird Obs. Report, 1972: 24 - 32.

Perrins, C.M. (1991). Lesser Black-backed Gulls on Skomer Island. Unpublished report to DWT.

Perrins, C.M. (1993). Study of puffinosis on Skomer. Unpublished report to Dyfed Wildlife Trust.

Perrins, C.M. (1997). The shearwaters and storm petrels of the Welsh islands. In *Welsh Islands: ecology, conservation & land use.* Proceedings of the Welsh Islands Conference 1995. (Editors: Rhind, P.M., Blackstock, T.H. & Parr, S.J., Countryside Council for Wales)

Perrins, C.M., Harris, M.P. & Britton, C.K. (1973). Survival of Manx Shearwaters *Puffinus puffinus.* Ibis, Vol. 115, pp. 535 - 548.

Plumb, W.J. (1965). Observations on the breeding biology of the Razorbill. *British Birds* 58: 449 - 456.

Pollock, C. (1994). Observations on the distribution of seabirds off south-west Ireland. Irish Birds 5(2): 173 - 182.

Purcell, T.V. & Thompson, G.V.F. (2002). A map showing the distribution and number of thalli of the lichens *Roccella fusiformis* and *R. phycopsis* on Skokholm Island in March 2002. Unpublished.

Ratcliffe, D.A. (1970). Changes attributable to pesticides in egg breakage frequency and eggshell thickness in some British Birds. Journal of Applied Ecology 7: 67 - 115.

Ratcliffe, D.A. (1977). A Nature Conservation Review: the Selection of Sites of Biological National Importance to Nature Conservation in Britain. Two volumes. Cambridge University Press.

Ratcliffe, D. (1980). The Peregrine Falcon. Poyser.

Richards, M. (1960). The attraction of birds to Bardsey lighthouse. Report of the Bardsey Bird & Field Observatory 1959, 7: 33 - 40.

Rodwell, J. (2000), editor. British Plant Communities, Volume 5: Maritime Communities and vegetation of open habitats. Cambridge University Press

Roscoe, D. (1975). Isopod communities in *Silene*. Fieldwork report. Univ. Coll. Cardiff. Unpublished.

Safriel, U. (1967). Population and food study of the oystercatcher. D. Phil. thesis, Oxford.

Salomonsen, F. (1955). The food production in the sea and the annual cycle of Faroese marine birds. Oikos 6: 92 - 146.

Sankey, J.H.P., 1949. Observations on food, enemies and parasites of British Harvest Spiders (Arachnida, Opiliones). The Entomologist's Monthly Magazine LXXXV: 246 - 247.

Schreiber, E. A., & Burger, J. (2002). Biology of Marine Birds. CRC Press, Boca Raton, Florida.
Scott, D.A. (1968). Macro-lepidoptera on Skokholm: 1968. Skokholm Bird Observatory Report 1968: pp. 28 - 32.

Scott, D.A. (1970). The breeding biology of the storm petrel *Hydrobates pelagicus*. D. Phil. thesis, Oxford.

Sea Empress Environmental Evaluation Committee (1998). The Environmental Impact of the *Sea Empress* oil spill. The Stationary Office, Norwich.

Seifert, B. (1992). A taxonomic revision of the Palaearctic members of the ant subgenus Lasius s. str. (Hymenoptera: Formicidae). Abhandlungen und Berichter des Naturkundermuseums Görlitz, 66: 1 - 67.

Sérusiaux, E. (1989). Liste Rouge des macrolichens dans la Communauté Européene. Centre de Recherches sur les Lichens. Université de Liège.

Sharrock, J.T.R. & Grant, P.J. (1982). Birds new to Britain and Ireland. Poyser.

Sheard, J.W. & Ferry, B.W. (1964). The Lichen Flora of Skokholm. Skokholm Bird Observatory Report 1964: 23 - 25.

Smith, A. (1995). A list of bryophytes found on Skokholm in May 1995. Unpublished list.

Smith, K.D. (1960). Migrants at The Smalls lighthouse. SBOR 1960: 21 - 23.

Smith, K.G.V. (1951). Hymenoptera, Microlepidoptera and other insects on Skokholm and Grassholm (Pembroke) in 1950. Journal of the Society for British Entomology 3, 244 - 246.

Smith, S., Thompson, G.V.F. & Perrins, C.M. (2001). A census of the Manx Shearwater *Puffinus puffinus* on Skomer, Skokholm and Middleholm, west Wales. Bird Study 48, 330 - 340.

Stace, C.A. (1991). New Flora of the British Isles. Cambridge University Press.

Stanbury, D.J. (1974). Some marking experiments on a population of *Monodonta lineata*, South Haven, Skokholm, Pembrokeshire. *Skokholm Bird Observatory Report* 1974. West Wales Naturalists' Trust.

Stanbury, D.J. (1997). Welsh "coney" islands: the history and importance of rabbits on Welsh islands. In *Welsh Islands: ecology, conservation & land use*. Proceedings of the Welsh Islands Conference 1995. (Editors: Rhind, P.M., Blackstock, T.H. & Parr, S.J., Countryside Council for Wales)

Stansfield, G. (1954). Collection of flat-flies on Skokholm Island. Skok. Bird Obs. Report 1954: pp 21 - 22:

Stansfield, G. (1955). Flat-flies and fleas from Skokholm birds, 1955. Skok. Bird Obs. Report 1955: pp 26 - 27.

Stansfield, G. (1957). The Fleas of Skokholm Island. *The Entomologist's Monthly Magazine*, Vol. XCIII, pp. 196 - 201.

Stewart, A.J.A. & Lees, D.R. (1996). The colour/pattern polymorphism of *Philaenus spumarius* (L.) (Homoptera: Cercopidae) in England and Wales. Philosophical Transactions of the Royal Society (B) 351, 69 - 89.

Thomas, D., (1992). Marine wildlife and net fisheries around Wales. Report published by the RSPB and The Countryside Council for Wales. 55pp.

Thompson, G.V.F. (1995). Fledging of Guillemot and Razorbill chicks on Skokholm in 1995. *The Island Naturalist* 30, 23 - 29.

Thompson, G.V.F. (1996a). Counting Lesser Black-backed Gulls on Skokholm. Unpublished report to the Islands Management Committee, Dyfed Wildlife Trust.

Thompson, G.V.F. (1996b). The number of Puffins bringing fish to burrows at Crab Bay, Skokholm in July 1996. *The Island Naturalist* 32: 18 - 21.

Thompson, G.V.F. (1996 - 2004). Warden's Annual Report to the Wildlife Trust of South & West Wales. Unpublished.

Thompson, G.V.F. & Purcell, T.V. (1997). The Status of the Harbour Porpoise around Skokholm. The Island Naturalist (Journal of the Friends of Skokholm & Skomer) 33 (Spring 1997): 6 - 7.

Thompson, G.V.F. & Purcell, T.V. (1998). The effects of the colour-change of the Skokholm light on the island's seabirds, 1996 - 1998. Unpublished Report to Dyfed Wildlife Trust and Trinity House Lighthouse Service.

Thompson, G.V.F. (1999). A trial installation of nest boxes for Storm Petrels *Hydrobates pelagicus* on Skokholm. Contract Science Report 317, Countryside Council for Wales.

Thompson, G.V.F. (2005). Storm petrel census on Skokholm in 2003. Countryside Council for Wales, Contract Science Report no. 672.

Tregenza, N.J.C., Berrow, S.D., Hammond, P.S. & Leaper, R. (1997). Harbour porpoise (*Phocoena phocoena* L.) by-catch in set gillnets in the Celtic Sea. ICES J. Mar. Sci., 54: 896 - 904.

Trout, R.C. (1995). Levels of Immunity to Rabbit Viral Haemorrhagic Disease in UK from Conservation Locations. A report to JNCC. Contract report no. F71-12-3304.

Tucker, G.M. & Heath, M.F. (1994). Birds in Europe: Their Conservation Status. BirdLife International, Cambridge.

Tutt, I.G. (1999). Skokholm Island light measurement and bird protection work. Development Department Report No.4, General Lighthouse Authorities of the UK and Ireland.

Twigg, G. & Cuerden C.M. (1967). Leptospirosis on Skomer and Skokholm islands. Nature in Wales 10 (4): 154 - 158.

Vaughan, D. and Gibbons, DW. (1996). Storm petrels on Skokholm Island in 1995. Report to CCW, RSPB and Dyfed Wildlife Trust.

Vaughan, D. and Gibbons, DW. (1998). The status of breeding storm petrels *Hydrobates pelagicus* on Skokholm Island in 1995. Seabird 20, 12 - 21.

Vaughan, D. (2001). Storm petrel census of Skokholm Island, Pembrokeshire. Report to JNCC and Wildlife Trust West Wales.

Vernon, I. (1973). Palmate Newts on Skokholm. Skokholm Bird Observatory Report, 1973.

Vernon, R.M. (1952). Some observations and breeding records of the Lapwing, Skokholm, 1952. Skok. Bird Obs. Report 1952: 25 - 30.

Warman, S.R. & Warman, C.E (1985). The food of Buzzards on Skokholm, Pembrokeshire. Bulletin of the Friends of Skomer & Skokholm 9: 8 - 9.

Walton, G.A. (1933). Water Beetles from Skokholm Island and the adjacent mainland of Pembrokeshire. Northwestern Naturalist 8: 301 - 303.

Waring, G.T., Gerior, P., Payne, M.P., Parry, B.L. & Nicolas, J.R. (1990). Incidental take of marine mammals in foreign fishery activities off the northeast United States, 1977 - 88. Fishery Bulletin, 88: 347 - 360.

Wernham, C.V., Toms, M.P., Marchant, J.H., Clark, J.A., Siriwardena, G.M. & Baillie, S.R. (eds.) (2002). The Migration Atlas: movements of the birds of Britain and Ireland. Poyser, London.

Werth (1947). The tendency of Blackbird and Song Thrush to breed in their birthplaces. British Birds 40: 328 - 330.

Weston, R. (1995). A report on findings of flint tools on Skokholm, May 1995. In Betts, M., Warden's Report to Dyfed Wildlife Trust for 1995. Unpublished.

Whilde, A., 1979. Auks trapped in salmon drift nets. Irish Birds, 1: 370 - 376.

Williamson, M.H. (1949). Note on the habitats of the Skokholm ants. Skokholm Bird Observatory Report 1949: p.26.

Index

(Note that page numbers in **bold** text denote that the subject is the main topic there)

Adderstongue fern *Ophioglossum vulgatum*: 29, 53, 69, 236.

Algae, freshwater: 47, 70.

Algae, marine: 35, 38, 72-73.

Banding (see Ringing)

Bat: 83.

Bluebell *Hyacinthoides non-scripta*: 11, 43, 51, 60, 64, 71, 206, 207, 223, 236, 265, 283, 284.

Bird, annotated systematic list of: 288-328.

Bracken *Pteridium aquilinum*: 29, 35, 37, 40, 41, 51, 56, 58, 60, 62, **70-71**, 74, 79, 80, 93, 103, 106, 112, 114, 122, 124, 128, 130, 149, 162, 165, 178, 179, 181, 182, 185, 187, 189, 192, 193, 201, 204, 205, 206, 207, 209, 212, 223, 224, 225, 228, 230, 231, 232, 236, 238, 239, 242, 243, 244, 246, 248, 251, 252, 253, 254, 256, 257, 258, 259, 260, 263, 275, 279, 281, 282, 283, 284, 285, 287, 295, 297, 313, 316, 319, 327.

Bracken, control of: 40, 71, 79, 114, 149, 209, 224, 225, 228, 230, 232, 236, 238.

Burrow use (invertebrate, bird, mouse or rabbit): 29, 35, 43, 61, 64, 72, 89, 91, 93, 105-106, 108, 109, 110, 111, 112, 114, 117, 119, 120, 121, 143, 144, 145, 164, 169, 177, 178, 179, 192, 197, 279, 281, 283, 284, 294.

Burrows, collapse of: 25, 71, 103, 110, 114, 122, 124, 130, 145, 148, 149, 209, 210, 220, 227.

Burrows, competition for: 111, 143, 148, 169, 197, 208, 228.

Burrows, flooding of: 114, 210, 213, 220.

Burrows, number of: 109, 110.

Burrowing by birds and mammals: 31, 38, 48, 53, 58, 64, 67, 111, 148, 177, 203-205, 224, 255.

Butterflies (see Lepidoptera)

Buzzard: 31, 95, 104, 148, **156-157**, 171, 197, 224, 282, 295.

By-the-wind Sailor *Velella velella*: 180.

Campion, Sea *Silene maritima*: 29, 35, 36, 51, 55, 56, 60, 62, 64, 70, 112, 146, 149, 168, 178, 184, 187, 191, 192, 199, 205, 209, 223, 230, 236, 242, 243, 244, 245, 246, 253, 257, 258, 259, 263, 281, 282, 284, 285.

Chough *Pyrrhocorax pyrrhocorax*: 31, 34, 35, 37, 42, 104, **167-169**, 195, 207, 224, 225, 227, 228, 322.

Cliff vegetation, see "Vegetation, cliff"

Cliff, suitability for nesting birds: 48, 133, 138, 139, 140, 150, 208.

Climate: 45-46, 220-221.

Crowfoot, Three-lobed *Ranunculus tripartitus*: 29, 35, 43, 52, 68, 70, 208, 226, 228, 230, 238, 282.

Countryside Council for Wales (CCW): 20, 37, 40, 43, 45, 50, 53, 72, 156, 158, 168, 179, 191, 209, 220.

Dale Castle Estate: 20, 23, 27, 114, 168.

Diptera (see Flies)

Disturbance (to wildlife): 13, 34, 40, 66, 86, 93, 99, 120, 122, 125, 130, 132, 137, 138, 142, 144, 149, 152, 154, 158, 159, 160, 169, 209, 210, 212, 217, 219, 220, 227, 229, 232.

Dolphin: 84, 95-97, 218, 219, 220.

Earthworms: 127, 157, 182, 330.

Eutrophication: 47, 60, 67, 68, 69, 130, 156, 180, 230.

Event Record Cards: 32-33.

Exclosure, rabbit: 51, 52, 58, 69, 72, 74, 75, 167, 204, 224, 230, 237, 238, 239, 241, 244, 246, 247, 248, 249, 250, 251, 256, 259, 260, 262, 264, 266, 324.

Farming: 23, 24, 27, 32, 33, 90, 194, 203, 224, 236, 241.

Fire: 32, 115, 149, 212, 226.

Fisheries: 86, 96, 99, 121, 127, 137, 148, 180, 215, **217- 219**.

Flea, general: 195, **196-197**, 343.

Flea, from birds: 195.

Flea, from rabbit: 29, 35, 89, 91, 92.

ISBN 142511469-5